ALGEBRAIC FUNCTIONS

ALGEBRAIC FUNCTIONS

GILBERT AMES BLISS

*Late Professor of Mathematics
in the University of Chicago*

DOVER PUBLICATIONS, INC.
NEW YORK

Published in Canada by General Publishing
Company, Ltd., 30 Lesmill Road, Don Mills,
Toronto, Ontario.
Published in the United Kingdom by Constable
and Company, Ltd., 10 Orange Street, London
WC 2.

This Dover edition, first published in 1966, is
an unabridged and unaltered republication of the
work originally published by the American Mathematical Society in 1933 as Volume XVI of the
Society's Colloquium Publications.
This edition is published by special arrangement
with the American Mathematical Society, P. O. Box
6248, Providence, Rhode Island 02904.

Library of Congress Catalog Card Number: 66-23747

Manufactured in the United States of America
Dover Publications, Inc.
180 Varick Street
New York, N. Y. 10014

PREFACE

THE THEORY of algebraic functions has been developed by three different methods which have been designated as transcendental, algebraic-geometric, and arithmetic. Two very illuminating comparisons of these theories have been made by Hensel and Landsberg [28, pages 694–702]* and Emmy Noether [37]. The transcendental method had its origin in a paper by Abel [1] in 1826, in which he announced the remarkable generalization of the addition formulas for elliptic integrals which is now called Abel's theorem. The theory has been greatly enriched by many writers, but especially by Riemann [11]. It is called transcendental because in it Abelian integrals play the fundamental role. The algebraic-geometric theory is a theory of algebraic plane curves. Early expositions were given by Clebsch and Gordan [3] in 1863–66, and by Brill and Noether [17] in 1871. A more recent account is that of Severi [39, 45] in 1921 and 1926, in which much emphasis is placed upon the properties of linear families of curves and their intersections. The title "arithmetic" is applied to a group of theories which differ greatly in detail but which have in common as central features the construction and analysis of the rational functions which are the integrands of Abelian integrals. One of the earliest suggestions of such a theory is found in a paper [7] which Kronecker presented to the Berlin Academy in 1862 but published first in 1881. More elaborate theories in the arithmetic group are those of Weierstrass [27] in his lectures of 1875–6, of Dedekind and Weber [9] in 1882, and of Fields [30] in 1906. The method of Weierstrass is an application to algebraic functions of his theory of analytic functions, and somewhat the same remark would apply to the method of Fields. Dedekind and Weber, however, emphasized the analogies between the theories of algebraic functions and algebraic numbers. Their methods have been elaborated and improved by Hensel and Landsberg in their book on algebraic functions [28] published in 1902, and in later memoirs.

In the following pages, after an introductory Chapter I, I have endeavored to give in Chapters II and III a concise but readable introduction to the arithmetic theory of algebraic functions. My purpose was

---

* The numbers in square brackets here and elsewhere in the text refer to the list of references at the end of this book.

to attain as directly as possible the proofs of the existence, and the methods of construction, of the integrands of the three kinds of elementary integrals, and the theorem of Riemann-Roch. These are fundamental results which it has always seemed to me desirable to have available early, rather than buried deeply, in the text of the theory. The methods used are those of Hensel and Landsberg with many variations. I have, for example, discarded almost entirely the nomenclature and use of the ideals of Dedekind and Weber, which are of great interest, but which are auxiliary rather than essential in the development of the theory.

An introduction to the methods of the transcendental theory is given in Chapters IV, V, and VI, the first of which is devoted to Riemann surfaces and Cauchy's theorem, the second to the definition and properties of Abelian integrals, and the third to the famous theorem of Abel which inaugurated the transcendental theory. An advantage of this order of presentation of the arithmetic and transcendental theories is that no preliminary transformation simplifying the singularities of the fundamental algebraic curve is required.

Chapters VII and VIII are devoted to birational transformations. In the former, fundamental properties and some simple applications of such transformations to the reduction of special algebraic curves to normal forms are explained. Chapter VIII is devoted to two famous transformation theorems. The first of these states that every algebraic curve can be reduced by a Cremona transformation to one having no singular points other than multiple points with distinct tangents, and the second asserts that by a less special birational transformation every such curve can be transformed into another having only double points with distinct tangents. These theorems have been important for the transcendental and algebraic-geometric methods, because these methods have a much simpler aspect when the only singularities of the algebraic curve under consideration are multiple points with distinct tangents.

The literature of the second of the transformation theorems mentioned above is very large. Many of the proofs of the theorem are incomplete, and very few of them have escaped amplification or criticism. It has not been generally recognized in the literature that there are really two theorems involved, one for the function-theoretic and one for the projective plane. In a paper [43] published in 1923 I have given a history of the theorem and have emphasized these remarks. In Chapter VIII below a proof of the theorem for the function-theoretic plane is given which was suggested in the paper of 1881 by Kronecker, and completed in 1902 by Hensel and Landsberg in their book on algebraic functions mentioned above [pages 402–9]. The theorem seems to me distinctly more difficult to prove for the projective plane. In a paper [41] published in 1922 I showed how the reasoning of Kronecker, and Hensel and Landsberg, can be extended to apply to the projective case also. The proof is reproduced in improved form in Chapter VIII. I find great differences of opinion among mathematicians concerning the validity and the advantages of the many different methods of proving these transformation theorems. The method given here has at any rate an especial interest from the standpoint of the arithmetic theories of algebraic functions.

Chapter IX below is devoted to the inversion problem for algebraic curves of genus zero or unity, and to the relations between the theories of elliptic functions and the rational functions associated with an algebraic curve of genus one. I have regretted the necessity of omitting the theory of the inversion problem for greater values of the genus. The presentation of it in a satisfactory manner would require a much larger book than this.

Illustrative examples have great value for a reader who is orienting himself in a mathematical theory for the first time. Chapter X is devoted to such examples, which may be studied in connection with the text from Chapter II on. Not all of these examples are merely exercises. The elliptic and hyperelliptic cases described in Section 70 have of course great importance and many applications. In the final sections of the chapter the methods of Baur [14, 19] for algebraic equations $f(x, y) = 0$ of the third degree in y are explained in detail. These have the advantage of requiring for their applications no more complex algebraic mechanisms than the highest common divisor process. Their generality is illustrated by the fact that they are applicable also to equations of the fourth degree in x and y after a suitable transformation.

Following Chapter X is a list of books and memoirs to which references are made above and elsewhere by numbers in square brackets. At the end of each chapter a brief note indicates reading which may be helpful in connection with the material presented in that particular chapter.

The book as a whole is introductory in character and not a comprehensive treatise. It is an account of lectures on algebraic functions which I have given at the University of Chicago a number of times, the most recent one being the Summer Quarter of 1931. In that year I prepared for students a mimeographed set of notes from which the following pages have been developed. In their preparation I have been ably assisted by Dr. M. R. Hestenes. He has read the manuscript with care and has made many valuable suggestions. I record here my appreciation of his helpful interest.

In conclusion I wish to acknowledge with gratitude the interest of the Editors of the Colloquium Publications of the American Mathematical Society, and the assistance of the National Research Council, which have made possible the publication of this book.

G. A. BLISS

The UNIVERSITY OF CHICAGO, 1932

TABLE OF CONTENTS

CHAPTER I

SINGLE-VALUED ANALYTIC FUNCTIONS

CHAPTER II

ALGEBRAIC FUNCTIONS AND THEIR EXPANSIONS

CHAPTER III

RATIONAL FUNCTIONS

CHAPTER IV

THE RIEMANN SURFACE OF AN ALGEBRAIC FUNCTION

ALGEBRAIC FUNCTIONS

SINGLE-VALUED ANALYTIC FUNCTIONS

1. **Introduction.** Many of the properties of single-valued functions on the Riemann surface of an algebraic function, described in later chapters, are generalizations of well-known properties of functions which are single-valued on the plane of the complex variable $z = x + iy$. In this first chapter it is proposed therefore to give a summary of theorems concerning such functions $f(z)$, with proofs of the more important ones. This will be helpful in pursuing later the theory of algebraic functions, not only because it will give an idea of some of the results to be generalized, but also because the theorems themselves are used in the proofs of the generalizations and their affiliated theorems.

Every function $f(z)$ to be considered is supposed to have a range Z of points of the z-plane at each of which it has a single value in the domain of complex numbers. Such a function is said to be *analytic at a point $z = a$* if there is a neighborhood N of $z = a$ entirely in Z, and such that at each point of N the function $f(z)$ has a unique derivative

$$f'(z) = \lim_{\Delta z \to 0} \frac{f(z + \Delta z) - f(z)}{\Delta z}.$$

Furthermore $f(z)$ is *holomorphic in a region R* of the z-plane if it is single-valued and analytic at each point of R. If a function $f(z)$ is represented in the form

$$f(z) = u(x, y) + i\,v(x, y)$$

then at each point where it is analytic the functions $u(x, y)$, $v(x, y)$ have first partial derivatives and satisfy the well-known equations

$$\partial u / \partial x = \partial v / \partial y, \qquad \partial u / \partial y = -\,\partial v / \partial x,$$

as one verifies readily from the relation

$$\partial f(z) / \partial x = \partial f(z) / i\,\partial y$$

expressing the equality of the derivatives in the directions of the x- and y-axes.

2. **Integrals of functions $f(z)$.** The theory of integration plays an important role in the theory of algebraic functions as well as for single-

valued analytic functions. It will be presented in this section in its simplest aspects for single-valued functions.

The arcs along which the integrals are taken will all be so-called *regular arcs*, that is, arcs with equations of the form

$$z = z(t) = x(t) + iy(t) \qquad (t_1 \leqq t \leqq t_2),$$

continuous and consisting of a finite number of sub-arcs on each of which the functions $x(t)$, $y(t)$ have continuous derivatives such that $x'^2 + y'^2 \neq 0$. The *definite integral* of $f(z)$ taken along a regular arc C has by definition the value

$$\int_C f(z)dz = \int_C (u + iv)(dx + i\,dy)$$

$$= \int_C (u\,dx - v\,dy) + i\int_C (v\,dx + u\,dy),$$

where the line integrals are to be evaluated by substituting for x, y, dx, dy their values as functions of t and dt from the equation of the curve and integrating from t_1 to t_2. The integral will surely exist when $f(z)$ is continuous at each point of C, since then the functions u, v are continuous functions of t on the interval $t_1 t_2$. Unless otherwise expressly stated we shall understand that our functions $f(z)$ are not only continuous but analytic at each point of the arcs C along which integrals are taken.

An important property of such an integral is that

$$\left| \int_C f(z)dz \right| \leqq Ml,$$

where M is the maximum of $|f(z)| = [u^2 + v^2]^{1/2}$ on C and l is the length of C. This is easy to justify since from the definition given above the integral is the limit of a sum of terms of the form

$$\{(u\cos\tau - v\sin\tau) + i(u\sin\tau + v\cos\tau)\}\Delta s,$$

where s is the length of arc measured along C and

$$\cos\tau = x'/(x'^2 + y'^2)^{1/2}, \qquad \sin\tau = y'/(x'^2 + y'^2)^{1/2},$$

and since each of these terms has an absolute value $\leqq M\Delta s$.

3. **Cauchy's theorem.** An arc C is *simply closed* if its end-values $z(t_1)$, $z(t_2)$ are identical while $z(t') \neq z(t'')$ for every other pair of distinct values t', t'' on the interval $t_1 t_2$. The theorem to be proved is then as follows:

THEOREM 3·1. CAUCHY'S THEOREM. *If a function $f(z)$ is holomorphic on a simply closed regular arc C and its interior then*

$$\int_C f(z)dz = 0.$$

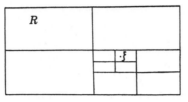

FIG. 3 · 1

It is convenient to prove the theorem first for a rectangle R such as is shown in Figure 3·1. Let R have perimeter l, and let η be the value

$$\eta = \left| \int_R f(z)dz \right|.$$

On at least one, say R_1, of the four quarter-rectangles of R we must have

$$\left| \int_{R_1} f(z)dz \right| \geq \eta/4.$$

Continuing this process of subdivision we obtain a sequence of rectangles $R_n (n = 1, 2, \cdots)$, each in the preceding, and with the properties

$$\left| \int_{R_n} f(z)dz \right| \geq \eta/4^n,$$

$$\text{Perimeter of } R_n = l/2^n,$$

$$\text{Diagonal of } R_n < l/2^{n+1}.$$

The rectangles condense upon a point ζ at which the function $f(z)$ has by hypothesis a derivative $f'(\zeta)$. If η were greater than zero there would therefore be a neighborhood N of ζ so small that in it the continuous function $D(z)$ defined by the equations

$$D(\zeta) = 0, \qquad D(z) = \frac{f(z) - f(\zeta)}{z - \zeta} - f'(\zeta) \text{ for } z \neq \zeta,$$

would satisfy the inequality $|D(z)| < \eta/l^2$. For a rectangle R_n in N we should have, with the help of preceding results,

$$\eta/4^n \leqq \left| \int_{R_1} f(z)dz \right| = \left| \int_{R_n} \{f(\zeta) + (z - \zeta)f'(\zeta) + (z - \zeta)D(z)\}dz \right|$$

$$= \left| \int_{R_n} (z - \zeta)D(z)dz \right| \leqq \frac{l}{2^{n+1}} \frac{\eta}{l^2} \frac{l}{2^n} .$$

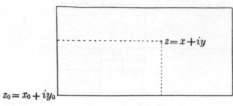

$$z = x + iy$$

$$z_0 = x_0 + iy_0$$

Fig. 3 · 2

But this would imply that $\eta \leqq \eta/2$, which is impossible, and we see that the absolute value η of the integral around the rectangle R is zero.

Having proved the theorem for a rectangle we may further infer easily that our integral vanishes on every closed regular curve C in a rectangle R on which $f(z)$ is holomorphic. For we may define a function $F(z)$ single-valued at every point z of R by the equations

$$F(z) = \int_{x_0}^{x} f(x + iy_0)dx + i \int_{y_0}^{y} f(x + iy)dy$$

$$= i \int_{y_0}^{y} f(x_0 + iy)dy + \int_{x_0}^{x} f(x + iy)dx.$$

We have then a function $F(z) = U + iV$ which is continuous and such that

$$\partial F/\partial x = f(x + iy) = u + iv = \partial F/i\,\partial y.$$

Hence U and V are continuous and

$$\partial U/\partial x = u = \partial V/\partial y, \qquad \partial V/\partial x = v = -\partial U/\partial y.$$

From this result and the definition of the integral in Section 2 above it follows that

$$\int_C f(z)dz = \int_C dU + i \int_C dV = 0.$$

The argument of this paragraph shows that the integral vanishes on closed regular curves in R which intersect themselves, as well as on those which are simply closed.

To prove Theorem $3 \cdot 1$ for an arbitrary simply closed regular arc C, as originally stated, we should first note that there is a constant $\epsilon > 0$ such that for every point ζ of C or its interior the function $f(z)$ is holomorphic on a square of side 2ϵ and center at ζ, on account of the hypothesis that $f(z)$ is holomorphic on C and its interior. Suppose then that the theorem were not true on C. If the interior of C is subdivided by a straight line segment, as shown in Figure $3 \cdot 3$, the conclusion of the theorem would fail to be true on one at least, say C_1, of the simply closed

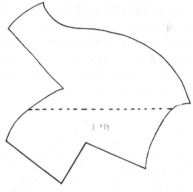

FIG. $3 \cdot 3$

curves formed by the line segment and C. By successive subdivisions of this sort a sequence of simply closed curves C_n could be constructed with maximum diameters approaching zero,* on each of which the theorem would fail. These curves would condense on a point ζ on C or its interior, and this would lead to a contradiction since from the preceding paragraph the theorem must be true for every closed regular arc in the square of side 2ϵ and center at ζ described above, and some of the curves C_n are certainly in this square.

A *connected region* is one such that every pair of its points can be joined by a continuous arc lying entirely in it; and a *simply connected region* R is a connected region which has the further property that the interior of every simply closed continuous curve in R is also in R. With these agreements we can prove the following modification of Cauchy's theorem for curves C which are closed but not necessarily simply closed:

THEOREM $3 \cdot 2$. *If a function $f(z)$ is holomorphic in a simply connected region R then*

---

* See, for example, Bliss, Princeton Colloquum Lectures, p. 29.

$$\int_C f(z)dz = 0$$

on every closed regular arc C interior to R.

The conclusion of the theorem is true for every simply closed polygon interior to R, by Theorem 3·1. It is also true for every closed polygon P whatsoever interior to R. For let the corners of P be designated by $z_0 z_1 \cdots z_n z_0$. Without loss of generality we may suppose that no two adjacent sides of the polygon have more than an end-point in common, since the sum of the values of the integral on a segment common to two adjacent sides is zero and the segment can be deleted. Furthermore we can if necessary move slightly the corners $z_k(k=2, 3, \cdots, n)$ successively without changing the value of the integral, as shown in Figure 3·4, so that no two sides of the resulting polygon are parallel. The result of this alteration is that two sides, if they intersect, do so at

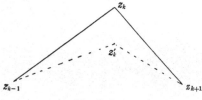

FIG. 3·4

a single point. Suppose now that $z_{l-1}z_l$ is the first side which meets a preceding one, say $z_{k-1}z_k$, and let ζ be the intersection point. The polygon $\zeta z_k \cdots z_{l-1}\zeta$ is simply closed and can be deleted without changing the value of the integral, by Theorem 3·1 Only a finite number of such deletions is possible since the number of sides of the polygon remaining after the deletion is at least one less than before. The final result is therefore a remaining simply closed polygon, and on such a polygon the integral is zero by Theorem 3·1.

A single-valued function $F(z) = U + iV$ can now be defined on the interior of the region R of Theorem 3·2 by the formula

$$F(z) = \int_P f(z)dz$$

where P is a polygon interior to R joining a fixed point z_0 to an arbitrary point z. By an argument similar to that used in proving Theorem 3·1, applied to the function $F(z)$ defined by the formulas

$$F(z) = F(\zeta) + \int_{\xi}^{x} f(x + i\eta)dx + i\int_{\eta}^{y} f(x + iy)dy$$

$$= F(\zeta) + i\int_{\eta}^{y} f(\xi + iy)dy + \int_{\xi}^{x} f(x + iy)dx,$$

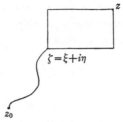

FIG. 3·5

interpreted with the help of Figure 3·5, it can readily be proved that

$$\int_{C} f(z)dz = \int_{C} dU + i\int_{C} dV = 0$$

for every closed regular arc C interior to R.

4. **Consequences of Cauchy's theorem.** If a function $f(z)$ is holomorphic in a neighborhood N of a point $z = a$, except possibly at $z = a$ itself, then the *residue of* $f(z)$ *at* $z = a$ is defined to be the number

$$R_a = \frac{1}{2\pi i}\int_{C} f(z)dz,$$

where C is a simply closed regular arc lying interior to the neighborhood N and having $z = a$ in its interior. Unless otherwise expressly stated it is understood in the following pages that integrals around simply closed curves are always taken in counter-clockwise direction. If Γ is a circle with center at $z = a$ and lying entirely interior to C, then by joining C to

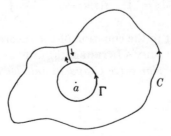

FIG. 4·1

Γ, as shown in Figure 4·1, and integrating around the boundary of the resulting region, Cauchy's theorem tells us that the value of the residue is the same if we replace C by Γ in the definition of R_a. It is then clear further that R_a is the same for all arcs C with the properties described in the definition of a residue.

THEOREM 4·1. *If a function $f(z)$ is holomorphic on a simply closed regular arc C and its interior, except possibly at a finite number of points a_k $(k=1, \cdots, n)$ interior to C, then*

$$\int_C f(z)dz = 2\pi i(R_1 + \cdots + R_n)$$

where R_k is the residue of $f(z)$ at $z=a_k$ $(k=1, \cdots, n)$.

The proof of this theorem is readily made by drawing for each a_k a circle Γ_k interior to C with center at a_k and containing no other singular point of $f(z)$. When the circles Γ_k are joined to C by cuts, as shown in Figure 4·2, Cauchy's theorem tells us that

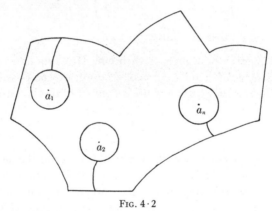

FIG. 4·2

$$\int_C f(z)dz = \int_{\Gamma_1} f(z)dz + \cdots + \int_{\Gamma_n} f(z)dz,$$

and this is equivalent to the equation of the theorem.

THEOREM 4·2. CAUCHY'S INTEGRAL FORMULA. *If $f(z)$ is holomorphic on a simply closed regular curve C and its interior then for every point z interior to C*

$$f(z) = \frac{1}{2\pi i} \int_C \frac{f(w)dw}{w - z},$$

where w is now a complex variable ranging on C.

The value of the integral in the theorem is unchanged if we replace C by a circle Γ with center at z and entirely interior to C, since the integrand $f(w)/(w-z)$ is holomorphic between C and Γ and on these two curves. Furthermore

$$\int_\Gamma \frac{f(w)dw}{w-z} = \int_\Gamma \frac{f(z)dw}{w-z} + \int_\Gamma \frac{f(w)-f(z)}{w-z}dw.$$

The value of the first integral on the right is $2\pi i\, f(z)$, and for the second we have

$$\left| \int_\Gamma \frac{f(w)-f(z)}{w-z}dw \right| < \frac{\epsilon}{r}2\pi r$$

provided that Γ is taken with radius r so small that for every w on it $|f(w)-f(z)| < \epsilon$. Since ϵ is arbitrary the theorem follows.

5. **Ordinary and singular points.** An *ordinary point* of a single-valued function $f(z)$ is one at which $f(z)$ is analytic. All other points are *singular points*. An *isolated singular point* $z = a$ is one for which there is a neighborhood in which $f(z)$ is holomorphic except at $z = a$.

THEOREM 5·1. THE LAURENT EXPANSION. *If $z = a$ is an ordinary or isolated singular point of $f(z)$, and if C is a circle with center at $z = a$ in and on which $f(z)$ is holomorphic except possibly at $z = a$, then the values of $f(z)$ are given at all points $z \neq a$ interior to C by a series of the form*

(5·1)
$$f(z) = A_0 + A_1(z - a) + A_2(z - a)^2 + \cdots$$
$$+ A_{-1}(z - a)^{-1} + A_{-2}(z - a)^{-2} + \cdots$$

which converges at every point interior to C except possibly at $z = a$.

To prove this we may draw a second circle C' with center at $z = a$ interior to C and denote the radii of C and C' by R and R'. If C and C' are joined by a cut, as shown in Figure 5·1, then Cauchy's integral for-

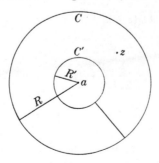

FIG. 5·1

mula gives the expression

$$f(z) = \frac{1}{2\pi i} \int_C \frac{f(w)dw}{w - z} - \frac{1}{2\pi i} \int_{C'} \frac{f(w)dw}{w - z}$$

for the value of $f(z)$ at an interior point z of the ring-shaped region between C' and C. For the first integral we find the formulas

$$\frac{1}{w - z} = \frac{1}{w - a} \frac{1}{1 - (z - a)/(w - a)}$$

$$= \frac{1}{w - a} + \frac{z - a}{(w - a)^2} + \cdots + \frac{(z - a)^{n-1}}{(w - a)^n} + \frac{1}{w - z}\left(\frac{z - a}{w - a}\right)^n,$$

$$\frac{1}{2\pi i} \int_C \frac{f(w)}{w - z} dw = A_0 + A_1(z - a) + \cdots + A_{n-1}(z - a)^{n-1} + R_n,$$

where

$$A_k = \frac{1}{2\pi i} \int_C \frac{f(w)dw}{(w - a)^{k+1}} \qquad (k = 0, 1, \cdots),$$

$$|R_n| = \left| \frac{1}{2\pi i} \int_C \frac{f(w)}{w - z}\left(\frac{z - a}{w - a}\right)^n dw \right| \leq \frac{M}{2\pi}\left(\frac{r}{R}\right)^n 2\pi R.$$

The constant M is the maximum of $|f(w)/(w-z)|$ for values of w on the circle C, and $r = |z-a|$. Since $(r/R) < 1$ it follows that R_n approaches zero as n approaches infinity. Similarly, for the second integral,

$$\frac{-1}{w - z} = \frac{1}{z - a} \frac{1}{1 - (w - a)/(z - a)}$$

$$= \frac{1}{z - a} + \frac{w - a}{(z - a)^2} + \cdots + \frac{(w - a)^{n-1}}{(z - a)^n} + \frac{1}{z - w}\left(\frac{w - a}{z - a}\right)^n,$$

$$\frac{-1}{2\pi i} \int_{C'} \frac{f(w)}{w - z} dw = A_{-1}(z - a)^{-1} + \cdots + A_{-n}(z - a)^{-n} + R_{-n},$$

where

$$A_{-k} = \frac{1}{2\pi i} \int_{C'} f(w)(w - a)^{k-1}dw \qquad (k = 1, 2, \cdots),$$

$$|R_{-n}| = \left| \frac{1}{2\pi i} \int_{C'} \frac{f(w)}{z - w}\left(\frac{w - a}{z - a}\right)^n dw \right| \leq \frac{M'}{2\pi}\left(\frac{R'}{r}\right)^n 2\pi R'.$$

The constant M' is the maximum of $|f(w)/(z-w)|$ for values of w on the circle C'. Since $(R'/r) < 1$ we see that R_{-n} also approaches zero as n

approaches infinity. Thus for every point z in the interior of the ring between C' and C the series $(5 \cdot 1)$ of Theorem $5 \cdot 1$ defined in this way converges and represents $f(z)$. With the help of Cauchy's theorem the values of the constants A_k, A_{-k} are seen to be independent of the radius of C', and for an arbitrary point $z \neq a$ interior to C the series of the theorem therefore converges to $f(z)$.

Let $z = a$ be a point having a neighborhood in which $f(z)$ is holomorphic except possibly at $z = a$. If the Laurent expansion for $f(z)$ at $z = a$ has no terms with negative exponents then $z = a$ is an *ordinary point* if $f(a) = A_0$. The point $z = a$ is called a *removable singularity*, when there are no terms with negative exponents, if $f(z)$ is not defined at $z = a$ or if $f(a) \neq A_0$, since in this case $z = a$ will become an ordinary point if the value A_0 is assigned to $f(z)$ at $z = a$. An isolated singular point at which the Laurent expansion has a term with negative exponent $-n$, but none with a larger negative exponent, is called *a pole of order* $-n$. If the series has an infinity of terms with negative exponents then $z = a$ is an *essential singularity of $f(z)$*. All singularities of $f(z)$ which are not poles are called essential singularities, but only those which are isolated from other singularities have Laurent expansions associated with them.

THEOREM $5 \cdot 2$. *Let $f(z)$ be a function which is holomorphic in a neighborhood N of $z = a$ except possibly at $z = a$ itself. If $|f(z)|$ is bounded in N then $z = a$ is an ordinary point or removable singularity of $f(z)$. If $|f(z)|$ is not bounded in N but $|(z - a)^n f(z)|$ is bounded for some positive integer n, then $z = a$ is a pole of $f(z)$ of order not less than $-n$. Similar statements hold for $z = \infty$ when $z - a$ is replaced by $1/z$.*

If $|f(z)|$ is bounded in N then it is easy to see that the product $g(z) = (z - a)^2 f(z)$ is holomorphic in the whole of N including $z = a$ and vanishes with its derivative at $z = a$. Hence for the Laurent expansion of $g(z)$ the integrals in the expressions for the coefficients A_{-k} are by Cauchy's theorem all zero, and the values of A_0 and A_1 are also zero since $g(a) = g'(a) = 0$. The Laurent expansion for $f(z)$ itself has therefore no terms with negative exponents.

If $|(z - a)^n f(z)|$ is bounded the Laurent expansion for $(z - a)^n f(z)$ can have no terms with negative exponents, according to the first part of the theorem. Consequently the Laurent expansion of $f(z)$ can have no terms with negative exponents less than $-n$. It must have some terms with negative exponents, however, if $|f(z)|$ is not bounded in N.

THEOREM $5 \cdot 3$. *Near every point $z = a$ at which the residue R_a is defined the function $f(z)$ is represented by a Laurent expansion and $R_a = A_{-1}$.*

This is readily proved by integrating $1/2\pi i$ times the series $(5 \cdot 1)$

term by term. The resulting integrals are all zero except that arising from the term $A_{-1}(z-a)^{-1}/2\pi i$ which has the value A_{-1}.

In the theory of functions the character of *the point* $z = \infty$ for a function $f(z)$ is determined by making the transformation $z = 1/\zeta$ and studying the character of the point $\zeta = 0$ for the function $f(1/\zeta)$. If there is a circle C about $z = 0$ as center outside of which $f(z)$ is holomorphic except possibly at $z = \infty$, then $f(z)$ is represented by a Laurent series

(5·2)
$$f(z) = A_0 + A_1(1/z) + A_2(1/z)^2 + \cdots$$
$$+ A_{-1}z + A_{-2}z^2 + \cdots$$

which converges to $f(z)$ at every point z outside of C.

The expansions of $f(z)$ at $z = \infty$ are

$$f(z) = A_0 + A_1(1/z) + A_2(1/z)^2 + \cdots,$$
$$f(z) = A_{-n}z^n + \cdots + A_{-1}z + A_0 + A_1(1/z) + \cdots$$
$$f(z) = \cdots + A_{-1}z + A_0 + A_1(1/z) + \cdots.$$

in the cases when $f(z)$ has, respectively, at $z = \infty$ an ordinary point or removable singularity, a pole of order $-n$, or an isolated essential singularity.

The residue of $f(z)$ at $z = \infty$, when $f(z)$ is holomorphic on a simply closed regular curve C and its exterior except possibly at $z = \infty$, is defined to be the number

$$R_\infty = -\frac{1}{2\pi i}\int_C f(z)dz,$$

where the integral is taken as usual in counter-clockwise sense. This residue has the same value when C is replaced by a circle with $z = 0$ as center entirely outside of C, and is therefore readily proved to be the same for all curves C with the properties described above. By integrating the Laurent series (5·2) term by term the residue at $z = \infty$ is readily found to have the value $R_\infty = -A_1$.

6. **Rational functions.** One of the most important classes of functions for the theory of algebraic functions, as well as for the theory of single-valued functions such as are considered in this chapter, is the class of rational functions. Most of the theorems given in this section can be generalized for algebraic functions, but there are important exceptions which will be indicated.

THEOREM 6·1. *A function $f(z)$ holomorphic and bounded in the whole finite z-plane, or a single-valued function $f(z)$ which has no singularity either in the finite z-plane or at $z = \infty$, is a constant.*

If a function $f(z)$ is holomorphic and satisfies the condition $|f(z)|$ $< M$ in the whole finite z-plane, then with the help of Cauchy's integral formula applied to a circle C with $z = 0$ as center and having the point z in its interior

$$\left| f(z) - f(0) \right| = \left| \frac{1}{2\pi i} \int_C \frac{f(w)dw}{w - z} - \frac{1}{2\pi i} \int_C \frac{f(w)dw}{w} \right|$$

$$= \left| \frac{1}{2\pi i} \int_C \frac{zf(w)dw}{w(w - z)} \right| \leqq \frac{1}{2\pi} \frac{rM}{R(R - r)} 2\pi R,$$

where R is the radius of C and $r = |z|$. As R approaches infinity the last expression approaches zero, and hence we must have $f(z) = f(0)$ for every z.

To prove that a single-valued function $f(z)$ with no singularity is a constant we may first prove that there is a constant M such that $|f(z)| < M$, and then apply the reasoning of the preceding paragraph. Or one may start from the fact that such a function has a Laurent expansion at $z = 0$,

$$f(z) = A_0 + A_1 z + A_2 z^2 + \cdots,$$

which is convergent in the whole finite z-plane. This is also the Laurent expansion of $f(z)$ at $z = \infty$, and since $z = \infty$ is not a singular point the coefficients $A_1, A_2, \cdots$ must all be zero.

THEOREM 6·2. *A polynomial of degree n has a pole of order $-n$ at $z = \infty$ and no other singularity. Conversely, a function with no singularity except a pole of order $-n$ at $z = \infty$ is a polynomial of degree n.*

The first part of the theorem is evident since the expression

$$P(z) = A_0 + A_1 z + \cdots + A_n z^n$$

for a polynomial of degree n is its Laurent expansion at $z = \infty$ and has the form which indicates a pole of order $-n$ at that point.

If, conversely, a function $f(z)$ has no singularity except a pole of order $-n$ at $z = \infty$, let

$$A_{-1} z + \cdots + A_{-n} z^n$$

be the sum of the terms with negative exponents, the so-called *principal part*, of its Laurent expansion at $z = \infty$. The difference

$$f(z) - A_{-1} z - \cdots - A_{-n} z^n$$

will then have no singularity at all and must be a constant.

THEOREM 6·3. *A rational function of z has no singularities except poles. Conversely, a function $f(z)$ which has no singularities except poles is rational in z.*

A rational function is by definition a function $f(z)$ which is equal to the quotient of two polynomials

$$f(z) = \frac{A_0 + A_1 z + \cdots + A_m z^m}{B_0 + B_1 z + \cdots + B_n z^n} = \frac{P(z)}{Q(z)} \qquad (A_m \neq 0,\ B_n \neq 0)$$

wherever the denominator is different from zero, and equal to the limit of this quotient at every point $z = a$ or $z = \infty$ where this limit is finite. In accordance with this definition we may just as well suppose from the start that the polynomials $P(z)$ and $Q(z)$ have no common factor.

The only singularities of such a function are at $z = \infty$ or at roots $z = a$ of the denominator $Q(z)$. If $Q(z)$ contains a factor $(z-a)^k$ and no higher power of $z-a$ then $z = a$ is a pole of order $-k$ of $f(z)$, as one sees with the help of Theorem 5·2. The product $(z-a)^k f(z)$ is, in fact, bounded near $z = a$ but $(z-a)^{k-1} f(z)$ is not. At $z = \infty$ the same theorem applied to the expression

$$f(z) = z^{m-n} \frac{A_0(1/z)^m + \cdots + A_m}{B_0(1/z)^n + \cdots + B_n}$$

shows that $z = \infty$ is a pole of order $n - m$ of $f(z)$ if $m > n$, but is otherwise an ordinary point. Hence a rational function has no singularities but poles.

If a function $f(z)$ has no singularities but poles then in a circle C with center at $z = 0$ there can be only a finite number of them. Otherwise the poles in C would have an accumulation point which would be a singularity of $f(z)$ but not a pole, since all ordinary points and poles of $f(z)$ are isolated from other singularities. Similarly after making the transformation $z = 1/\zeta$ it appears that there are only a finite number of poles of $f(z)$ outside of C. Suppose now that the finite poles of $f(z)$ are the points $z = a_i$ $(i = 1, \cdots, p)$ and that their orders are numbers $-k_i$. Then

$$f(z)(z - a_1)^{k_1} \cdots (z - a_p)^{k_p}$$

has no singularity except possibly a pole at $z = \infty$ and is equal to a polynomial $P(z)$. Hence $f(z)$ is a rational function.

THEOREM 6·4. *If a function $f(z)$ is holomorphic in the whole z-plane except for isolated singular points then the number of its singularities is finite and the sum of its residues is zero. In particular this is true for rational functions.*

The argument used in the proof of Theorem 6·3 can be applied again to show that the number of singularities of $f(z)$ is finite. Let C be a circle about $z=0$ as center and so large that all of the singularities of the function $f(z)$ in the finite part of the z-plane are interior to C. Then by Theorem 4·1

$$\int_C f(z)dz = 2\pi i \ \{\text{sum of residues of } f(z) \text{ at finite points } z\}.$$

But according to the definition of the residue of $f(z)$ at $z=\infty$ we have

$$\int_C f(z)dz = -2\pi i R_\infty.$$

Hence the sum of all of the residues of $f(z)$ is zero.

THEOREM 6·5. *The sum of the orders of the zeros and poles of a rational function $f(z)$ is zero.*

At a point $z=a$ which is a zero or pole of $f(z)$ we may express $f(z)$, by means of its Laurent series, in the form

$$f(z) = (z-a)^k \{A_0 + A_1(z-a) + \cdots \} = (z-a)^k g(z),$$

where $g(z)$ is holomorphic near $z=a$, $g(a)=A_0\neq0$, and k is the order of the zero or pole. Then the quotient

$$\frac{f'(z)}{f(z)} = \frac{k}{z-a} + \frac{g'(z)}{g(z)}$$

has the residue k at $z=a$. Similarly the residue of $f'(z)/f(z)$ at $z=\infty$ is the order of the zero or pole of $f(z)$ at $z=\infty$. The quotient $f'(z)/f(z)$ has no singularities other than the zeros and poles of $f(z)$, and the theorem is therefore proved, since the sum of the residues of $f'(z)/f(z)$ is zero.

A very important corollary to this theorem is the *fundamental theorem of algebra* which says that every polynomial has at least one root. Since a polynomial of degree n has one pole of order $-n$ at $z=\infty$, the sum of the orders of its zeros, according to Theorem 6·5, must be n.

It is understood that the *principal part* of the Laurent expansion at an isolated singular point $z=a$ of a function $f(z)$ is the sum of the terms of the expansion which have negative exponents. With this definition in mind we can prove the following theorem:

THEOREM 6·6. *If $P_1(z), \cdots, P_n(z)$ are the principal parts of the Laurent expansions at the poles of a rational function $f(z)$, then $f(z)$ is expressible in the form*

(6·1) $$f(z) = P_1(z) + \cdots + P_n(z) + c.$$

If a finite number of poles and principal parts are selected arbitrarily then there exists a rational function which has these poles and principal parts and no other singularities. The most general such function is of the form (6·1), *where c is an arbitrary constant.*

Each of the expressions $P_k(z)$, for a given rational function $f(z)$, has no other singularity except the pole at which it is the principal part. The difference

$$f(z) - P_1(z) - \cdots - P_n(z)$$

has therefore no singularities whatsoever and is constant.

If $P_1(z), \cdots, P_n(z)$ are selected arbitrarily the sum

$$g(z) = P_1(z) + \cdots + P_n(z)$$

is evidently rational and has the required singularities and principal parts and no others. For every other function $f(z)$ with these properties the difference $f(z) - g(z)$ has no singularities and is a constant.

THEOREM 6·7. *If $a_1, \cdots, a_m, b_1, \cdots, b_n$ are the zeros and poles of a rational function $f(z)$ in the finite part of the z-plane, each repeated a number of times equal to the absolute value of its order, then $f(z)$ is expressible in the form*

$$(6·2) \qquad f(z) = c \frac{(z - a_1) \cdots (z - a_m)}{(z - b_1) \cdots (z - b_n)}.$$

If the numbers $a_1, \cdots, a_m$ and $b_1, \cdots, b_n$ are selected arbitrarily in the finite part of the z-plane there exists a rational function having them as its finite zeros and poles. The most general such function is of the form (6·2) *where c is an arbitrary constant. At $z = \infty$ the function has a zero of order $n-m$ if $n > m$, a pole of order $n-m$ if $n < m$, or an ordinary point which is neither a zero nor a pole if $n = m$.*

The truth of the first statement of this theorem follows readily from the fact that the rational function

$$g(z) = \frac{(z - a_1) \cdots (z - a_m)}{(z - b_1) \cdots (z - b_n)} = z^{m-n} \frac{(1 - a_1/z) \cdots (1 - a_m/z)}{(1 - b_1/z) \cdots (1 - b_n/z)}$$

has the finite zeros $a_1, \cdots, a_m$ and poles $b_1, \cdots, b_n$, and also the order which $f(z)$ must have at $z = \infty$, as one readily verifies from the fact that the sum of the orders of the zeros and poles is zero. The quotient $f(z)/g(z)$ has no zeros or poles and hence is a constant. The last part of the theorem is now evident.

The theorems numbered 6·1 and 6·3 to 6·5 above all have corresponding theorems of similar forms which hold for the rational functions, associated with an algebraic function, which are to be studied in later chapters. The last two theorems are in a quite different category, however. They imply that the principal parts, or the zeros and poles of a rational function in the finite z-plane, can be selected arbitrarily. On the contrary, it is not in general possible to prescribe arbitrarily the principal parts or the zeros and poles of a rational function on the Riemann surface of an algebraic function, as will be seen in Theorems $40 \cdot 2$ and $40 \cdot 4$ of Chapter V.

7. **An expansion theorem.** The theorem to be explained in this section is a fundamental one for the development of the properties of algebraic functions and it has also many other applications. It is the theorem which characterizes a curve $f(x, y) = 0$ in a neighborhood of a non-singular point where the partial derivatives f_x, f_y are not both zero.

THEOREM $7 \cdot 1$. THE EXPANSION THEOREM. *Let $f(x, y)$ be a function of the two complex variables x, y with the properties*

(1) *it is expressible near (a, b) by a convergent power series in $x - a$ and $y - b$,*

(2) $f(a, b) = 0$,

(3) $f_y(a, b) \neq 0$.

Then there is one and but one power series of the form

$$y = b + c_1(x - a) + c_2(x - a)^2 + \cdots$$

which satisfies $f(x, y) = 0$ identically. In a suitably chosen neighborhood $|x - a| \leq \delta$ this power series converges and defines a holomorphic solution $y(x)$ of the equation $f(x, y) = 0$ with the further property that there is a constant $\epsilon > 0$ such that no solution $(x, y') \neq \{x, y(x)\}$ exists satisfying the inequalities

$$(7 \cdot 1) \qquad |x - a| \leq \delta, \qquad |y' - y(x)| \leq \epsilon.$$

There is no loss in generality in taking $(a, b) = (0, 0)$, or in supposing the equation $f(x, y) = 0$ in the form $y = h(x, y)$ with $h(0, 0) = h_y(0, 0) = 0$. The first simplification can be brought about by a transformation $x - a = x'$, $y - b = y'$; and the second by transferring all of the terms of the equation $f(x, y) = 0$ to the right side except the linear term in y which has a coefficient different from zero by (3).

Suppose then that we try to make the series

$$(7 \cdot 2) \qquad y = c_1 x + c_2 x^2 + \cdots$$

satisfy the equation

$$(7 \cdot 3) \qquad y = h(x, y)$$

formally. By substituting and comparing coefficients we see successively that this will be accomplished if each c_k is set equal to a uniquely determined polynomial with positive integral coefficients in a finite number of the coefficients of h. Hence there is one and but one series $(7 \cdot 2)$ which satisfies $(7 \cdot 3)$ formally.

In order to prove the convergence of $(7 \cdot 2)$ we lose no generality in assuming $h(x, y)$ convergent for $|x| \leqq 1$, $|y| \leqq 1$, since if the series $h(x, y)$ converges for $|x| \leqq \rho$, $|y| \leqq \sigma$ we can always secure convergence for $|x'| \leqq 1$, $|y'| \leqq 1$ by making the transformation $x = \rho x'$, $y = \sigma y'$. Under these circumstances the coefficients of $h(x, y)$ have absolute values all less than a certain constant M, since by hypothesis the series of absolute values of the terms of $h(x, y)$ now converges when $x = 1$, $y = 1$. The equation

$$(7 \cdot 4) \qquad y = H(x, y) = \frac{M}{(1 - x)(1 - y)} - M - My$$

has no constant term and no linear term in y on the right, and has each coefficient in $H(x, y)$ greater than or equal to M and hence greater than the absolute value of the corresponding coefficient of $h(x, y)$. Its unique solution series through $(x, y) = (0, 0)$,

$$(7 \cdot 5) \qquad\qquad y = C_1 x + C_2 x^2 + \cdots ,$$

has therefore positive coefficients each greater than the absolute value of the corresponding coefficients of $(7 \cdot 2)$. But the series $(7 \cdot 5)$ represents the solution

$$y = \frac{1 - \{1 - 4M(1 + M)x/(1 - x)\}^{1/2}}{2(1 + M)}$$

of equation $(7 \cdot 4)$ which vanishes at $x = 0$, and therefore surely converges when $|x| < 1/(1 + 2M)^2$. Hence the series $(7 \cdot 2)$ converges also on this interval.

To prove the last statement in the theorem we may write

$$f(x, y') - f(x, y) = (y' - y)A(x, y, y')$$

where $A(a, b, b) = f_y(a, b) \neq 0$. Hence in a sufficiently small region $(7 \cdot 1)$ we have $A[x, y(x), y'] \neq 0$, and we see that $f(x, y)$ and $f(x, y')$ can not both vanish unless $y = y'$.

8. **Resultants and discriminants.** For the developments in later chapters we shall need some properties of the resultant of two poly-

nomials and of the discriminant of a single polynomial. The *resultant of two polynomials*

$$f(y) = f_0 y^m + f_1 y^{m-1} + \cdots + f_m,$$
$$g(y) = g_0 y^n + g_1 y^{n-1} + \cdots + g_n,$$

may be represented by the symbol

$$R = \begin{vmatrix} y^{n-1}f \\ \cdots \\ yf \\ f \\ y^{m-1}g \\ \cdots \\ yg \\ g \end{vmatrix}$$

which stands for the determinant whose rows are the coefficients of the powers of y in the polynomials indicated. The resultant is not identically zero in the coefficients of f and g since for the special case $f = y^m$, $g = y^n + 1$ its value is unity. By multiplying the polynomials in the symbol for R by the co-factors of the last column of R we find an identity

$$(8 \cdot 1) \qquad\qquad R = M(y)f(y) + N(y)g(y)$$

where the coefficients M and N are polynomials in y with degrees not greater than $n-1$ and $m-1$, respectively.

THEOREM 8·1. *When the polynomials f and g have numerical coefficients a necessary and sufficient condition that they shall have a finite or infinite common root is $R = 0$.*

If R is different from zero the coefficients f_0 and g_0 are not both zero and the equation $(8 \cdot 1)$ shows that f and g cannot have a common finite root. If $R = 0$ there are constants not all zero satisfying the linear equations whose coefficients are the columns of R. When the polynomials in the symbol for R are multiplied by these constants and added, an identity in y of the form

$$(8 \cdot 2) \qquad\qquad 0 = M(y)f(y) + N(y)g(y)$$

is found, where M and N have degrees not exceeding $n-1$ and $m-1$ as before. It follows readily from this equation that when f_0 and g_0 are not both zero the polynomials f and g have a common linear factor and therefore a common finite root. When f_0 and g_0 both vanish f and g have a common infinite root.

The resultant R becomes a polynomial in f_0, g_0 and the roots ξ_i, η_k of f and g when the values of f_i and g_k are substituted from the expressions for f_i/f_0 and g_k/g_0 as symmetric functions of the roots. It is easy to see that R has the factor $f_0^n g_0^m$, and we can prove that R is homogeneous and of degree mn in the roots ξ_i, η_k. For if we multiply each root by a factor ρ the coefficients f_i and g_k are multiplied by ρ^i and ρ^k. If we multiply the k-th row of R by ρ^{k-1} for $k=1, \cdots, n$, and the $(n+i)$-th row by ρ^{i-1} for $i=1, \cdots, m$, it turns out that a factor ρ^{s-1} can be taken out of the s-th column for $s = 1, 2, \cdots, m+n$. Hence R is multiplied by ρ to the power

$$(1 + \cdots + m + n - 1) - (1 + \cdots + n - 1)$$
$$- (1 + \cdots + m - 1) = mn,$$

and we see that R is homogeneous and of degree mn in the roots ξ_i, η_k. Since R vanishes in every numerical case for which a root ξ_i is equal to a root η_k it must contain each of the factors $\xi_i - \eta_k$, and since the degree of R in the roots is mn it follows that

$$(8 \cdot 3) \qquad R = c f_0^n g_0^m \prod (\xi_i - \eta_k),$$

where the product is taken for all the mn differences. The value of the constant c is readily found to be 1 since for the special case $f = y^m$, $g = y^n + 1$ the values of Π, f_0, g_0 and the determinant for R, are all unity. From the expression $(8 \cdot 3)$ for R it is evident also that

$$(8 \cdot 4) \qquad R = f_0^n \prod g(\xi_i) = g_0^m \prod f(\eta_k),$$

where the products are taken, respectively, for all the roots ξ_i of f and all the roots η_k of g.

The *discriminant D of a polynomial* $f(y)$ is by definition the resultant of the derivative $f'(y)$ and the polynomial

$$g(y) = mf - yf' = f_1 y^{m-1} + \cdots + (m - 1) f_{m-1} y + m f_m.$$

From equation $(8 \cdot 1)$ it follows readily that the discriminant satisfies an identity

$$D = P(y)f(y) + Q(y)f'(y)$$

where the coefficients P and Q are polynomials of degrees at most $m-2$ and $m-1$, respectively.

THEOREM $8 \cdot 2$. *When* $f(y)$ *has numerical coefficients a necessary and sufficient condition that it shall have a finite or infinite multiple root is* $D = 0$.

From Theorem $8 \cdot 1$ we know that when $D = 0$ the polynomials $f'(y)$ and $g(y)$ have a finite or infinite common root. If the common root is finite it must be a root of both $f(y)$ and $f'(y)$, on account of the form of $g(y)$, and hence is a multiple root of f. If it is infinite then the leading coefficients mf_0, f_1 of $f'(y)$ and $g(y)$ both vanish, and f itself has a multiple infinite root.

In the determinant for D we may substitute the values of the coefficients f_i from the expressions for the quotients f_i/f_0 as symmetric functions of the roots ξ_i of f. It is easy to see then that D has the factor f_0^{2m-2} and is a symmetric function of the ξ_i. By an argument similar to that used for the resultant it can be shown further that D is homogeneous and of degree $m(m-1)$ in the roots. Since D vanishes when $\xi_i = \xi_k$ it must contain the factor $\xi_i - \xi_k$, and consequently the square of this factor, since it is symmetric in the roots. It follows readily then that

$$D = cf_0^{2m-2} \prod_{i<k}(\xi_i - \xi_k)^2,$$

where c is a constant, since the degree of each side of the equation in the variables ξ_i is $m(m-1)$. From the relation

$$f'(\xi_1) = f_0(\xi_1 - \xi_2) \cdots (\xi_1 - \xi_m),$$

and similar ones for the other roots, we find

$$D = c(-1)^{m(m-1)/2} f_0^{m-2} \prod f'(\xi_i).$$

The value of the constant c can be found from the special case $f = y^m + 1$ for which the value of the determinant for D is m^{2m-2} and the value of the product in the last equation is m^m, as one readily calculates. Hence we have the two final formulas for D

$$(8 \cdot 5) \qquad D = (-1)^{m(m-1)/2} m^{m-2} f_0^{2m-2} \prod_{i<k}(\xi_i - \xi_k)^2$$

$$(8 \cdot 6) \qquad = m^{m-2} f_0^{m-2} \prod f'(\xi_i)$$

which will be useful in later chapters.

9. **Reducibility of a polynomial** $f(x, y)$. The polynomials to be studied in this section are all supposed to have their coefficients in the domain of real or complex numbers. A polynomial $f(x, y)$ with coefficients in this domain is said to be *reducible* if it is equal to the product of two other such polynomials in x and y neither of which is a constant; otherwise it is *irreducible*. For the study of the irreducible factors of a polynomial the following lemma is fundamental:

LEMMA 9·1. *If the functions f, g, P, L, in the equation*

$$f(x, y)g(x, y) = P(x, y)L(x, y)$$

are polynomials in x and y, with P irreducible, and if the equation is an identity in x and y, then P is a factor of either f or g.

This can easily be proved when $P = x - a$. For suppose the lemma not true in this case and set $x = a$ in the equation. The coefficients of the powers of y in $f(a, y)$ would not all vanish, and similarly for $g(a, y)$. We could then select a value b for y which is not a root of either $f(a, y)$ or $g(a, y)$ and the equation of the lemma would then not be true. Hence $P = x - a$ must be a factor in all the coefficients of powers of y in f, or else in all the similar coefficients for g.

In the general case when P involves both x and y suppose that P is not a factor in f so that f and P have no common factor at all, since P is irreducible. The resultant of f and P as polynomials in y will then be a polynomial $R(x)$ not identically zero and satisfying an identity, analogous to (8·1), of the form

$$(9·1)\qquad R(x) = M(x, y)f(x, y) + N(x, y)P(x, y)$$

in which $R(x)$, $M(x, y)$, $N(x, y)$ are polynomials. The equation (9·1) multiplied by g, with the equation of the lemma, then imply an equation of the form

$$R(x)g(x, y) = P(x, y)Q(x, y).$$

According to the preceding paragraph the factors $x - a$ of $R(x)$ must be divisible into the coefficients of the powers of y in $Q(x, y)$, since P is by hypothesis irreducible, and hence g has the factor P.

COROLLARY. *For two irreducible polynomials $f(x, y)$ and $P(x, y)$, both of which contain powers of y, there are only a finite number of values of x for which f and P have equal roots y unless f is a constant times P.*

This follows from equation (9·1) in which $R(x)$ would be identically zero if f and P had equal roots y for an infinity of values of x. Since $M(x, y)$ in this equation is at least one degree lower in y than P, it follows that P would have to be divisible into $f(x, y)$ and hence f and P would differ only by a constant factor.

LEMMA 9·2. *Every polynomial $f(x, y)$ is expressible as the product $f = P_1 P_2 \cdots P_k$ of a finite number of irreducible factors, and every other such expression for f has factors which are the same except possibly for constant multipliers.*

The existence of such a product for f, consisting of at least one factor, is evident. Suppose that a second one is $f = Q_1 \cdots Q_l$. According to the preceding lemma Q_1 must be a factor in P_1 or else in the product $P_2 \cdots P_k$. Repeating this argument we conclude finally that Q_1 is divisible into some P_i, in which case Q_1 coincides with P_i except for a constant multiplier. If we divide out by $Q_1 = P_i$ we may similarly show that the second factor Q_2 is identical with a new factor P_j, and so on.

THEOREM 9·1. *A necessary and sufficient condition that a polynomial* $f(x, y)$ *shall have no repeated irreducible factors involving* y *is* $D(x) \not\equiv 0$, *where* $D(x)$ *is the discriminant of* $f(x, y)$ *as a polynomial in* y.

If $f(x, y)$ has such a repeated factor then for every x the equation $f(x, y) = 0$ has multiple roots y and $D(x)$ must vanish identically. Hence the condition of the theorem is sufficient.

The condition is also necessary since if $D(x) \equiv 0$ then by the argument in Section 8 there is an identity of the form

$$M(x, y)f(x, y) + N(x, y)f_y(x, y) = 0$$

analogous to equation (8·2), in which $M(x, y)$ and $N(x, y)$ are polynomials of degrees at most $n-2$, $n-1$, respectively, in y, and not identically zero. By Lemma 9·1 all of the irreducible factors of f must divide either N or f_y, and one at least of those which involve y, say $P(x, y)$, must be a factor of f_y, since the degree of $N(x, y)$ in y is too low for N to contain all of them. The equations

$$f = P(x, y)h(x, y), \qquad f_y = P_y h + P h_y$$

show that if P is a factor in f_y it must also be a factor of h, so that P occurs at least twice in $f(x, y)$.

REFERENCES FOR CHAPTER I

For the theory presented in Chapter I above the reader may consult the standard books on the theory of functions of a complex variable, for example, the references numbered 13, 24, 34 and 35 in the list at the end of this book. For the theory of resultants and discriminants see the references numbered 25 and 31.

CHAPTER II

ALGEBRAIC FUNCTIONS AND THEIR EXPANSIONS

10. **Introduction.** In the preceding chapter it was shown that the values of a single-valued analytic function of a complex variable x in a neighborhood of an isolated singular point $x=a$ are the values of a Laurent series in positive and negative integral powers of $x-a$, convergent in a suitably chosen circle with $x=a$ as center except possibly at $x=a$ itself. In the following paragraphs we shall see that an algebraic function of x is a multiple-valued function, and that its values near an arbitrary point $x=a$ are given, not by one, but in general by a finite number of Laurent expansions, each in powers of a variable $t=(x-a)^{1/r}$ where r is a positive integer. The purpose of this chapter is the definition of an algebraic function and the determination of its expansions.

11. **Definition of an algebraic function.** Let $f(x, y)$ be a polynomial in y of the form

$$f(x, y) = f_0(x)y^n + f_1(x)y^{n-1} + \cdots + f_n(x)$$

where each coefficient $f_k(x)$ is itself a polynomial in x with coefficients in the domain of complex numbers. The largest exponent of x occurring in one of these coefficients will be denoted by m. An *algebraic function* is then a function $y(x)$ defined for values x in the complex x-plane by an equation of the form $f(x, y)=0$. The values of such a function $y(x)$ are points in the complex y-plane, and there are in general more than one value of $y(x)$ corresponding to each x. At $x=\infty$ the values of the function $y(x)$ are, by definition, the roots of the equation $g(0, y)=0$ where $g(x', y)=x'^m f(1/x', y)$.

Unless otherwise expressly stated it will be understood always that the conditions

(a) $f_0(x), \cdots , f_n(x)$ have no common factor involving x,

(b) $f_0(x) \not\equiv 0$,

(c) $D(x) \not\equiv 0$

are satisfied, where $D(x)$ is the discriminant of $f(x, y)$ thought of as a polynomial in y. It can be seen without great difficulty that these conditions are not serious restrictions. When, for example, the discriminant $D(x)$ is identically zero it has been shown that the polynomial $f(x, y)$

24

has repeated factors involving y, and the exclusion of all except one of these factors in each case would reduce the polynomial to one with the properties indicated. The condition $D(x) \neq 0$ implies further that at all except a finite number of values $x = a$ where $D(a) = 0$ the values of $y(x)$ are distinct and exactly n in number.

A point $x = a$ in the complex x-plane where $f_0(a) \neq 0$, $D(a) \neq 0$ is called an *ordinary point* for the algebraic function $y(x)$. A point at which one or both of $f_0(a)$, $D(a)$ vanish is a *singular point*. The point $x = \infty$ is ordinary or singular according as $x' = 0$ is ordinary or singular for the algebraic function $y(x')$ defined by the equation $g(x', y) = x'^m f(1/x', y) = 0$. The number of singular points is evidently finite.

THEOREM 11·1. *Near an ordinary point $x = a$ the n values of the algebraic function $y(x)$ are defined by n convergent series*

$$(11 \cdot 1) \qquad y = b_i + c_{i1}(x - a) + c_{i2}(x - a)^2 + \cdots$$
$$(i = 1, \cdots, n)$$

where the numbers b_i are the n distinct roots of $f(a, y) = 0$.

~ To prove this it is evident that at each pair (a, b_i) we have $f(a, b_i) = 0, f_y(a, b_i) \neq 0$. Hence Theorem 7·1 tells us that there is a convergent series $(11 \cdot 1)$ which satisfies $f(x, y) = 0$ identically.

12. **Continuations of the values of an algebraic function.** If the values of an algebraic function $y(x)$ at a non-singular point $x = x'$ are designated by the symbols $y_1', \cdots, y_n'$, then as x describes a continuous arc C joining x' to x'' and consisting only of ordinary points of $y(x)$ these values go over continuously into values $y_1'', \cdots, y_n''$ of $y(x)$ at x''. The theorems of this section describe properties of such continuations.

THEOREM 12·1. *If $x = x(t)$ $(t_1 \leq t \leq t_2)$ is a continuous arc C consisting entirely of ordinary points of an algebraic function $y(x)$ then the values of $y(x)$ along C form a set $y_k(t)$ $(t_1 \leq t \leq t_2; k = 1, \cdots, n)$ of n distinct continuous functions on $t_1 t_2$.*

The theorem is easily seen to be true with the help of Theorem 11·1 for each arc $x_1 x'$ of C sufficiently near x_1. Suppose that there were a largest arc $x_1 \xi$ for each interior point x' of which the arc $x_1 x'$ of C has this property. There would then be a circle about ξ as center in which the values of $y(x)$ would be defined by n distinct series $Y_l(x)$ $(l = 1, \cdots, n)$, as indicated in Theorem 11·1. Let x' be a point on C such that the arc $x' \xi$ is in this circle, and let $y_k(t)$ $(k = 1, \cdots, n)$ be the continuous functions representing $y(x)$ on $x_1 x'$. The functions $Y_l(x)$ could then be numbered so that $Y_k(x') = y_k(t')$, and on the interval $t't''$

corresponding to the arc x' x'' indicated in Figure 12·1 the functions $y_k(t) = Y_k[x(t)]$ would be continuous extensions of the functions $y_k(t)$ on $t_1 t'$. Hence the arc $x_1 \xi$ could not be the largest arc with the properties presupposed above and the theorem is true for the whole arc C.

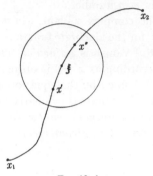

FIG. 12·1

COROLLARY. *There is always a polygon with the same end-points as C, consisting entirely of ordinary points of $y(x)$, and having continuation functions $Y_k(t)$ which can be so numbered that they have the same end-values as the functions $y_k(t)$ belonging to C.*

The corollary is easily seen to be true on sub-arcs of C with initial point x_1 and which lie entirely within a circle with center at x_1 where the algebraic function is represented by n distinct series (11·1). If there were a largest arc $x_1 \xi$ of C for which each interior arc $x_1 x'$ has the property of the corollary, then for an arc $x_1 x'$ as in Figure 12·1 the polygon could be extended to x'' by the addition of the straight line segment $x'x''$, and $x_1 \xi$ could not be the largest arc as described. The conclusion of the corollary is therefore true for the whole arc C.

In the following pages a *region R* of the x-plane is understood to be a set of points all of which are interior points of the set. A region R is *connected* if every pair of its points can be joined by a continuous arc entirely within R, and it is *simply connected* if further the interior of every simply closed curve in R is also in R.

THEOREM 12·2. *Let R be a simply connected region of the x-plane containing only ordinary points of an algebraic function $y(x)$, and let P be a simply closed polygon in R with the equation $x = x(t)$ $(t_1 \leq t \leq t_2)$. Then the continuation functions $y_k(t)$ $(k = 1, \cdots, n)$ along P have initial- and end-values which are identical, i.e., $y_k(t_1) = y_k(t_2)$ $(k = 1, \cdots, n)$.*

The theorem is certainly true for every simply closed polygon which

lies in a circle about an ordinary point $x = \xi$ as center in which the value
of $y(x)$ are represented by n distinct power series in $x - \xi$ similar to those
of the set (11·1).

Suppose then that the theorem were not true on a certain polygon
P in R. If the interior of P is divided by a segment $x_3 x_4$ parallel to the
real axis in the x-plane, the continuation functions in one at least of the
polygons $x_1 x_3 x_4 x_1$, $x_4 x_3 x_5 x_4$ would have different initial and end-values.
Otherwise the continuation functions belonging to these polygons, when
so numbered that they coincide at x_4, would form a set of continuation
functions on P for which the theorem would be true, which is a contra-

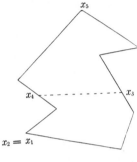

FIG. 12·2

diction. By repeating this process of subdivision by lines parallel to the
co-ordinate axes a sequence $\{P_i\}$ of simply closed polygons could be
determined, with maximum diameters approaching zero,* on each of
which the theorem fails. Select a point ξ_i arbitrarily on each P_i. The
points ξ_i must have an accumulation point ξ on P or its interior, in
every neighborhood of which there are polygons P_i. But since ξ is an
ordinary point it has a neighborhood N such that the continuation
functions on every simply closed polygon in N have the same initial
and end-values, which is a contradiction.

COROLLARY 1. *The conclusion of Theorem* 12·2 *holds for every closed
polygon P in R, even if it is not simply closed.*

To prove this let the corners of P be designated by $x_1 x_2 \cdots x_n x_1$.
Without changing the initial and end-values of its continuation functions at x_1 the polygon P can be simplified in two ways. In the first place
segments common to adjacent sides, as shown in Figure 12·3, can be
deleted. After this has been done the corners x_k $(k = 2, \cdots, n)$ can be

* See pages 29–30 of the reference in the footnote on page 5 of this book.

ccessively moved slightly if necessary so that in each case the side $x_{k-1}x_k$ is not parallel to any other side. The possibility of doing this, as shown in Figure 12·4, is due to the fact that when the new sides $x_{k-1}x_k'\,x_{k+1}$ are also in R there are continuation functions along them with

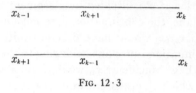

FIG. 12·3

the same end-values as those of the continuation functions along x_{k-1} $x_k x_{k+1}$, according to Theorem 12·2. The result of these modifications is that two sides of the polygon P have at most one point in common.

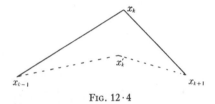

FIG. 12·4

Suppose now that the side $x_{l-1}x_l$ is the first one which intersects a preceding side $x_{k-1}x_k$, and let the common point be ξ. Then the polygon $\xi x_k \cdots x_{l-1}\xi$ is simply closed and can be discarded because, according to Theorem 12·2, its continuation functions have the same initial and end-values at ξ. This process of discarding loops can be repeated at most a finite number of times since the number of sides of the remaining polygon after each discard is at least one less than before. After all such loops have been deleted the remaining polygon is itself simply closed and has the same initial and end-values of its continuation functions as P. By Theorem 12·2 these initial and end-values must be identical.

THEOREM 12·3. *In a simply connected region R of the x-plane containing only ordinary points of an algebraic function $y(x)$ the values of $y(x)$ form a set $y_k(x)$ $(k=1, \cdots, n)$ of n distinct holomorphic functions.*

In order to show this let the values of $y(x)$ at an arbitrarily chosen point x_1 of R be denoted by $b_k(k=1, \cdots, n)$. On all polygons P in R joining x_1 to a second point x_2 the continuation functions $y_k(t)$ for which $y_k(t_1) = b_k$ will have the same end-values at x_2. Hence numbering the values of $y(x)$ at x_1 numbers them by continuation at every other point x_2 of R.

The single-valued functions $y_k(x)$ so defined in R are holomorp
each point x_2 of R. For let $Y_k(x)$ be the series in $x - x_2$ defining the va
of $y(x)$ near x_2, so numbered that $y_k(x_2) = Y_k(x_2)$. The values $y_k(x)$ th
coincide with the values $Y_k(x)$ at every point x near x_2 since the con

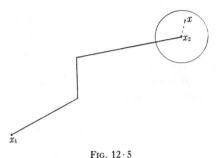

FIG. 12·5

tinuation function on the straight line segment x_2x which starts with
the value $y_k(x_2) = Y_k(x_2)$ has the end-value $Y_k(x)$, and the function
$Y_k(x)$ is analytic at x_2.

THEOREM 12·4. *At an ordinary point $x = a$ of an algebraic function the
radii of convergence of the n series in powers of $x - a$ representing the functions $y_k(x)$ $(k = 1, \cdots, n)$ are at least equal to the distance from $x = a$ to
the nearest singular point of the algebraic function.*

This is evident since the interior of the circle C with center at $x = a$
and passing through the nearest singular point is a simply connected
region in which the functions $y_k(x)$ of Theorem 12·3 are holomorphic.
Hence their Laurent expansions at $x = a$ are convergent everywhere in
the interior of C.

13. **The expansions for an algebraic function.** In the preceding pages
it has been shown that near an ordinary point $x = a$ of an algebraic
function $y(x)$ the values of $y(x)$ are given by n distinct power series in
$x - a$ of the form (11·1), and these series are convergent in a circle which
reaches to the nearest singular point. In this section it will be shown that
the values of $y(x)$ near a singular point are also representable by power
series, but series which may have terms with fractional powers of $x - a$.
A first property of such series is given by the following lemma and its
corollary.

LEMMA 13·1. *In a properly chosen neighborhood N of a point $x = a$
for which $f_0(x) = (x - a)^p g(x)$ with $g(a) \neq 0$ the products $z = (x - a)^p y$, where
y is a root of $f(x, y) = 0$, are bounded.*

prove this select N so small that $g(x) \neq 0$ in it. Then every product
en different from zero satisfies the equation

$$\frac{f(x, y)}{y^n f_0} = 1 + \frac{f_1}{zg} + \frac{(x-a)^p f_2}{z^2 g} + \cdots + \frac{(x-a)^{(n-1)p} f_n}{z^n g} = 0.$$

If z were not bounded in N there would be points $x \neq a$ in N at which
this equation could not be true, since every function $(x-a)^{(k-1)p} f_k/g$
is bounded in N.

We may note in passing that if $p = 0$ the roots y themselves are
bounded in N. If $p > 0$ it may be that there is a smaller integer q such
that the products $(x-a)^q y$ are bounded in N.

COROLLARY. *If a Laurent series*

$$
\begin{aligned}
(13 \cdot 1) \qquad y &= c_0 + c_1 t + c_2 t + \cdots \\
&\quad + d_1 t^{-1} + d_2 t^{-2} + \cdots
\end{aligned}
$$

*satisfies the equation $f(x, y) = 0$ identically in t when $t = (x-a)^{1/r}$, or when
$t = (1/x)^{1/r}$, r being a positive integer, then the number of terms with negative exponents must be finite.*

For the case when $t = (x-a)^{1/r}$ the product $(x-a)^p y = t^{pr} y$, where y
is the series $(13 \cdot 1)$, is bounded, according to the lemma above. It is
readily seen then that the product $t^{pr+2} y$ is holomorphic in a neighborhood of the point $t = 0$ including $t = 0$ itself. Hence the Laurent expansion for $t^{pr+2} y$ at $t = 0$ has no terms with negative exponents for t, and
the expansion $(13 \cdot 1)$ for y, found by dividing this Laurent expansion
by t^{pr+2}, can have only a finite number of terms with negative exponents.

When $t = (1/x)^r$ we may make the transformation $x = 1/x'$ and draw
similar conclusions with the help of the polynomial $g(x', y) = x'^m
f(1/x', y)$ and the expression $t = x'^{1/r}$ for t.

We can now determine the character of the expansions which represent an algebraic function in a neighborhood of an arbitrary point $x = a$.
Let C be a circle with $x = a$ as center containing no singularity of the
algebraic function except possibly $x = a$. If a cut ab is made, as indicated
in Figure $13 \cdot 1$, the part of the interior of the circle which remains is
a simply connected region R containing no singularities of the algebraic
function. In R the values of the algebraic function $y(x)$ form n distinct
holomorphic functions $y_k(x)$ $(k = 1, \cdots, n)$, as indicated in Theorem
$12 \cdot 3$. The same is true in the region $R' + R''$ shown in the figure, and
we can number the functions $Y_k(x)$ for $R' + R''$ so that in R' each will
be identical with the corresponding $y_k(x)$. In the region R'' the function

$Y_k(x)$ may be equal to $y_k(x)$, but if not it will at any rate be identical with another one of the set, say $y_l(x)$.

Suppose now that the region R is replaced by a pile of n such regions, one for each of the functions $y_k(x)$, and let the point over x in the k-th sheet represent the pair $[x, y_k(x)]$. The pile can be made to represent

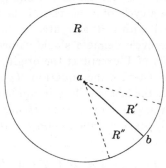

Fig. 13·1

the functions continuously, even along the edges of the cut ab, if the edge ab' in the k-th sheet is joined to the edge ab'' of the l-th sheet for which the identity $Y_k(x) = y_l(x)$ holds in R'', as indicated in Figure 13·2, and if the points of the edges so joined are associated with the values of $Y_k(x)$ along ab. The points P of the surface so formed are in one-to-one

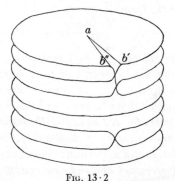

Fig. 13·2

correspondence with the pairs of values (x, y) satisfying the equation $f(x, y) = 0$ for values x on the circle C and its interior exclusive of $x = a$, and the correspondence is such that the single-valued function $y(P)$ so defined on the surface is holomorphic. By a holomorphic function $y(P)$ we mean one that is single-valued on the surface and such that for each point P_0 on the surface there is a neighborhood in which the points P of the surface are in one-to-one correspondence with their values x, and in which furthermore the corresponding values $y(P)$ define a holomorphic function of x. The surface evidently falls into cycles, each containing one or more sheets, as indicated in the figure.

The transformation $x - a = t^r$ establishes a one-to-one correspondence between the points of a cycle of r sheets and the interior, exclusive of the origin, of a circle Γ with $t = 0$ as center in the t-plane. The values $y(P)$ belonging to the cycle define a single-valued function $y(t)$ holomorphic on the interior of Γ except at the origin. The Laurent expansion for this function satisfies the equation $f(x, y) = 0$ with $x = a + t^r$ identically in t, and by the last corollary it can have only a finite number of terms in t with negative exponents. Hence we see that for each cycle of sheets there exists a so-called *branch* of the algebraic function with equations of the form

$$x = a + t^r, \qquad y = bt^\mu + b't^{\mu'} + \cdots ,$$

where r is a positive integer and the exponents of t are positive or negative integers or zero with $\mu < \mu' < \cdots$. Only those coefficients b, b', $\cdots$ are indicated which are different from zero. We can now prove the following theorem:

THEOREM 13·1. *In a neighborhood N of every finite point $x = a$ the n distinct values of an algebraic function $y(x)$ are determined by a finite number of branches of the form*

$$(13 \cdot 2) \qquad x = a + t^r, \qquad y = bt^\mu + b't^{\mu'} + \cdots$$

in which r is a positive integer, the coefficients b, b', $\cdots$ indicated are all different from zero, and the exponents of t are integers, possibly zero or negative, such that $\mu < \mu' < \cdots$. For a value $x \neq a$ in N each branch determines r distinct values of $y(x)$ when the r values of the root $t = (x - a)^{1/r}$ are substituted in the series for y. The sum of the numbers r for the different branches is n. The branches for $x = \infty$ have $x = 1/t^r$ in place of $x = a + t^r$.

A branch will be designated as primitive if its integers $r, \mu, \mu', \cdots$ have no common divisor. A necessary and sufficient condition that a branch shall define distinct values of y near $x = a$ is that it be primitive.

Two primitive branches will be called equivalent when their expansions (13·2) become identical after a transformation of the form $t = \omega t'$, where ω is one of the r-th roots of unity. A necessary and sufficient condition that two primitive branches define distinct values y near $x = a$ is that they are not equivalent.

If a set S of non-equivalent primitive branches represents the values of an algebraic function y(x) near x = a, then every other set S' with these properties must have each of its branches equivalent to one of S.

The statements in the first paragraph of the theorem are justified by preceding arguments.

If t is one value of the root $(x-a)^{1/r}$ then the totality of such roots is the set of numbers $\omega^k t$ $(k = 0, 1, \cdots, r-1)$ where $\omega = e^{2\pi i/r}$ is a primitive r-th root of unity. The r values of y defined by a primitive branch (13·2) are then

$$y_k = b\omega^{k\mu}t^\mu + b'\omega^{k\mu'}t^{\mu'} + \cdots \quad (k = 0, 1, \cdots, r-1).$$

Two such values y_i and y_k are distinct near $t = 0$ unless their series have the same coefficients, which would imply that the numbers $(j-k)\mu$, $(j-k)\mu'$, $\cdots$ are all divisible by r. But in this case r, μ, μ', $\cdots$ would have a common divisor, and the branch would not be primitive.

Let two branches have exponents $(r, \mu, \mu', \cdots)$ and $(s, \nu, \nu', \cdots)$, and let d, m be respectively the greatest common divisor and least common multiple of r, s so that $r = \rho d$, $s = \sigma d$, $m = \rho\sigma d$. If t is now a particular m-th root of $x-a$ and ω a primitive m-th root of unity, then t^σ is an r-th root of $x-a$ and ω^σ is a primitive r-th root of unity, and it is readily seen that the r-th and s-th roots of $x-a$ are the sets

$$\omega^{j\sigma}t^\sigma(j = 0, 1, \cdots, r-1), \qquad \omega^{k\rho}t^\rho(k = 0, 1, \cdots, s-1).$$

The values of $y(x)$ defined by the two branches are given by series

$$y_j = b\omega^{j\sigma\mu}t^{\sigma\mu} + \cdots, \qquad y_k = c\omega^{k\rho\nu}t^{\rho\nu} + \cdots.$$

There will be a neighborhood of $t = 0$ in which the values defined by these series are all distinct unless some two of the series are identical. In case of such identity the equality of exponents would require $\sigma\mu = \rho\nu$, $\sigma\mu' = \rho\nu'$, $\cdots$, which in turn would require $\rho = \sigma = 1$ and the identity of the sets $(r, \mu, \mu', \cdots)$ and $(s, \nu, \nu', \cdots)$, since ρ and σ are relatively prime and the branches both primitive. The equality of the coefficients would then give the relations

$$b = c\omega^{(k-i)\mu}, \qquad b' = c'\omega^{(k-i)\mu'}, \qquad \cdots,$$

which show that the series for y_i and y_k would be equivalent by the transformation $t = \omega^{k-i}t'$.

The uniqueness, in the sense of equivalence, of the set of branches representing the values of an algebraic function $y(x)$ near $x = a$, as stated in the last paragraph of the theorem, is evident, since $y(x)$ has but n values and any new branch not equivalent to one already in the set would define new values for y.

In Figure 13·2 it is understood that over the point $x = a$ the sheets of a cycle are joined, but that two different cycles are distinct over $x = a$. The vertex of a cycle, or a point on one of the sheets of a cycle, may be called a *place* to distinguish it from the corresponding point x of the x-plane below it. Thus at a point x of the x-plane an algebraic function $y(x)$ has in general n values, while at a place on a cycle it has but one value.

An *ordinary place* is one at which the Laurent expansion for y in (13·2) has no terms with negative exponents. The constant term of the expansion is clearly one of the roots of the equation $f(a, y) = 0$, a value of the algebraic function. A *singular place* is one which is not ordinary. If the first exponent μ of the expansion (13·2) is different from zero the corresponding place is called a *pole of order* μ if μ is negative, or a *zero of order* μ if μ is positive. The only singular places for an algebraic function are poles since the Laurent series (13·2) has only a finite number of terms with negative exponents.

A pair of values $(x, y) = (a, b)$ may belong to the vertices of a number of different cycles. The following theorem relates the number of sheets in these cycles to the multiplicity of $y = b$ as a root of $f(a, y) = 0$.

THEOREM 13·2. *If $y = b$ is a finite root of $f(a, y) = 0$ of order q, then the pair $(x, y) = (a, b)$ belongs to vertices of cycles over $x = a$ possessing in all exactly q sheets.*

To prove this let D be a circle in the y-plane with center at $y = b$ and containing no root of $f(a, y) = 0$ except $y = b$. Let C be a circle in the x-plane with center at $x = a$ and so small that for x in C all the values $y(x)$ on sheets of cycles belonging to (a, b) are inside D, while all the values of $y(x)$ on other sheets are outside of D. Then for a fixed x in C the number of roots of $f(x, y) = 0$ in D is equal to the number q' of sheets in the cycles belonging to (a, b). We have then

$$(13\cdot3) \qquad \int_D \frac{f_y(x, y)dy}{f(x, y)} = 2\pi i\{\text{no. of roots of } f(x, y) \text{ in } D\} = 2\pi i q'.$$

As x approaches a we find therefore

$$(13\cdot4) \qquad \int_D \frac{f_y(a, y)dy}{f(a, y)} = 2\pi i q'.$$

But the value of the last integral is readily seen to be $2\pi i q$ when $y = b$ is a multiple root of $f(a, y) = 0$ of order q, so that $q = q'$.

COROLLARY. *If $y = \infty$ is a root of $f(a, y) = 0$ of order q, then the $(x, y) = (a, \infty)$ belongs to vertices of cycles over $x = a$ possessing exactly sheets. Both the theorem and this corollary apply at $x = \infty$ as well as finite values $x = a$.*

The value $y = \infty$ is by definition a root of order q of $f(a, y) = 0$ if

$$f_0(a) = \cdots = f_{q-1}(a) = 0, \qquad f_q(a) \neq 0.$$

The finite roots of $f(a, y) = 0$ are consequently $n - q$ in number, and according to Theorem 13·2 they belong to cycles containing exactly $n - q$ sheets. Hence $y = \infty$ must belong to the remaining q sheets.

The truth of the theorem at $x = \infty$ can be established as usual by a discussion of the expansions for the polynomial $g(x', y) = x'^m f(1/x', y)$ at the point $x' = 0$.

In conclusion it is important to note that the branches

$$y = bt^\mu + b't^{\mu'} + \cdots, \qquad t = (x - a)^{1/r} \text{ or } (1/x)^{1/r},$$

which satisfy the equation $f(x, y) = 0$ are the important elements of the algebraic function, rather than the points (x, y) which satisfy the equation. At an ordinary point $x = a$ the points $(x, y) = (a, b_i)$ satisfying $f = 0$ are in one-to-one correspondence with the branches, so that either the number pairs (a, b_i) or the branches can be used to characterize the n places over $x = a$. At a singular point $x = a$, however, the same pair (a, b) may belong to a number of different branches, and the places over $x = a$ on the corresponding cycles are distinguishable only by the expansions which belong to them.

14. **Determination of the expansions by means of Newton's polygons.** The arguments of the preceding section establish the existence of the expansions representing an algebraic function, but they do not provide a convenient method for actually computing successively the terms of these expansions. The purpose of this section is the development of such a method of computation applicable to numerical examples.

Let $y = b$ be a q-tuple root of $f(a, y) = 0$. If $q = 1$, Theorem 7·1 tells us that there is a unique convergent expansion

$$y = b + c_1(x - a) + \cdots$$

which satisfies the equation $f(x, y) = 0$. If $q > 1$ the theorem gives no information. In this case $f(x, y)$ can be expanded by Taylor's formula in the form

$$f(x, y) = \sum A_{\alpha\beta}(x - a)^\alpha (y - b)^\beta,$$

for $x = a$ the term of lowest degree in $y - b$ has exponent q. When pairs (α, β) belonging to the terms in $f(x, y)$ are plotted on the β-plane a polygon can be drawn, as illustrated in Figure 14·1, by rotating the y-axis counter-clockwise around the point $(0, q)$ until it

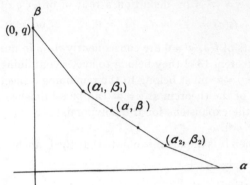

FIG. 14·1

meets a first point (α, β), then rotating about the lowest point (α_1, β_1) on it until it meets a new point (α, β), and so on. The polygon so formed is convex toward the origin and all the points (α, β) belonging to terms of $f(x, y)$ are on it or on the side of it opposite to the origin.

Let (α_1, β_1) and (α_2, β_2) with $\beta_1 > \beta_2$ be the end-points of a side of the polygon, the points between them on the side being denoted by (α, β) and the remaining points by (α', β'). Then

$$f(x, y) = A_{\alpha_1\beta_1}(x - a)^{\alpha_1}(y - b)^{\beta_1} + \sum A_{\alpha\beta}(x - a)^{\alpha}(y - b)^{\beta}$$
$$+ A_{\alpha_2\beta_2}(x - a)^{\alpha_2}(y - b)^{\beta_2} + \sum A_{\alpha'\beta'}(x - a)^{\alpha'}(y - b)^{\beta'},$$

where the two sums are taken in each case for all terms of the type indicated. Let $\phi(u)$ denote the polynomial

$$(14 \cdot 1) \qquad \phi(u) = A_{\alpha_1\beta_1}u^{\beta_1-\beta_2} + \sum A_{\alpha\beta} u^{\beta-\beta_2} + A_{\alpha_2\beta_2}.$$

The equation of the side in question may be written in the form

$$(14 \cdot 2) \qquad r\alpha + s\beta = p$$

where r, s, p are positive integers and r is prime to s. After the substitution

$$(14 \cdot 3) \qquad x = a + t^r, \qquad y = b + t^s u$$

the equation $f = 0$ takes the form

$$f(x, y) = t^p \{ u^{\beta_2} \phi(u) + t \text{ (polynomial in } t, u) \} = t^p g(t, u) = 0.$$

If c is a simple root of $\phi(u)$ this equation is satisfied by a uniquely det
mined series

$$u = c + dt + \cdots$$

according to Theorem 7·1. Hence the functions

$$x = a + t^r, \qquad y = b + ct^s + dt^{s+1} + \cdots$$

satisfy $f(x, y) = 0$ identically. If c is a multiple root of $\phi(u)$ then the method described above must be re-applied to the polynomial $g(t, u)$ at the point $(t, u) = (0, c)$.

It will be proved in the next section that all of the expansions in fractional powers of $x - a$ for the algebraic function $y(x)$ can be secured by pursuing the following program:

(1) Find the finite roots $y = b$ of $f(a, y) = 0$ and apply the above process to each of the pairs (a, b) so determined. This will give all of the expansions for $y(x)$ in fractional powers of $x - a$ which have no terms with negative exponents.

(2) According to Lemma 13·1 there can be expansions in powers of $x - a$ having terms with negative exponents only if $f_0(a) = 0$. Suppose that $f_0(a) = \cdots = f_{q-1}(a) = 0$, $f_q(a) \neq 0$. To find the expansions set $y = 1/y'$ and apply the method described above to the q-tiple root $y' = 0$ of the polynomial $g(a, y')$ where $g(x, y') = y'^n f(x, 1/y')$. The reciprocals of these expansions for y' are the expansions of $y(x)$ which have poles at $x = a$.

(3) To find the expansions at $x = \infty$, set $x = 1/x'$ and apply the processes described in (1) and (2) to the polynomial $g(x', y) = x'^m f(1/x', y)$ at the point $x' = 0$.

15. **The polygon method gives all expansions.** In simple numerical cases it will readily be found that the polygon method provides all of the expansions for an algebraic function $y(x)$ at $x = a$, but it requires a proof to show that this will always be the case. The following theorems establish this result.

THEOREM 15·1. *After a finite number of transformations of the form* $x = a + t^r$, $y = b + t^s u$ *a polynomial* $\phi(u)$, *as in equation* (14·1), *will be reached which has only simple roots.*

To prove this it should be noted first that if c is a multiple root of order q_1 of $\phi(u)$ so is ωc where ω is an arbitrary r-th root of unity, since the exponents $\beta - \beta_2$ in $\phi(u)$ all satisfy equations of the form $r(\alpha - \alpha_2) + s(\beta - \beta_2) = 0$ with r prime to s, deducible from equation (14·2), and are consequently integral multiples of r. It follows readily that

$\cdot 1$)
$$q \geqq \beta_1 - \beta_2 \geqq rq_1,$$

where q is the multiplicity of the original root b. For successive transformations it follows then that

$$q \geqq rq_1 \geqq rr_1q_2 \geqq rr_1r_2q_3 \geqq \cdots ,$$

and after a finite number of transformations the numbers r_i must all be unity and the numbers q_i all be equal.

Let us denote now by the original notations (a, b) and $f(x, y)$ a point and polynomial at which the stage just described has been reached. The transformation

(15·2)
$$x = a + t, \qquad y = b + t^s u$$

then gives a polynomial $\phi(u)$ with a single multiple root of order q, since in (15·1) we have now $r=1$, $q_1=q$. It is easy to see in this case that the polygon for the root (a, b) has a single side with an equation of the form

$$\alpha + s\beta = p$$

where $p = sq$, as shown in Figure 15·1, since if there were more sides the degree of $\phi(u)$ would be less than q. By means of the equations

$$f(a + t, b + t^s u) = t^p g(t, u),$$
$$f_y(a + t, b + t^s u) = t^{p-s} g_u(t, u) = t^{(q-1)s} g_u(t, u),$$
$$D(x) = Pf + Qf_y = Pt^p g + Qt^{(q-1)s} g_u,$$

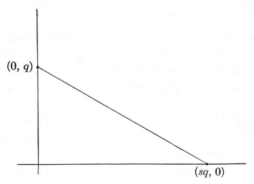

FIG. 15·1

it is clear that $D(x)$ has the factor $t^{(q-1)s} = (x-a)^{(q-1)s}$, and therefore at least the factor $(x-a)^{q-1}$. After each successive transformation (15·2) it is seen that the discriminant $D(x)$ will have a further factor $(x-a)^{(q-1)}$ which is impossible unless $q=1$, since $D(x)$ is a polynomial with a finite degree. Thus we see that after a finite number of transformations $(14 \cdot 3)$ a polynomial $\phi(u)$ will be attained which has only a single simple root.

THEOREM $15 \cdot 2$. *The program described at the end of Section 14 will provide a complete set of non-equivalent branches, in the sense of Theorem $13 \cdot 1$, defining the n distinct values of the algebraic function $y(x)$ near $x=a$.*

If a branch

$$(15 \cdot 3) \qquad x = a + t^r, \qquad y = b + b't^{\mu'} + \cdots$$

is provided by the polygon method for a finite root $y=b$ of $f(a, y) = 0$ after k transformations

$$x = a + t_1{}^{r_1}, \qquad y = b + t_1{}^{s_1} u_1,$$

$$t_{i-1} = t_i{}^{r_i}, \qquad u_{i-1} = b^{(i-1)} + t_i{}^{s_i} u_i \ (i = 2, \cdots, k),$$

its exponents for the variable $t = t_k$ will have the values

$$r = r_1 r_2 \cdots r_k, \qquad \mu' = s_1 r_2 \cdots r_k,$$

$$\mu^{(i)} = \mu^{(i-1)} + s_i r_{i+1} \cdots r_k \qquad (i = 2, \cdots, k),$$

as one readily verifies. Such a branch is primitive in the sense of Theorem $13 \cdot 1$ since the pairs r_i, s_i, and hence also the numbers r, μ', $\cdots$, $\mu^{(k)}$, are relatively prime.

The expansions $(15 \cdot 3)$ arising from different sides of the polygon for (a, b) in Figure $14 \cdot 1$ are distinct since the exponents $\mu'/r = s_1/r_1$ of the first terms in $x-a$ are distinct for the different sides. The expansions provided by the same side but by different roots of the polynomial $\phi(u)$ have unequal coefficients for these first terms. Hence after the first polygon for (a, b) has been constructed and the expansions for simple roots of the various polynomials $\phi(u)$ determined, the number of distinct expansions plus the orders of the multiple roots remaining to be considered is equal to the sum of the degrees of the polynomials $\phi(u)$. This sum is equal to the multiplicity q of the root $y=b$ of $f(a, y) = 0$. If this is true after a finite number of polygons have been constructed it will similarly be true after one more polygon and its expansions corresponding to simple roots have been determined. Since after a finite number of transformations all of the roots c become simple it follows that the number of distinct expansions provided by the root $y=b$ is exactly equal to its multiplicity q.

If the sum of the orders of the finite roots of $f(a, y) = 0$ is ν then the argument of the preceding paragraph shows that the polygon method provides ν distinct expansions (15·3) corresponding to these roots. Each of the expansions belongs to a cycle of a number r of expansions, satisfying $f(x, y) = 0$, equivalent in the sense of Theorem 13·1, and found by replacing t by $\omega^i t$ $(i = 0, 1, \cdots, r-1)$ in (15·3), where ω is a primitive r-th root of unity. Every one of the expansions found by such a substitution in one of the ν expansions must belong to the set of ν expansions described above, since otherwise the number of distinct values of $y(x)$ belonging to cycles corresponding to finite roots of $f(a, y)$ would be greater than ν. Each of the cycles is a primitive branch, and no two such branches are equivalent.

The multiplicity of $y = \infty$ as a root of $f(a, y)$ must be $n - \nu$. After the transformation $y = 1/y'$ the argument above shows that there are non-equivalent primitive branches providing precisely $n - \nu$ distinct values of $y'(x)$ near $x = a$. The reciprocals of these will be branches providing $n - \nu$ distinct values of $y(x)$. We know that they must be primitive branches for $y(x)$ as well as for $y'(x)$ since otherwise they could not define distinct values for $y(x)$. The conclusion of the theorem is thus justified, since the branches for finite roots $y = b$ cannot be equivalent to branches for $y = \infty$.

16. **Special types of singular points.** The variety of singular points possible for an algebraic curve is very great, and the expansions associated with one of them may be very numerous and complicated. There are a number of simple types, however, which are of frequent occurrence in special examples and whose expansions can be readily calculated.

At a point (a, b) which satisfies $f(x, y) = 0$ let the expansion of $f(x, y)$ be

$$\begin{aligned}
f(x, y) &= A_{10}(x - a) + A_{01}(y - b) \\
&\quad + A_{20}(x - a)^2 + A_{11}(x - a)(y - b) + A_{02}(y - b)^2 \\
&\quad + \cdots \\
&= [x - a, y - b]_1 + [x - a, y - b]_2 + \cdots,
\end{aligned}$$

where the bracket $[x - a, y - b]_k$ is a symbol for the terms of degree k.

A *point (a, b) with a simple vertical tangent* is by definition one at which $A_{10} \neq 0$, $A_{01} = 0$, $A_{02} \neq 0$. It is so called because if its co-ordinates were real the graph of the equation $f(x, y) = 0$ in the real xy-plane would have a single branch through (a, b) with a tangent at (a, b) parallel to the y-axis. A *k-tiple point having tangents with distinct finite slopes* is a point at which the expansion for $f(x, y)$ has the form

$$f(x, y) = [x - a, y - b]_k + [x - a, y - b]_{k+1} + \cdots$$

with the further property that the k roots μ_i $(i = 1, \cdots, k)$ of the polynomial $[1, m]_k$ are finite and distinct. The tangents at such a point are the lines $y - b = \mu_i(x - a)$. A double point with tangents having distinct finite slopes is the simplest case. A *simple cusp* with a tangent having a finite slope is a point (a, b) at which $A_{10} = A_{01} = 0$, $A_{02} \neq 0$, and $[1, m]_2$ has a double root μ for which $[1, \mu]_3 \neq 0$.

THEOREM 16·1. *A point (a, b) on $f(x, y) = 0$ with a simple vertical tangent is a vertex of a single cycle of two sheets at which the algebraic function $y(x)$ has an expansion of the form*

$$(16·1) \qquad x = a + t^2, \qquad y = b + c_1 t + c_2 t^2 + \cdots$$

where $c_1 = [-A_{10}/A_{02}]^{1/2}$.

This can be readily verified by constructing the Newton polygon corresponding to (a, b). The transformation for $(16·1)$ is $x = a + t^2$, $y = b + tu$, and

$$f(x, y) = t^2\{A_{10} + A_{02}u^2 + tP(t, u)\} = t^2 g(t, u),$$

where $P(t, u)$ is a symbol for a polynomial in t and u. For a value $c_1 = (-A_{10}/A_{02})^{1/2}$ there is an expansion for u in powers of t giving a branch of the form $(16·1)$. There is a second such expansion corresponding to $-c_1$, but it is identical with the expansion found by changing t to $-t$ in $(16·1)$ since there are two and only two expansions for u in powers of t satisfying the equation $g(t, u) = 0$.

THEOREM 16·2. *A k-tiple point (a, b) having tangents with distinct finite slopes belongs to k cycles of one sheet each with expansions of the form*

$$(16·2) \qquad x = a + t, \qquad y = b + \mu_i t + c_{i2} t^2 + \cdots \qquad (i = 1, \cdots, k)$$

where the constants μ_i are the k distinct finite roots of $[1, m]_k$.

If $[1, m]_k$ has no root zero the Newton polygon has a single side giving the transformation

$$x = a + t, \qquad y = b + tu,$$
$$f(x, y) = t^k\{[1, u]_k + tP(t, u)\} = t^k g(t, u).$$

There are evidently k expansions for u in powers of t giving branches of the form $(16·2)$. If $[1, m]_k$ has a root equal to zero the polygon has two sides, but the resulting expansions have still the form $(16·2)$.

THEOREM 16·3. *A simple cusp (a, b) with a tangent having a finite slope is a vertex of a single cycle of two sheets with an expansion of the form*

$$(16 \cdot 3) \qquad x = a + t^2, \qquad y = b + \mu t^2 + \nu t^3 + \cdots ,$$

where μ is the double root of $[1, m]_2$ and $\nu = \{ - [1, \mu]_3 / A_{02} \}^{1/2}$.

This result is found when $A_{20} \neq 0$ by two successive transformations or by direct substitution of

$$x = a + t^2, \qquad y = b + \mu t^2 + u t^3$$

and subsequent determination of u. When $A_{20} = 0$ only a single substitution $x = a + t^2$, $y = b + t^3 u$ is necessary.

REFERENCES FOR CHAPTER II

References for the various sections of Chapter II above, in the list at the end of this book, are the following: 13, Chapter IV; 15, Chapter XIII; 18. Chapter IV; 28, Vorlesung IV; 34, Chapters XXVII, XXVIII; 42, Chapters I, II.

CHAPTER III

RATIONAL FUNCTIONS

17. Introduction. The three principal methods of attacking the theory of rational functions of the pairs of values (x, y) which satisfy an algebraic equation $f(x, y) = 0$ have been briefly described in the preface of this book. The arithmetic theory, in particular, is applicable without any preliminary transformation simplifying the singularities of the equation. The purpose of this chapter is an exposition of this theory which will lead as directly as possible to the fundamental theorems concerning the construction of rational functions with prescribed singularities, such as will be required in later chapters for the integrands of Abelian integrals of various types, and to the famous theorem of Riemann-Roch. The developments in Sections 18 and 19 are preliminary in character. In Sections 20 and 21 the important notions of a divisor and of its basis and multiples are presented, and in Section 22 the very useful theory of the complementary basis is discussed. The remaining sections of the chapter contain the applications of these results to the proofs of the theorems mentioned above and related topics.

18. First properties of rational functions. Let $f(x, y)$ be an irreducible polynomial in x and y and let $\eta(x, y)$ be a rational function of x and y whose properties at the values (x, y) satisfying the equation $f = 0$ are to be studied.

If $\eta(x, y)$ is a polynomial in x and y it will either have $f(x, y)$ as a factor, or else there will be only a finite number of values x for which $\eta(x, y)$ and $f(x, y)$ have common roots y, as one may see with the help of the corollary to Lemma $9 \cdot 1$. In the latter case the polynomial $\eta(x, y)$ cannot vanish identically on any cycle P satisfying the equation $f = 0$. At each such cycle it will have an expansion of the form

$$(18 \cdot 1) \qquad \eta(x, y) = ct^\nu + c't^{\nu'} + \cdots$$

with coefficients $c, c', \cdots$ not zero and exponents $\nu, \nu', \cdots$ positive or negative integers or zero, found by substituting the expressions $(13 \cdot 2)$ for x and y, or by substituting $x = 1/t^r$ and the corresponding expansion for y if the cycle P is at $x = \infty$. There are only a finite number of cycles for which ν is negative, since there are only a finite number where the

43

expansions for x and y in powers of t have negative exponents. Furthermore there can be only a finite number of cycles for which ν is positive, since $\eta(x, y)$ and $f(x, y)$ have common roots y at only a finite number of values x.

If $\eta(x, y)$ is a quotient of two polynomials having no common factor we make the hypothesis once for all that the denominator does not have $f(x, y)$ as a factor. Then with the help of the preceding paragraph we see that $\eta(x, y)$ will either vanish identically on the cycles of $f = 0$, if its numerator contains $f(x, y)$ as a factor, or else it will have at each cycle P an expansion of the form (18·1). Furthermore there will in the latter case be only a finite number of cycles for which $\nu \neq 0$. Such a cycle will be called a zero or pole of order ν of $\eta(x, y)$ when the exponent ν is, respectively, positive or negative.

There are two expressions associated with every rational function $\eta(x, y)$ which are important for the developments of the following pages. These are the so-called *norm* and *trace* of η defined by the equations

$$N(\eta) = \eta(x, y_1) \cdots \eta(x, y_n),$$

$$T(\eta) = \eta(x, y_1) + \cdots + \eta(x, y_n),$$

where $y_1, \cdots, y_n$ are the n roots of the equation $f(x, y) = 0$ corresponding to the value x. The values $\eta(x, y_i)$ of η corresponding to the different values y_i are called *conjugate values* of η. The norm and the trace are both representable as rational functions of x since they are symmetric in the roots $y_1, \cdots, y_n$ and therefore expressible rationally in terms of the coefficients of the powers of y in the equation $f = 0$.

By means of the norm we can prove the well-known and useful theorem that *the sum of the orders of a rational function $\eta(x, y)$ is zero*. The r values of $\eta(x, y)$ corresponding to the r values of y defined by a cycle of the form (13·2) for a finite value $x = a$ are found by substituting in the expansion (18·1) the r values of the root $t = (x - a)^{1/r}$. Since the product of these r values of $\eta(x, y)$ occurs in the norm it follows that $N(\eta)$ has corresponding to each cycle P the factor $(x - a)^\nu$, and that its order at $x = a$ is the sum of the orders ν of $\eta(x, y)$ at the cycles for $x = a$. Similar remarks hold of course for the cycles for which $t = (1/x)^{1/r}$. We know that the sum of the orders of a rational function of x is zero, this being true in particular for $N(\eta)$, and the same result must therefore hold for the function $\eta(x, y)$.

The residue of a function $\eta(x, y)$ at a cycle is defined to be the coefficient of $1/t$ in the expansion for the product $\eta \, dx/dt$, or, what is the same thing, it is the value of the integral

$$\frac{1}{2\pi i}\int_\Gamma \eta \frac{dx}{dt} dt$$

taken around a circle Γ in the t-plane with center at the origin $t=0$. Since when t describes this circle once the value $x=a+t^r$ describes r times a circle C about $x=a$ in the x-plane it follows that the residue is also expressible as an integral

$$\frac{1}{2\pi i}\int_C [\eta(x, y_1) + \cdots + \eta(x, y_r)]dx$$

where $y_1, \cdots, y_r$ are the r values of y corresponding to the cycle. Evidently the residue at $x=a$

$$\frac{1}{2\pi i}\int_C T(\eta)dx$$

of the rational function of x designated by $T(\eta)$ is the sum of the residues of $\eta(x, y)$ at the cycles corresponding to $x=a$. Since the sum of the residues of a rational function of x is zero we now have the result that *the sum of the residues of a rational function $\eta(x, y)$ is also zero.*

If a *rational function $\eta(x, y)$ has no pole it must be a constant.* For the symmetric functions of the conjugate values $\eta(x, y_i)$ are then all rational in x and everywhere finite, and hence by a well known theorem are equal to constants. Consequently the values $\eta(x, y_i)$ are the roots of a polynomial with constant coefficients. For some particular one, say β, of these roots the different $\eta(x, y) -\beta$ must vanish at an infinity of cycles and, by the argument of a preceding paragraph, must contain $f(x, y)$ as a factor. It follows readily that $\eta(x, y) = \beta$ at every cycle.

A final remark concerning the expansions for the trace $T(\eta)$ will be helpful. The sum of the r values of $\eta(x, y)$ defined for a cycle by the series $(18\cdot 1)$ has an expansion beginning with the term

$$(1 + \omega^\nu + \omega^{2\nu} + \cdots + \omega^{(r-1)\nu})c\, t^\nu,$$

where ω is a primitive r-th root of unity. This is true because the r values of the root t are exactly the values $\omega^k t$ $(k=0, 1, \cdots, r-1)$. The value of the parenthesis is r when ν is an integral multiple of r, since then each term in it is unity, but zero otherwise since the sum of the roots of unity of every index is zero. *If the quotient ν/r for a particular cycle at $x=a$ is smaller than the similar quotients for all the other cycles corresponding to $x=a$, then the first term in the expansion of $T(\eta)$ in powers of $(x-a)$ will have exactly the exponent ν/r when this quotient is an integer, and a larger exponent when it is not an integer.*

19. Bases for all rational functions. A set of functions $\eta_k(x, y)$ $(k = 1, \cdots, n)$ is called a *basis for the totality of rational functions* $\eta(x, y)$ if the determinant $\left| \eta_k(x, y_i) \right|$ of their conjugate values is not identically zero at the cycles of $f(x, y) = 0$.

THEOREM 19·1. *The values of a rational function* $\eta(x, y)$ *at the cycles of* $f(x, y) = 0$ *are expressible in terms of a basis in the form*

$$(19·1) \qquad \eta = R_1(x)\eta_1 + \cdots + R_n(x)\eta_n,$$

where the coefficients $R_k(x)$ *are rational in* x, *and there is only one such expression for* η.

To prove this we notice in the first place that a function $\zeta(x, y)$ for which the traces

$$T(\zeta\eta_k) = \zeta(x, y_1)\eta_k(x, y_1) + \cdots + \zeta(x, y_n)\eta_k(x, y_n) \ (k = 1, \cdots, n)$$

of the products $\zeta\eta_k$ all vanish identically must itself be identically zero, since the determinant $\left| \eta_k(x, y_i) \right|$ does not vanish identically. Since the determinant $\left| T(\eta_i\eta_k) \right| = \left| \eta_k(x, y_i) \right|^2$ is not identically zero the equations

$$T(\eta \ \eta_i) = R_1 T(\eta_1\eta_i) + R_2 T(\eta_2\eta_i) + \cdots + R_n T(\eta_n\eta_i) \qquad (i = 1, \cdots, n)$$

determine the coefficients $R_1, \cdots, R_n$ uniquely as rational functions of x in such a way that the traces of the products $\zeta\eta_i$ for the function

$$\zeta = \eta - R_1\eta_1 - \cdots - R_n\eta_n$$

all vanish identically. Hence ζ is identically zero and η is expressible uniquely as described in the theorem.

It is clear that the determinant $\left| T(\eta_i\eta_k) \right| = \left| \eta_k(x, y_i) \right|^2$ for a basis is symmetric in $y_1, \cdots, y_n$ and therefore rational in x. Since it is not identically zero, it can have only a finite number of poles and zeros. At all other values of x it is different from zero.

If $\zeta_1, \cdots, \zeta_n$ are expressible in terms of a basis in the form

$$\zeta_k = R_{k1}\eta_1 + \cdots + R_{kn}\eta_n \qquad (k = 1, \cdots, n),$$

then the determinant $\left| \zeta_k(x, y_i) \right|$ is the product of $\left| R_{ik} \right|$ and $\left| \eta_k(x, y_i) \right|$ and a necessary and sufficient condition that $\zeta_1, \cdots, \zeta_n$ form a basis is that the determinant $\left| R_{ik} \right|$ of the rational functions $R_{ik}(x)$ be different from zero.

A special case of a basis is the set of functions $1, y, \cdots, y^{n-1}$. The determinant of the conjugates of these powers of y is the product of the differences of the roots $y_i(i = 1, \cdots, n)$, as is well known, and it can not vanish identically since the roots of an irreducible polynomial $f(x, y)$ are distinct except at special values of x. All other bases are obtainable from this one by linear transformations such as are described in the last paragraph.

COROLLARY. *A function $\eta(P)$ which is single-valued and has no singularities except poles at the cycles P of an algebraic function is expressible as a rational function $\eta(x, y)$ of x and y.*

When we say that $\eta(P)$ has no singularities except poles, we mean that its values are given on the cycles P by expansions of the form (18·1). The trace $T(\eta\eta_i)$ of the product of η by one of the functions η_i of a basis for rational functions is a rational function of x. For one may readily prove that it is single-valued and analytic at every point $x = a$ or $x = \infty$ except possibly at values of x corresponding to poles of η or η_i. If $x = a$ is a value corresponding to such a pole there is an integer n such that the product $(x - a)^n T(\eta\eta_i)$ is bounded near $x = a$, and by Theorem 5·2 it follows that $T(\eta\eta_i)$ has at most a pole at $x = a$. A similar argument holds for $x = \infty$. We see then that $T(\eta\eta_i)$ is holomorphic in the whole x-plane except for poles, and by Theorem 6·3 it is rational in x. The proof of the last theorem now shows that η is expressible in the form (19·1) and hence is rational in x and y.

20. **Divisors and their bases.** If $P_1, \cdots, P_s$ are symbols for distinct cycles of an algebraic function and $\mu_1, \cdots, \mu_s$ a corresponding set of positive or negative integers, then the symbol $Q = P_1^{\mu_1} \cdots P_s^{\mu_s}$ is called a *divisor*, and the sum $q = \mu_1 + \cdots + \mu_s$ is called the order of the divisor. Such a divisor is not to be interpreted as a product of expansions. It is merely a symbol used to designate a set of cycles or places P_k with a corresponding set of orders μ_k. A rational function $\eta(x, y)$ is a *multiple of the divisor Q* if its order at each cycle P_k is greater than or equal to μ_k, and if its orders at all other cycles of the algebraic function are greater than or equal to zero. The problem of determining the multiples of a divisor and their properties is a fundamental one for the theory of algebraic functions, as we shall see in the following pages. When it has been solved the determination of the Abelian integrals of various types associated with the algebraic function, and the proof of the important Riemann-Roch Theorem, are relatively simple matters.

As a preliminary to the determination of the multiples of a divisor Q we may study those rational functions $\eta(x, y)$ which have the properties of multiples except at the cycles corresponding to $x = \infty$ where no restriction whatever is now placed upon their behavior. A function of this sort is called a *multiple of Q except at infinity,* and the totality of such functions constitute the *ideal of Q* which may be denoted by the symbol $I(Q)$. In the determination of such an ideal only the places of Q which correspond to finite values $x = x_0$ have any effect, and we may without loss of generality suppose that Q contains only such places.

A *basis for the divisor Q* is a basis whose elements $\eta_1, \cdots , \eta_n$ are multiples of Q except at infinity, and which has the further property that the totality of such multiples is identical with the totality of functions $\eta(x, y)$ expressible in the form

$$(20 \cdot 1) \qquad \eta(x, y) = g_1(x)\eta_1 + \cdots + g_n(x)\eta_n,$$

where the coefficients $g_k(x)$ are polynomials.

It is not a priori evident that there will be a basis with these properties for every divisor Q, and one of our first tasks will be to prove that such a basis exists. Before attempting the proof, however, it will be useful to deduce a characteristic property of such a basis. To do this let us consider a finite value x_0 where the algebraic function $y(x)$ has three cycles A, B, C providing, respectively, a, b, c values for $y(x)$, and at which the orders required by Q are λ, μ, ν. The methods to be used would be quite analogous if there were more or fewer than three cycles for $x = x_0$, but the notations would be more complicated.

If a basis $\eta_1, \cdots , \eta_n$ has its elements all multiples of Q except at infinity then the expansions for η_k at the three places over x_0 will have the forms

$$\text{at } A : \qquad \eta_k = \alpha_{k0}t^\lambda + \cdots + \alpha_{ka-1}t^{\lambda+a-1} + \cdots ,$$

$$\text{at } B : \qquad \eta_k = \beta_{k0}t^\mu + \cdots + \beta_{kb-1}t^{\mu+b-1} + \cdots ,$$

$$\text{at } C : \qquad \eta_k = \gamma_{k0}t^\nu + \cdots + \gamma_{kc-1}t^{\nu+c-1} + \cdots .$$

The determinant

$$
\Delta = \begin{vmatrix}
\alpha_{10} & \cdots & \alpha_{n0} \\
\cdots & \cdots & \cdots \\
\alpha_{1a-1} & \cdots & \alpha_{na-1} \\
\beta_{10} & \cdots & \beta_{n0} \\
\cdots & \cdots & \cdots \\
\beta_{1b-1} & \cdots & \beta_{nb-1} \\
\gamma_{10} & \cdots & \gamma_{n0} \\
\cdots & \cdots & \cdots \\
\gamma_{1c-1} & \cdots & \gamma_{nc-1}
\end{vmatrix}
$$

has numerous applications in the following pages and will be refer.
always as the determinant Δ for the basis $\eta_1, \cdots, \eta_n$ at the value x
It is clear that an analogous determinant can be constructed for ev
finite value x_0 no matter how many cycles the algebraic function $y($
may have corresponding to it. We can now prove the following theorem

THEOREM 20·1. *A necessary and sufficient condition that a set $\eta_1, \cdots,$*
η_n of multiples of Q except at $x = \infty$ be a basis for the divisor Q is that at
every finite value x_0 their determinant Δ be different from zero.

To prove the necessity of this condition suppose that the deter-
minant Δ is equal to zero at a value x_0 for a set $\eta_1, \cdots, \eta_n$ of multiples
of Q except at infinity. Then there is a set of constants $C_1, \cdots, C_n$
satisfying the linear equations whose coefficients are the rows of Δ, and
the numerator of the function

$$\eta = \frac{C_1\eta_1 + \cdots + C_n\eta_n}{x - x_0}$$

has orders at least equal to $\lambda+a, \mu+b, \nu+c$ at the cycles A, B, C, while
the denominator has orders a, b, c. Hence η is a multiple of Q except at
infinity, not expressible in the form (20·1), and $\eta_1, \cdots, \eta_n$ can not be a
basis for Q.

The condition is also sufficient. For in the first place a set of functions $\eta_1, \cdots, \eta_n$ having the property of the theorem necessarily has its
determinant $| \eta_k(x, y_i) |$ not identically zero, because at a non-singular
value x_0 having n cycles distinct from those of Q the determinant
$| \eta_k(x, y_i) |$ is exactly the determinant Δ and therefore different from zero
by hypothesis. Every function $\eta(x, y)$ is therefore expressible in terms of
$\eta_1, \cdots, \eta_n$ with rational coefficients and may be written in the form

$$\eta = \frac{g_1(x)\eta_1 + \cdots + g_n(x)\eta_n}{d(x)}$$

where $g_1(x), \cdots, g_n(x), d(x)$ are polynomials having no common factor.
When a function η is a multiple of Q except at $x = \infty$ the denominator
$d(x)$ must be a constant. For in case $d(x) = (x-x_0)d_1(x)$ the first two
terms in the equation

$$d_1(x)\eta = \sum \frac{g_i(x) - g_i(x_0)}{x - x_0}\eta_i + \sum \frac{g_i(x_0)}{x - x_0}\eta_i$$

would be multiples of Q and hence also the last term. But since the determinant Δ is different from zero at $x = x_0$ it follows readily that the last

would surely have a lower order than that prescribed by Q at one ast of the places over $x=x_0$, which is a contradiction. Hence the ominator $d(x)$ has no factor $x-x_0$ and is constant. Every multiple $x, y)$ of Q except at infinity is therefore surely expressible in the form 20·1).

With the help of the last theorem we may proceed to the proof that there is a basis for every divisor Q. In the first place it is evident that a function $\eta(x, y)$ which is not a multiple of Q except at infinity can be made into one by multiplying it by a polynomial in x. For if $\eta(x, y)$ is multiplied by a sufficiently high power of $x-x_0$ the orders of the product at the cycles corresponding to x_0 may be made to exceed those required by Q. It is clear from this remark that a basis $\eta_1, \cdots, \eta_n$ can always be easily made over into one whose functions are all multiples of Q except at infinity.

If a basis $\eta_1, \cdots, \eta_n$ has its functions all multiples of Q except at infinity then the order of the determinant $|\eta_k(x, y_i)|$ at a value x_0 is surely not less than the sum of the orders required by Q at the cycles corresponding to x_0. For if at such a cycle Q requires the expansion of its multiples to begin with a term in $(x-x_0)^{\mu/r}$, then r rows of the determinant $|\eta_k(x, y_i)|$ will have the factor $(x-x_0)^{\mu/r}$ in each element and the determinant itself will have at least the factor $(x-x_0)^{\mu}$. The theorem which we wish to prove with the help of these remarks is now the following one:

THEOREM 20·2. *For every divisor Q there exists a basis $\eta_1, \cdots, \eta_n$ such that the totality of multiples of Q except at infinity is identical with the totality of functions expressible in the form*

$$\eta(x, y) = g_1(x)\eta_1 + \cdots + g_n(x)\eta_n$$

where the coefficients $g_k(x)$ are polynomials in x.

To prove this, suppose that $\eta_1, \cdots, \eta_n$ is a basis of functions each of which is a multiple of Q except at infinity. If it is not a basis for Q, there will be a value x_0 at which its determinant Δ vanishes. Let $C_1, \cdots, C_n$ be constants satisfying the linear equations whose coefficients are the rows of Δ, and suppose that C_k is one of them which is different from zero. Then the set of functions

$$\eta_1, \cdots, \eta_{k-1}, \quad \frac{C_1\eta_1 + \cdots + C_n\eta_n}{x - x_0}, \quad \eta_{k+1}, \cdots, \eta_n$$

is also a basis with elements multiples of Q except at infinity, and the determinant of its conjugates is that of the original basis multiplied by

$C_k/(x-x_0)$. Furthermore $\Delta \neq 0$ for the new basis wherever it w
for the old one. If Δ for the new basis still vanishes at x_0, this pro
may be repeated. It can be repeated a finite number of times or.
however, before reaching a basis for which Δ is different from zer
since after each repetition the order of the determinant $| \eta_k(x, y_i) |$ at
$x = x_0$ is decreased by unity, and we have seen just preceding Theorem
20·2 that for a basis of multiples of Q except at infinity the order of
this determinant at $x = x_0$ has a minimum. If Δ has been made different
from zero at all the values x_0 corresponding to places in Q or branch
places and at the places where the determinant of the conjugates of the
basis originally vanished, then the basis will have $\Delta \neq 0$ at every x_0
and will be a basis for Q. We know that there are only a finite number
of values x_0 at which such alterations must be made since Q has only
a finite number of factors and the square of the determinant of conjugates is a rational function of x and has only a finite number of zeros.

21. **Multiples of a divisor.** We have seen in Section 19 that a basis
$\eta_1, \cdots, \eta_n$ for the totality of rational functions $\eta(x, y)$ can be transformed into an equivalent basis $\zeta_1, \cdots, \zeta_n$ by a linear transformation
of the form

$$(21 \cdot 1) \qquad \zeta_k = g_{k1}\eta_1 + \cdots + g_{kn}\eta_n \qquad (k = 1, \cdots, n)$$

in which the coefficients g_{kl} are rational in x and have a determinant not
identically zero. A similar relationship can be established for every pair
of bases for a divisor Q, as indicated in the following theorem:

THEOREM 21·1. *If $\eta_1, \cdots, \eta_n$ is a basis for a divisor Q then a necessary and sufficient condition for $\zeta_1, \cdots, \zeta_n$ to be also such a basis is that
$\zeta_1, \cdots, \zeta_n$ be expressible in the form* $(21 \cdot 1)$ *with coefficients $g_{kl}(x)$ poly-
nomials in x and with a determinant $| g_{kl} |$ equal to a constant different from
zero.*

We know that if $\zeta_1, \cdots, \zeta_n$ is to be a basis for Q its functions must
be multiples of Q except at $x = \infty$ and hence uniquely expressible in
terms of $\eta_1, \cdots, \eta_n$ with polynomial coefficients g_{ki}, since every such
multiple is so expressible. Similarly $\eta_1, \cdots, \eta_n$ must be expressible in
terms of $\zeta_1, \cdots, \zeta_n$ with polynomial coefficients h_{kl}. The determinants
$| g_{kl} |$ and $| h_{kl} |$ are both polynomials in x and their product is unity.
Hence both must be constants. Conversely one may easily see that a set
of functions $\zeta_1, \cdots, \zeta_n$ related to $\eta_1, \cdots, \eta_n$ as described in the
theorem will surely be a basis for Q, so that the theorem is completely
established.

our application of the transformation of bases of a divisor Q ..ibed in the last theorem we shall find it convenient to have first ..lied a simple transformation of the form $x_1 = 1/(x-\alpha)$, where $x = \alpha$ a non-singular point of the algebraic function belonging to none of the places of Q. After such a transformation each cycle at $x_1 = \infty$ has but a single sheet. Furthermore a multiple $\eta(x, y)$ of Q before the transformation will still be a multiple of Q. For the transformation takes $x = a$ into $x_1 = a_1 = 1/(a-\alpha)$, and is equivalent to

$$x - a = - (x_1 - a_1)/a_1 x_1 = - (x_1 - a_1)a_1^{-2}\left(1 - \frac{x_1 - a_1}{a_1} + \cdots\right).$$

Hence the variables $t = (x-a)^{1/r}$ and $t_1 = (x_1 - a_1)^{1/r}$ are related by an equation

$$t = t_1(- a_1^{-2})^{1/r}(1 - t_1^r/ra_1 + \cdots).$$

By substitution of this value for t we see that each branch $(13 \cdot 2)$ goes over into a branch of the form

$$x_1 = a_1 + t_1^r, \qquad y = b_1 t_1^\mu + \cdots$$

at which the expansion for $\eta(x, y)$ analogous to $(18 \cdot 1)$ retains the initial exponent ν, and that a multiple $\eta(x, y)$ of a divisor Q will retain this property after the transformation. In the remaining sections of this chapter we shall suppose that such a transformation has already been made, so that the expansions of a rational function $\eta(x, y)$ at $x = \infty$ contain only integral powers of $1/x$ and so that none of the places over $x = \infty$ belongs to Q.

By means of the transformations described in Theorem $21 \cdot 1$ bases for Q can be found which have special properties of great assistance in the proofs which we shall discuss in this and the following sections. We may define the *column order* of a function $\eta(x, y)$ at $x = \infty$ as the minimum of the exponents in its n expansions at the cycles for $x = \infty$. If the column orders of the functions of a basis $\eta_1, \cdots, \eta_n$ for Q are the numbers $r_k(k = 1, \cdots, n)$, then the conjugates of these functions will have at $x = \infty$ expansions of the form

$$(21 \cdot 2) \qquad \eta_k(x, y_i) = C_{ik}\left(\frac{1}{x}\right)^{r_k} + \cdots, \qquad (i, k = 1, \cdots, n),$$

where one at least of each set $C_{1k}, \cdots, C_{nk}$ is different from zero. A basis for Q is said to be *normal at $x = \infty$* if the determinant $|C_{ik}|$ is different from zero. It is evident that for such a basis the order of terminant $|\eta_k(x, y_i)|$ at $x = \infty$ is exactly $r_1 + \cdots + r_n$.

THEOREM 21·2. *For every divisor Q there exists a basis $\eta_1, \cdots$ which is normal at $x = \infty$. When expressed in terms of such a basis a multi*

$$(21·3) \qquad \eta(x, y) = g_1(x)\eta_1 + \cdots + g_n(x)\eta_n$$

of Q except at $x = \infty$ has its column order at $x = \infty$ the smallest of the numbers $r_k - \mu_k (k = 1, \cdots, n)$ where r_k is the column order of η_k and μ_k is the degree of the polynomial $g_k(x)$.

To establish these statements let us order the functions $\eta_1, \cdots, \eta_n$ of an arbitrarily selected basis for Q so that their column orders satisfy the inequalities $r_1 \geqq r_2 \geqq \cdots \geqq r_n$. If the determinant $|C_{ik}|$ of coefficients from the expansions $(21·2)$ is equal to zero there will exist constants $C_1, \cdots, C_n$ not all zero satisfying the linear equations whose coefficients are the rows of this determinant. Let C_k be the last one which is different from zero. Then the basis $\eta_1, \cdots, \eta_{k-1}, \eta_k', \eta_{k+1}, \cdots, \eta_n$, with

$$\eta_k' = C_1 x^{r_1 - r_k} \eta_1 + \cdots + C_{k-1} x^{r_{k-1} - r_k} \eta_{k-1} + C_k \eta_k,$$

is also a basis for Q, by Theorem 21·1, and has the same column orders except that the order r_k' for η_k' is at least one greater than r_k. If the new basis is not normal at $x = \infty$ the process can be repeated. It can be repeated only a finite number of times before attaining a normal basis, however, since at each step the sum of the column orders of the basis is increased by at least unity, and this sum is at most equal to the order at $x = \infty$ of the determinant of the conjugates of the basis, which is unchanged by the transformation.

Let μ be the smallest of the numbers $r_k - \mu_k$ for the function $\eta(x, y)$ in $(21·3)$, after the basis has been made normal, so that $r_k - \mu_k \geqq \mu$ $(k = 1, \cdots, n)$. Then the degree μ_k of the coefficient $g_k(x)$ satisfies the inequality $-\mu_k \geqq \mu - r_k$, and $g_k(x)$ has at $x = \infty$ an expansion of the form

$$g_k(x) = c_k \left(\frac{1}{x}\right)^{\mu - r_k} + \cdots .$$

At least one of the coefficients c_k is different from zero. The expansions of the function $(21·3)$ at the cycles for $x = \infty$ have from $(21·2)$ the form

$$\eta(x, y_i) = \left(\frac{1}{x}\right)^{\mu} \sum_k C_{ik} c_k + \cdots \qquad (i = 1, \cdots, n),$$

at least of the coefficients of $(1/x)^\mu$ is necessarily different from
~~~ce the determinant $|C_{ik}|$ is not zero. The column order of η is
~ore μ.

~o far we have considered only "multiples of a divisor Q except at
~ ∞," whose usefulness is of an auxiliary sort. The multiples which
~re of greater importance are those which have orders greater than or
equal to the orders prescribed by Q at every cycle whatsoever of the
algebraic function $y(x)$, including those at $x = \infty$. It is evident that some
divisors will have no multiples, an example being a divisor Q which has
positive but no negative exponents. A multiple $\eta(x, y)$ of such a divisor
would necessarily have all of its orders greater than or equal to zero,
and the sum of the orders of η could not be equal to zero as we know it
must be. The following theorem describes the character and the number
of the multiples of a divisor Q.

THEOREM 21·3. *If a divisor Q has a multiple, it has a set $\sigma_1(x, y), \cdots,$
$\sigma_\nu(x, y)$ of linearly independent ones such that every multiple of Q is expressible in the form*

$$\sigma = c_1\sigma_1 + \cdots + c_\nu\sigma_\nu$$

*with constant coefficients. If Q has no cycles at infinity and if $\eta_1, \cdots, \eta_n$ is
a basis for Q normal at $x = \infty$, with column orders r_k such that*

$$(21·4) \qquad r_1 \geqq r_2 \geqq \cdots \geqq r_s \geqq 0 > r_{s+1} \geqq \cdots \geqq r_n,$$

then the number ν of linearly independent multiples of Q is

$$\nu = (r_1 + 1) + \cdots + (r_s + 1).$$

When $\eta_1, \cdots, \eta_n$ is a basis for Q with the properties presupposed in
the theorem the function

$$\eta = g_1(x)\eta_1 + \cdots + g_n(x)\eta_n$$

will be a multiple of Q at all cycles, including those at $x = \infty$, if and only
if its column order at $x = \infty$ is greater than or equal to zero. According
to Theorem 21·2 this can never be so if all of the column orders r_k are
negative, since then all the numbers $r_k - \mu_k$ are negative, and in this
case the divisor Q has no multiples. When some of the column orders
are positive, as indicated in the arrangement $(21·4)$, the function η will
have its column order greater than or equal to zero at $x = \infty$, according
to Theorem 21·2, if and only if it is expressible in the form

$$(21·5) \qquad \eta = g_1(x)\eta_1 + \cdots + g_s(x)\eta_s$$

with $r_k - \mu_k \geqq 0$ for each coefficient $g_k(x)$ $(k = 1, \cdots, s)$. It is clear from this remark that the degree μ_k of each $g_k(x)$ can be r_k but no greater. The functions

$$\eta_1, \quad x\eta_1, \quad \cdots, \quad x^{r_1}\eta_1, \quad \cdots, \quad \eta_s, \quad x\eta_s, \quad \cdots, \quad x^{r_s}\eta_s$$

therefore constitute a set of multiples of Q in terms of which all such multiples are expressible linearly with constant coefficients, and their number ν is that given in the theorem. They are linearly independent since no linear expression of the form (21·5) can vanish identically when the determinant $|\eta_k(x, y_i)|$ is different from zero. This completes the proof of the theorem. We can infer in a similar manner the truth of the following useful corollary.

COROLLARY. *Let D be the divisor which is the product of the cycles at $x = \infty$, and let Q be a divisor having no cycles at $x = \infty$. If $\eta_1, \cdots, \eta_n$ is a basis for Q normal at $x = \infty$ and having there the column orders indicated in the arrangement* (21·4) *then the number of multiples of the divisor DQ is $\nu = r_1 + \cdots + r_s$. Furthermore if*

$$r_1 \geqq r_2 \geqq \cdots \geqq r_t \geqq 2 > r_{t+1} \geqq \cdots \geqq r_n,$$

then the number of multiples of D^2Q is

(21·6) $$\nu = (r_1 - 1) + \cdots + (r_t - 1).$$

The proof of the first part of the corollary is like that of the theorem except that the degree of each $g_k(x)$ in the expression (21·5) can now not exceed $r_k - 1$ if we wish $\eta(x, y)$ to have a zero of order one at least at each cycle for $x = \infty$.

Similarly the multiples of D^2Q are the multiples of Q which have zeros of order two at least at the cycles for $x = \infty$. By an argument similar to the one just made it follows that these multiples are the functions

$$\eta = g_1(x)\eta_1 + \cdots + g_t(x)\eta_t$$

for which each polynomial $g_k(x)$ $(k = 1, \cdots, t)$ has degree at most equal to $r_k - 2$. Hence their number is the number ν of the corollary.

It is not always easy to compute the number of linearly independent multiples of a divisor from the criteria given in the theorem above and its corollary, but we shall see that in a number of important cases this computation can be readily made with the help of the next theorem. Let the values of x corresponding to the cycles of a divisor $Q = P_1{}^{\mu_1} \cdots P_s{}^{\mu_s}$ be the finite values $x_1, \cdots, x_s$. Then the *ideal norm of the divisor Q* is defined to be the product

$$N(Q) = (x - x_1)^{\mu_1} \cdots (x - x_s)^{\mu_s}.$$

If a divisor has cycles at $x = \infty$ they are neglected in forming the ideal norm, but otherwise the definition is the same.

We have seen in Section 13 that there are only a finite number of cycles for the algebraic function $y(x)$ at which $r > 1$. Such a cycle will be called a *branch cycle*. The *divisor of the branch cycles* is defined to be the divisor $X = \Pi P^{r-1}$, where P is a branch cycle and r the number of roots y_i of the equation $f(x, y) = 0$ furnished by it, and the product is taken for all of the branch cycles. With the help of these notations the theorem now to be proved is as follows:

THEOREM 21·4. *For every basis* $\eta_1, \cdots, \eta_n$ *of a divisor Q we have*

$$\left| \eta_k(x, y_i) \right|^2 = cN(Q)^2 N(X)$$

where c is a constant factor.

It is clear that the power of a factor $x - x_0$ which occurs in the determinant $\left| \eta_k(x, y_i) \right|$ is the same for all bases of Q since for two equivalent bases the values of this determinant differ only by a constant factor (Theorem 21·1). Let us suppose therefore that the basis $\eta_1, \cdots, \eta_n$ has already been prepared by a linear transformation (21·1) with constant coefficients g_{kl} so that the determinant Δ for $\eta_1, \cdots, \eta_n$ at $x = x_0$ is the identity determinant. For the illustrative case used above, in which there are three cycles corresponding to $x = x_0$, the following table then indicates the exponents of the lowest powers of $(x - x_0)$ in the expansions of the elements of the determinant $\left| \eta_k(x, y_i) \right|$ at the three cycles. Out of each of the first a rows we may take the factor $(x - x_0)^{\lambda/a}$, and out of the $a - 1$ columns following the first the factor $(x - x_0)$ raised to the power $1/a + \cdots + (a-1)/a$. Hence in all we have from these rows and columns the factor $(x - x_0)$ raised to the power $\lambda + (a-1)/2$. A similar process applied to the two remaining principal minors indicated in the diagram gives for the squared determinant $\left| \eta_k(x, y_i) \right|^2$ the factor $(x - x_0)$ raised to the power

$$2\lambda + 2\mu + 2\nu + (a - 1) + (b - 1) + (c - 1),$$

which is exactly the power of $(x - x_0)$ occurring in the product $N(Q)^2$ $N(X)$. The same method of proof applies when there are more or fewer than three cycles at $x = x_0$.

If we can show that, after the power of $(x - x_0)$ described above has been removed, the constant term in the expansion for $\left| \eta_k(x, y_i) \right|$ is different from zero, we shall have proved our theorem, for then the

	$\eta_1 \quad \eta_2 \quad \cdots \quad \eta_a$	$\eta_{a+1} \quad \cdots \quad \eta_{a+b}$	$\eta_{a+b+1} \quad \cdots \quad \eta_n$
$\eta(x, y_1)$	$\dfrac{\lambda}{a} \quad \dfrac{\lambda+1}{a} \quad \cdots \quad \dfrac{\lambda+a-1}{a}$		
$\cdots$	$\cdots\cdots\cdots\cdots$	$\geqq \dfrac{\lambda}{a}+1$	$\geqq \dfrac{\lambda}{a}+1$
$\eta(x, y_a)$	$\dfrac{\lambda}{a} \quad \dfrac{\lambda+1}{a} \quad \cdots \quad \dfrac{\lambda+a-1}{a}$		
$\eta(x, y_{a+1})$		$\dfrac{\mu}{b} \quad \cdots \quad \dfrac{\mu+b-1}{b}$	
$\cdots$	$\geqq \dfrac{\mu}{b}+1$	$\cdots\cdots \quad \cdots$	$\geqq \dfrac{\mu}{b}+1$
$\eta(x, y_{a+b})$		$\dfrac{\mu}{b} \quad \cdots \quad \dfrac{\mu+b-1}{b}$	
$\eta(x, y_{a+b+1})$			$\dfrac{\nu}{c} \quad \cdots \quad \dfrac{\nu+c-1}{c}$
$\cdots$	$\geqq \dfrac{\nu}{c}+1$	$\geqq \dfrac{\nu}{c}+1$	$\cdots\cdots \quad \cdots$
$\eta(x, y_n)$			$\dfrac{\nu}{c} \quad \cdots \quad \dfrac{\nu+c-1}{c}$

zeros and poles in the finite x-plane of the two rational functions $|\eta_k(x, y_i)|^2$ and $N(Q)^2 N(X)$ are identical, and these two can differ only by a constant factor. When we set $x = x_0$ in the determinant $|\eta_k(x, y_i)|$ deprived of the factors $(x-x_0)$ as described, the three principal minors in the squares indicated in the diagram are the only ones which remain. The first one of these, for example, is

$$\begin{vmatrix} 1 & 1 & \cdots & 1 \\ \omega^\lambda & \omega^{\lambda+1} & \cdots & \omega^{\lambda+a-1} \\ \cdots & \cdots & \cdots & \cdots \\ \omega^{(a-1)\lambda} & \omega^{(a-1)(\lambda+1)} & \cdots & \omega^{(a-1)(\lambda+a-1)} \end{vmatrix}$$

where ω is a primitive a-th root of unity, and it is different from zero since no two of the roots $\omega^{\lambda+k}$ ($k=0, 1, \cdots, a-1$) are equal. A similar argument applies to the other minors, and the theorem is therefore proved.

As an immediate consequence of the preceding theorems we have

COROLLARY 1. *For every basis* $\eta_1, \cdots, \eta_n$ *of a divisor* Q *normal at* $x = \infty$ *the equation*

$$(21 \cdot 7) \qquad r_1 + \cdots + r_n + q + \frac{w}{2} = 0$$

is true, where the integers r_k *are the column orders of the basis at* $x = \infty$, q *is the order of the divisor* Q, *and* w *the order of the divisor* X *of the branch places.*

To prove the corollary we note first that the order at $x = \infty$ of the determinant $|\eta_k(x, y_i)|^2$ for a basis normal at infinity is $2(r_1 + \cdots + r_n)$, as has been remarked above in the paragraph just preceding Theorem $21 \cdot 2$. According to the last theorem the sum of the orders of $|\eta_k(x, y_i)|^2$ at finite values of x is the same as that of the product $N(Q)^2 N(X)$ which we know to be $2q+w$. The equation $(21 \cdot 7)$ then expresses the known fact that the sum of all the orders of the rational function $|\eta_k(x, y_i)|^2$ is zero.

COROLLARY 2. *The number*

$$(21 \cdot 8) \qquad p = \frac{w}{2} - n + 1 = \tfrac{1}{2} \sum (r - 1) - n + 1,$$

which is called the genus of the algebraic function defined by the equation $f(x, y) = 0$, *is always a positive integer or zero.*

It is evident from the equation $(21 \cdot 7)$ that $w/2$ is an integer and hence that the number p in the last corollary is an integer. To prove that it is not negative consider a basis $\eta_1, \cdots, \eta_n$ normal at $x = \infty$ for the particular divisor $Q = 1$. This basis must have all of its column orders $r_1, \cdots, r_n$ at $x = \infty$ zero or negative since no rational function can have positive orders at all cycles at $x = \infty$ and no negative ones elsewhere. One at least of the column orders must be zero since otherwise the column order of the function

$$\eta = g_1(x)\eta_1 + \cdots + g_n(x)\eta_n$$

would always be negative (Theorem $21 \cdot 2$), and this is impossible since the function $\eta(x, y) = $ constant is certainly a multiple of the divisor

$Q = 1$. On the other hand, two of the numbers $r_1, \cdots, r_n$ could not be zero since then both of the corresponding functions of the basis would have no singularities and would be constants, and they would not be linearly independent. Since now $r_1 = 0$ while all other integers $r_2, \cdots, r_n$ are negative, it follows with the help of equation $(21 \cdot 7)$, since the order of the divisor $Q = 1$ is $q = 0$, that

$$p = \frac{w}{2} - n + 1 = - r_1 - \cdots - r_n - n + 1 \geqq 0.$$

22. **Complementary bases.** A basis $\zeta_1, \cdots, \zeta_n$ is said to be *complementary* to the basis $\eta_1, \cdots, \eta_n$ if the traces of the products of the functions composing the two bases satisfy the relations

$$(22 \cdot 1) \qquad T(\eta_k \zeta_k) = 1, \qquad T(\eta_k \zeta_l) = 0 \qquad (k \neq l).$$

We have seen in Section 19 that the coefficients R_k for the function

$$\zeta = R_1 \eta_1 + \cdots + R_n \eta_n$$

will be uniquely determined when the traces

$$T(\eta_i \zeta) = R_1 T(\eta_i \eta_1) + \cdots + R_n T(\eta_i \eta_n) \qquad (i = 1, \cdots, n)$$

are assigned. It follows readily that the functions ζ_k of a basis complementary to $\eta_1, \cdots, \eta_n$ are uniquely determined, and that the relation between the two bases is a reciprocal one.

THEOREM $22 \cdot 1$. *If a basis* $\eta_1, \cdots, \eta_n$ *is normal at* $x = \infty$ *with column orders* $r_1, \cdots, r_n$, *then its complementary basis* $\zeta_1, \cdots, \zeta_n$ *is also normal at* $x = \infty$ *and has the column orders* $-r_1, \cdots, -r_n$.

Let us denote the column orders which are to be determined for the basis $\zeta_1, \cdots, \zeta_n$, by $s_1, \cdots, s_n$, and let d_{ik} be the matrix of coefficients for this basis corresponding to the matrix C_{ik} in equation $(21 \cdot 2)$ for the original basis. Then at $x = \infty$ we have the expansion

$$T(\eta_i \zeta_k) = \left(\frac{1}{x}\right)^{r_i + s_k} \sum_{j=1}^{n} C_{ji} d_{jk} + \cdots .$$

These expansions must vanish identically when $i \neq k$ and be identically equal to 1 when $i = k$, on account of the relations $(22 \cdot 1)$. Since the determinant $|C_{jk}|$ is different from zero, and since the constants d_{jk} $(j = 1, \cdots, n)$ for a fixed k are not all zero, it follows that the relations

$$\sum_{j=1}^{n} C_{ji} d_{jk} = 0 \quad (i \neq k), \qquad \sum_{j=1}^{n} C_{jk} d_{jk} = 1, \qquad r_k + s_k = 0$$

must hold. We see that $s_k = -r_k$, and that the determinant $|d_{jk}|$ is different from zero since it is, except for interchange of rows and columns, the reciprocal of $|C_{jk}|$.

THEOREM 22·2. *If $\eta_1, \cdots, \eta_n$ is a basis for a divisor Q, then its complementary basis $\zeta_1, \cdots, \zeta_n$ is a basis for the divisor R defined by the equation $QRX = 1$, in which X is the divisor of the branch places.*

To prove this consider again the illustrative case of a value $x = x_0$ having three cycles A, B, C providing, respectively, a, b, c roots of $f(x, y) = 0$. The argument to be made would be quite similar if there were more or fewer than three places. At the three cycles A, B, C, respectively, let λ, μ, ν be the orders of Q and λ', μ', ν' be the minima of the orders of the functions of the complementary basis $\zeta_1, \cdots, \zeta_n$. To prove the theorem we may prove first that λ', μ', ν' are the orders of the divisor R at the cycles A, B, C, by establishing the relations

$$(22\cdot2)\quad \lambda + \lambda' + a - 1 = 0, \ \mu + \mu' + b - 1 = 0, \ \nu + \nu' + c - 1 = 0,$$

and second that the determinant Δ of Section 20 formed with respect to the divisor R for the set $\zeta_1, \cdots, \zeta_n$ cannot be zero.

We suppose the notations for the cycles A, B, C so chosen that

$$(22\cdot3)\qquad (\lambda + \lambda')/a \leqq (\mu + \mu')/b \leqq (\nu + \nu')/c.$$

It will be simpler if we assume that the first of the relations (22.2) is true and prove the second, since the proof of the first requires similar but fewer arguments. Consider now two functions

$$\eta = u_1\eta_1 + \cdots + u_n\eta_n, \qquad \zeta = v_1\zeta_1 + \cdots + v_n\zeta_n,$$

for which the coefficients u_i, v_i are constants. Since the determinant Δ of Section 20 is different from zero at the value x_0 it follows that when a number h of the set $0, 1, \cdots, b-1$ has been selected arbitrarily, the coefficients u_i can be determined so that the function η has at A, B, C, respectively, the expansions

$$\eta = \alpha(x - x_0)^{\lambda/a+1} + \cdots,$$
$$\eta = (x - x_0)^{(\mu+h)/b} + \beta(x - x_0)^{\mu/b+1} + \cdots,$$
$$\eta = \gamma(x - x_0)^{\nu/c+1} + \cdots.$$

The coefficients v_i can then be selected so that ζ has orders exactly λ', μ', ν' at A, B, C, respectively, and so that

$$(22\cdot4)\qquad T(\eta\zeta) = u_1v_1 + \cdots + u_nv_n \neq 0.$$

With the help of the first equation $(22 \cdot 2)$ it is clear that the smallest exponents possible for the expansions of the product $\eta\zeta$ at A, B, C are then

$$(\lambda' + \lambda)/a + 1 = 1/a, \qquad (\mu' + \mu + h)/b, \qquad (\nu' + \nu)/c + 1.$$

If the first of these were the smallest the trace $T(\eta\zeta)$ would have to vanish at $x = x_0$, contrary to $(22 \cdot 4)$. The second is less than the third, by $(22 \cdot 3)$, and hence must be the smallest. Since $T(\eta\zeta)$ is a constant different from zero it follows from the last paragraph of Section 18 that $(\mu' + \mu + h)/b$ must be negative when it is a fraction and zero when it is an integer. We see readily then that the largest of the values $(\mu' + \mu + h)/b$ for $h = 0, 1, \cdots, b - 1$ must be zero, and the second relation $(22 \cdot 2)$ is therefore proved. The proofs of the other two are similar.

We can prove that at the value x_0 the determinant Δ of Section 20 formed with respect to the divisor R for the basis $\zeta_1, \cdots, \zeta_n$ can not be zero. For if it had this value, constants v_k not all zero could be selected so that at A, B, C the function ζ would have, respectively, the expansions

$$\zeta = \alpha'(x - x_0)^{1+\lambda'/a} + \cdots,$$
$$\zeta = \beta'(x - x_0)^{1+\mu'/b} + \cdots,$$
$$\zeta = \gamma'(x - x_0)^{1+\nu'/c} + \cdots.$$

Since for every choice of the constants u_k the orders of η at the cycles A, B, C are at least λ, μ, ν, the exponents of the terms in $T(\eta\zeta)$ would then all be greater than zero, on account of the relations $(22 \cdot 2)$. The trace $(22 \cdot 4)$ would be zero for every choice of the constants u_k, which is impossible.

Since the above reasoning applies at every finite value x_0 it follows that $\zeta_1, \cdots, \zeta_n$ is a basis for the divisor R, as stated in the theorem.

As a first application of the properties of the complementary basis we may establish formulas for the number of multiples of divisors of the form $D^2/(P_1 \cdots P_\mu X)$ which will be of service in a later section. Let $\eta_1, \cdots, \eta_n$ be a basis for the divisor $Q = 1/(P_1 \cdots P_\mu X)$, normal at $x = \infty$ and with column orders

$$(22 \cdot 5) \qquad r_1 \geqq r_2 \geqq \cdots \geqq r_t \geqq 2 > r_{t+1} \geqq \cdots \geqq r_n.$$

Since the order of Q is $q = -(\mu + w)$, the formula $(21 \cdot 7)$ gives the relation

$$(22 \cdot 6) \qquad r_1 + \cdots + r_n - (\mu + w) + \frac{w}{2} = 0.$$

The basis $\zeta_1, \cdots, \zeta_n$ complementary to $\eta_1, \cdots, \eta_n$ is a basis for the divisor $R = 1/XQ = P_1 \cdots P_\mu$ and has at $x = \infty$ the column orders $-r_1$, $\cdots, -r_n$. Each of the functions ζ_k must have a negative column order at $x = \infty$ since each has zeros at the cycles $P_1, \cdots, P_\mu$ and must therefore have some poles at infinite places which are the only places where such poles are possible. The numbers r_k are therefore all positive, and those following r_t in the arrangement $(22 \cdot 5)$ are unity. Formula $(22 \cdot 6)$ and the equation $(21 \cdot 6)$ therefore give

$$\nu = (r_1 - 1) + \cdots + (r_n - 1) = \frac{w}{2} - n + \mu = p + \mu - 1$$

as the number of multiples of $D^2/(P_1 \cdots P_\mu X)$. When no cycles P_1, $\cdots, P_\mu$ are present, we have $R = 1$ and it follows from the argument of the last paragraph of Section 21 that $r_n = 0$, while the other column orders are positive. Hence we now have, from formulas $(21 \cdot 6)$ and $(22 \cdot 6)$ with $\mu = 0$,

$$\nu = (r_1 - 1) + \cdots + (r_n - 1) + 1 = \frac{w}{2} - n + 1 = p$$

as the number of multiples of D^2/X. This proves the following theorem:

THEOREM $22 \cdot 3$. *Let D be the divisor whose factors are the cycles at $x = \infty$, X the divisor of the branch cycles, and $P_1, \cdots, P_\mu$ arbitrarily chosen cycles. Then the number of linearly independent multiples of the divisor D^2/X is exactly $\nu = p$, and the number for $D^2/(P_1 \cdots P_\mu X)$ $(\mu \geqq 1)$ is $\nu = p + \mu - 1$.*

23. **The invariant property of the genus number.** If the poles and zeros of a rational function $\eta(x, y)$ are at the cycles $P_1, \cdots, P_s$ and have the orders $\mu_1, \cdots, \mu_s$, then the divisor $Q_\eta = P_1^{\mu_1} \cdots P_s^{\mu_s}$ is called *the divisor of η*. Since the sum of the orders of a rational function is always zero, it follows that the order of the divisor Q_η must be zero. Conversely one might expect that there would be a rational function corresponding in this way to every divisor Q of order zero, but this is not always the case. It is true in the case of functions of a single variable x which may be regarded as rational functions of the algebraic function defined by the equation $y - x = 0$. For we can easily construct out of factors of the type $(x - x_0)^\lambda$ a rational function of x with arbitrarily prescribed poles and zeros in the complex x-plane, provided only that the sum of the orders of these poles and zeros is zero. But for rational functions $\eta(x, y)$ of a more general algebraic function no such simple

construction is possible, and it may be that for some divisors of order zero no corresponding rational function exists.

Some of the factors in Q_η have positive exponents and some negative. We may agree to denote the product of those with positive exponents by N_η, and may express the divisor in the form $Q_\eta = N_\eta/D_\eta$, where the meaning of D_η is evident. At every cycle P of a factor P^a of the denominator D_η the expansions $(18\cdot1)$ for the rational function η and its derivative have the forms

$$(23\cdot1) \qquad \eta = \frac{\beta}{t^a} + \cdots, \qquad \frac{d\eta}{dt} = -a\beta\frac{t^{a-1}}{t^{2a}} + \cdots,$$

where β is a constant different from zero. At other cycles these expansions have the form

$$(23\cdot2) \qquad \eta = \alpha + \beta t^a + \cdots, \qquad \frac{d\eta}{dt} = a\beta t^{a-1} + \cdots,$$

where β is again different from zero and α a constant which vanishes at the factors of N_η but not elsewhere. A cycle P of either type is called a *branch cycle for* $\eta(x, y)$ if $a \neq 1$. The *divisor of the branch cycles for* η is defined to be $X_\eta = \Pi P^{a-1}$, where the product is taken for all the branch cycles P of η. We may for convenience denote the orders of X_η and D_η by w_η and n_η, respectively. For the function $\eta = x$, the notations which have just been introduced give the special cases X_x, D_x, w_x, n_x which have been denoted in the preceding pages by X, D, w, n.

THEOREM $23\cdot1$. *The divisor whose orders are identical with those of the derivative* $d\eta/dt$ *at the various cycles of an algebraic function is* X_η/D_η^2. *The order* $w_\eta - 2n_\eta$ *of this divisor is the same for all rational functions* η.

The first part of the theorem is evident after an examination of the exponents in the expressions $(23\cdot1)$ and $(23\cdot2)$ for $d\eta/dt$. To prove the second part we notice that, by elimination of y from the two equations

$$\eta = \eta(x, y), \qquad f(x, y) = 0,$$

a relation $\phi(x, \eta) = 0$ can always be found in which $\phi(x, \eta)$ is a polynomial. Since all of the expansions for x and η satisfy this equation identically it follows that

$$\frac{d\eta}{dt} = -\left(\frac{\partial\phi}{\partial x}\bigg/\frac{\partial\phi}{\partial\eta}\right)\frac{dx}{dt},$$

which shows that at every cycle the order of $d\eta/dt$ is the sum of the order of a rational function of x, y and the order of dx/dt. The divisor of $d\eta/dt$ is therefore the product of the divisor of dx/dt by that of a rational function, and the orders of the divisors of $d\eta/dt$ and dx/dt are therefore always equal.

As a result of the invariance of the expression $w_\eta - 2n_\eta$, we see that the genus of our algebraic function is also expressible in the form

$$p = \tfrac{1}{2}w_\eta - n_\eta + 1,$$

since, according to Theorem 23·1, this number will have the same value no matter what rational function $\eta(x, y)$ is used in its computation. From Corollary 2 at the end of Section 21 we know that p is always a positive integer or zero and hence that $w_\eta/2$ is always an integer.

24. **Construction of elementary integrals.** Integrals of the form

$$I = \int \eta(x, y)dx,$$

where $\eta(x, y)$ is a rational function of x and y, are the so-called Abelian integrals associated with the algebraic equation $f(x, y) = 0$. They play a most important and interesting role in the theory of the algebraic functions defined by such equations. If we write such an integral in the form

$$I = \int \eta(x, y)\frac{dx}{dt}dt$$

and substitute the expansions of η and dx/dt, it is evident that at each cycle the value of the integral will be expressible in terms of t by means of a series of the form

$$(24·1) \qquad \frac{A_{-p}}{t^p} + \cdots + \frac{A_{-1}}{t} + A \log t + A_0 + A_1 t + \cdots.$$

If the series has no logarithmic term or terms with negative exponents, the cycle is called an ordinary cycle for the integral; if terms with negative exponents are present but no logarithmic term, it is a pole; if a logarithmic term is present, it is a logarithmic singularity. Integrals which have no singularities are called *integrals of the first kind*; those which have poles but no logarithmic singularities are of the *second kind*; while those with logarithmic singularities are of the *third kind*.

All integrals of the first kind may be thought of as elementary integrals, but an integral of the second kind is called an elementary integral only when it has no singularity except a single pole with an expansion of the form

$$\frac{1}{t^\mu} + A_0 + A_1 t + \cdots .$$

An integral of the third kind is an elementary integral if it has only two singularities at which its expansions are

$$\log t + A_0 + A_1 t + \cdots , \qquad - \log t + B_0 + B_1 t + \cdots .$$

The coefficient A in the expansion (24·1) is a residue of the function $\eta(x, y)$ and we have found in Section 18 that for every such function the sum of the residues is zero. We see then that the elementary integral of the third kind is as simple as one could hope to find, since every such integral must have at least two logarithmic singularities.

We shall see presently that every Abelian integral whatsoever is expressible as a sum of elementary integrals of the first, second, and third kinds multiplied by constant coefficients, but for this result to have significance we must be certain that elementary integrals of the three kinds actually exist. For integrals w of the first kind it is evident that at every cycle the expansion for $\eta \, dx/dt$ must be without terms in negative powers of t, and the sum of the orders of η and dx/dt must therefore be positive or zero. This means that η is a multiple of the reciprocal of the divisor of dx/dt, and according to Theorem 23·1 this reciprocal is D^2/X. From Theorem 22·3 the number of linearly independent multiples of this divisor is p, and we have the following theorem:

THEOREM 24·1. *The number of linearly independent integrals of the first kind is exactly the genus p. If $w_1, \cdots , w_p$ are such integrals of the first kind then every other integral of the first kind is expressible uniquely with constant coefficients in the form*

$$w = c_1 w_1 + \cdots + c_p w_p + c.$$

For an elementary integral of the second kind with no singularity except a simple pole at a cycle P the product $\eta \, dx/dt$ can have no singularity except a pole of order two at P. It follows readily that the number of linearly independent functions η for which the product $\eta \, dx/dt$ has these properties is the same as the number of multiples of the divisor $D^2/P^2 X$. According to Theorem 22·3 this number is $\nu = p+1$. One at least of the multiples η must give the product $\eta \, dx/dt$ a negative order at P since otherwise all would be integrands of integrals of the first kind,

and only p of these are linearly independent. For an η which provides
a negative order the expansion at P must have the form

$$\eta \frac{dx}{dt} = \frac{A_{-2}}{t^2} + A_0 + A_1 t + \cdots , \qquad (A_{-2} \neq 0),$$

the term in $1/t$ being absent since the sum of the residues of η is zero.
The integrand $-\eta/A_{-2}$ gives the integral of the following theorem for
the case when $\mu = 0$.

THEOREM 24·2. *For every cycle P and every integer $\mu \geq 0$ there exists
an elementary integral $\zeta_\mu(P)$ of the second kind with an expansion at P of
the form*

$$\zeta_\mu(P) = \mu!/t^{\mu+1} + A_0 + A_1 t + \cdots$$

in which it is understood that $\mu! = 1$ when $\mu = 0$. The integrals

$$\zeta_\mu(P) + c_1 w_1 + \cdots + c_p w_p + c$$

are also of this type and there are no others.

The last statement is evident since the difference of two integrals
$\zeta_\mu(P)$ with the same μ is necessarily an integral of the first kind.

If the theorem is true for $\mu - 1$ and preceding integers the proof for
μ is similar to that for $\mu = 0$. An integrand function η for an integral
$\zeta_\mu(P)$ must give $\eta dx/dt$ no singularities except a pole of order $-(\mu+2)$
at the cycle P. The number of linearly independent functions η providing orders $\geq -(\mu+2)$ for $\eta dx/dt$ at P is the number $p + \mu + 1$ of
linearly independent multiples of the divisor $D^2/(P^{\mu+2}X)$ given by
Theorem 22·3. The number providing orders $\geq -(\mu+1)$ for $\eta dx/dt$ at
P is similarly $p + \mu$. Hence among the $p + \mu + 1$ multiples there must be
one at least which gives $\eta dx/dt$ exactly the order $-(\mu+2)$. By subtracting a suitable linear combination of $\zeta_0, \cdots, \zeta_{\mu-1}$ from the integral
having this η as its integrand, and multiplying finally by a constant
if necessary, an integral $\zeta_\mu(P)$ can be constructed with the properties
of the theorem.

THEOREM 24·3. *For an arbitrary pair of distinct cycles P_1, P_2 there
exists an elementary integral of the third kind $\pi(P_1, P_2)$ with expansions
at P_1 and P_2, respectively, of the forms*

$$+ \log t + A_0 + A_1 t + \cdots , \qquad - \log t + B_0 + B_1 t + \cdots .$$

The integrals

$$\pi(P_1, P_2) + c_1 w_1 + \cdots + c_p w_p + c$$

are also of this type and there are no others.

To construct such an integral $\pi(P_1, P_2)$ one must find an integrand function η which gives $\eta \, dx/dt$ no singularities except simple poles at P_1 and P_2, and which is therefore a multiple of the divisor D^2/P_1P_2X. According to Theorem $22 \cdot 3$ there are $\nu = p+1$ linearly independent multiples of this divisor, one at least of which must give $\eta \, dx/dt$ a pole at one at least of the cycles P_1, P_2. But if η gives $\eta \, dx/dt$ a simple pole at P_1 with an expansion

$$\frac{A}{t} + A_0 + A_1 t + \cdots,$$

it must also provide a simple pole at P_2 with an expansion

$$-\frac{A}{t} + B_0 + B_1 t + \cdots,$$

since the sum of the residues of η is zero. The integrand η/A furnishes the integral $\pi(P_1, P_2)$ of the theorem.

THEOREM $24 \cdot 4$. *Every Abelian integral I is expressible linearly in terms of elementary integrals with constant coefficients.*

To prove this let L be a cycle at which the integral I has a logarithmic singularity and at which the residue of the integrand function η of I is denoted by A, and let L_0 be a cycle distinct from all the singularities L. The difference

$$I - \sum_L A\pi(L, L_0),$$

where the sum is taken for all the logarithmic singularities L, has no logarithmic singularities at the cycles L, and also none at L_0 since the sum of the residues A is zero. It may still have poles, however, at cycles P with expansions of the form

$$\frac{B_{-\mu}}{t^\mu} + \cdots + \frac{B_{-1}}{t} + B_0 + B_1 t + \cdots.$$

The difference

$$I - \sum_L A\pi(L, L_0) - \sum_P \left[\frac{B_{-\mu}}{(\mu-1)!} \zeta_{\mu-1}(P) + \cdots + B_{-1}\zeta_0(P) \right],$$

where the last sum is taken for all the poles P, is an integral of the first kind linearly expressible as indicated in Theorem $24 \cdot 1$.

25. **The Riemann-Roch theorem.** The theorem designated by this name is a famous one in the theory of algebraic functions, with many

applications in both geometry and analysis. The purpose of this section is the presentation of a proof of the theorem free from restrictive assumptions on the singularities of the algebraic function defined by the equation $f(x, y) = 0$, and based upon the theory of multiples of a divisor. We shall need the following two lemmas:

LEMMA 25·1. *The number of linearly independent multiples of a divisor Q is the same as the number for the product $Q_\xi Q$, where Q_ξ is the divisor of a rational function $\xi(x, y)$.*

This is evident because if $\sigma(x, y)$ is a multiple of Q then the product $\xi\sigma$ is a multiple of $Q_\xi Q$; and if σ is a multiple of $Q_\xi Q$ then σ/ξ is a multiple of Q. Hence $\xi\sigma_k$ $(k = 1, \cdots, \nu)$ is a complete set of linearly independent multiples of $Q_\xi Q$ if $\sigma_k(k = 1, \cdots, \nu)$ is such a set for Q.

LEMMA 25·2. *If $P_1, \cdots, P_m$ are cycles selected arbitrarily among those of a divisor Q, there is always a rational function $\eta(x, y)$ such that the divisor $Q_\eta Q$ contains none of the cycles $P_1, \cdots, P_m$.*

In proving the lemma we may suppose that none of the cycles $P_1, \cdots, P_m$ is at $x = \infty$, since a transformation of the form $x_1 = 1/(x - \alpha)$ will bring this about if it is not already so. Let $\eta_1, \cdots, \eta_n$ be a basis for the divisor $Q_1 = P_1^{-\mu_1} \cdots P_m^{-\mu_m}$, where μ_k is the exponent which P_k has in Q. Since at every finite value x_0 the determinant Δ of the basis is different from zero, we may select the constants c_i in the expression

$$\eta = c_1\eta_1 + \cdots + c_n\eta_n$$

so that they do not satisfy any of the linear equations whose coefficients are the rows of the determinants Δ corresponding to the values x_0 for the cycles $P_1, \cdots, P_m$. Then η will have exactly the orders $-\mu_k$ at the cycles P_k, and the divisor $Q_\eta Q$ will contain none of these cycles.

We are now ready to prove the following principal theorem of this section:

THEOREM 25·1. (RIEMANN-ROCH.) *If the product QQ' of two divisors is equal to the divisor $Q_\xi X/D^2$ of a product $\xi dx/dt$, where $\xi(x, y)$ is a rational function, then the orders q, q' of Q and Q' and the numbers μ, μ' of linearly independent multiples of $1/Q$ and $1/Q'$ satisfy the relations*

$$(25·1) \qquad \mu = \mu' + q - p + 1, \qquad q + q' = 2p - 2.$$

These equations may also be written in the form

$$2\mu - q = 2\mu' - q', \qquad q + q' = 2p - 2.$$

In making a proof of the theorem there will be no loss of generality in assuming that none of the cycles of the divisor X are at $x = \infty$, since this can be brought about by a transformation $x_1 = 1/(x-\alpha)$, and such a transformation does not disturb the character of the product QQ'. We may see this because $Q_{x_1} = D/D_{x_1}$, and because the argument on page 52 following the proof of Theorem 21·1 shows that the transformation takes the cycles of X into those of X_{x_1}, so that

$$QQ' = Q_\xi X/D^2 = Q_\xi (D_{x_1}/D)^2 X/D_{x_1}^2 = Q_{\xi/x_1}^2 X_{x_1}/D_{x_1}^2.$$

It is easy to see that the relation between Q and Q' can be expressed in the form $X/Q_1 Q_1' = 1$, where

$$(25 \cdot 2) \qquad Q_1 = DQQ_\eta/Q_\xi, \qquad Q_1' = DQ'/Q_\eta.$$

Furthermore the function $\eta(x, y)$ can be so chosen that Q_1 has no cycles at $x = \infty$, according to Lemma 25·2. The same will then be true of $Q_1' = X/Q_1$, since X has also no cycles at $x = \infty$. The numbers μ, μ' of multiples of $1/Q$ and $1/Q'$ are the same as those of D/Q_1 and D/Q_1', by $(25 \cdot 2)$ and Lemma 25·1.

Let $\eta_1, \cdots, \eta_n$ be a basis for the divisor $1/Q_1$ normal at $x = \infty$ and with column orders

$$r_1 \geqq r_2 \geqq \cdots \geqq r_s \geqq 0 > r_{s+1} \geqq \cdots \geqq r_n.$$

According to the Corollary to Theorem 21·3 the number of linearly independent multiples of D/Q_1 is

$$\mu = r_1 + \cdots + r_s.$$

The basis complementary to $\eta_1, \cdots, \eta_n$ is a basis for $1/Q_1'$ and has column orders

$$-r_1 \leqq -r_2 \leqq \cdots \leqq -r_s \leqq 0 < -r_{s+1} \leqq \cdots \leqq -r_n,$$

by Theorems 22·1 and 22·2. Hence the number of multiples of D/Q_1' is

$$\mu' = -r_{s+1} - r_{s+2} - \cdots - r_n.$$

The last two equations with $(21 \cdot 7)$ and $(21 \cdot 8)$ give the formula

$$\mu - \mu' = r_1 + \cdots + r_n = q + n - w/2 = q - p + 1$$

since the order of $1/Q_1$, from $(25 \cdot 2)$, is $-n - q$. Furthermore the orders of the two sides of the equation $QQ' = Q_\xi X/D^2$ must be equal, so that

$$q + q' = w - 2n = 2p - 2.$$

Thus the theorem is proved.

26. **Rational functions with prescribed poles.** In Section 6 it was shown that a rational function of the variable x can always be constructed with arbitrarily selected poles and zeros provided only that the sum of the orders of the zeros is equal to the sum of the orders of the poles. The analogous theorem is not true for rational functions $\xi(x, y)$ on the Riemann surface of an algebraic function. The problem of constructing rational functions $\xi(x, y)$ which have poles only among an arbitrarily selected set of cycles $P_1, \cdots, P_q$ is one of the fundamental problems of algebraic function theory. The theorems of this section have to do with this problem.

We shall adopt the notation $\psi_i(P) = \psi_i(x, y)$ $(i = 1, \cdots, p)$ for the p linearly independent multiples of the divisor D^2/X whose existence is asserted in Theorem 22·3. All other such multiples are then expressible in the form

$$(26\cdot1) \qquad\qquad \psi = c_1\psi_1 + \cdots + c_p\psi_p.$$

These functions ψ are the integrands of integrals of the first kind described in Theorem 24·1. The divisor Q_ψ of every such function has the form $Q_\psi = RD^2/X$ where R is a divisor having only positive exponents and of order $w - 2n = 2p - 2$, since the divisor D^2/X has order $2n - w = 2 - 2p$ and Q_ψ has order zero.

LEMMA 26·1. *If the rational functions $\eta_i(i = 1, \cdots, \mu)$ are linearly independent then for every integer $q > 0$ it is possible to select finite non-singular places P_k $(k = 1, \cdots, q)$, distinct from any finite number of other places given in advance, and such that the rank of the matrix $|| \eta_i(P_k) ||$ is the smaller of the numbers μ and q.*

If this were not the case let ρ be the maximum rank attainable for the matrix, and suppose $P_1, \cdots, P_q$ selected so that the matrix has this rank. Then the linear equations

$$c_1\eta_1(P_k) + \cdots + c_\mu\eta_\mu(P_k) = 0 \qquad (k = 1, \cdots, q)$$

would have solutions c_i not all zero. The function

$$\eta(x, y) = c_1\eta_1(x, y) + \cdots + c_\mu\eta_\mu(x, y)$$

would vanish at all finite non-singular places P permitted by the lemma, since otherwise the maximum rank attainable for the matrix would be greater than ρ. Hence $\eta(x, y)$ would have an infinity of zeros and be identically zero, and the functions η_i could not be linearly independent.

Let $P_1, \cdots, P_q$ be a set of places distinct from the places of the divisor D^2/X and chosen as described in the lemma for the integrands $\psi_i (i=1, \cdots, p)$ of integrals of the first kind. The number of linearly independent integrands of this sort vanishing at $P_1, \cdots, P_q$ is evidently the larger of the two numbers $p-q$ and 0. It is also the number of linearly independent multiples of the divisor $P_1 \cdots P_q D^2/X$ since the integrands ψ are multiples of D^2/X. Thus we see that for a set of places $P_1, \cdots, P_q$ chosen as above the number of linearly independent multiples of the divisor $P_1 \cdots P_q D^2/X$ is the larger of the two numbers $p-q$ and 0.

A *special set of places* $P_1, \cdots, P_q$ is by definition one for which the number of linearly independent multiples ψ of $P_1 \cdots P_q D^2/X$ is greater than the larger of $p-q$ and 0. Evidently for such sets $q \leq 2p-2$ since the divisor $P_1 \cdots P_q D^2/X$ would otherwise have order greater than $2p-2+2n-w=0$ and would therefore have no multiples. A *special divisor* $Q=P_1 \cdots P_q$ is one for which the set $P_1, \cdots, P_q$ is special. A *special rational function* is by definition one whose poles occur only among the places of a special set $P_1, \cdots, P_q$.

THEOREM 26·1. *There is no place P' which is common to all the divisors R in the formulas $Q_\psi = R D^2/X$ for integrands ψ of integrals of the first kind. The integrands ψ have therefore no zero in common other than those prescribed by the divisor D^2/X, and for every place P some of these integrands have consequently exactly the order prescribed by D^2/X.*

To prove this suppose that P' were a place common to all of the divisors R, and that the places $P_1, \cdots, P_{p-1}$ were selected distinct from P' and so that the matrix $||\psi_i(P_k)||$ has rank $p-1$, as in Lemma 26·1. There would then be exactly one linearly independent multiple ψ of the divisor $Q D^2/X$, where $Q=P_1 \cdots P_{p-1}$, and its divisor would have the form $Q_\psi = Q Q' D^2/X$ with Q' containing the fixed place P'. Evidently there would also be exactly one multiple of $1/Q'$, by Lemma 25·1. In the Riemann-Roch theorem applied to Q and Q' we should have $q=p-1$, $\mu'=1$, and hence $\mu=1$ from (25·1). But this number μ of multiples of $1/Q$ would be the same as the number of multiples ψ of $Q'D^2/X$, by Lemma 25·1, and to obtain multiples of the latter divisor we should have only to find integrands ψ which vanish at the places of Q'/P'. The equation $Q_\psi = Q Q' D^2/X$ implies that the order of Q' is $p-1$, so that the number μ of integrands ψ vanishing at the places of Q'/P' would be at least $p-(p-2)=2$, and this would contradict the value $\mu=1$. Thus the theorem is proved.

THEOREM 26·2. *For a divisor* $Q = P_1 \cdots P_q$ *the number* q *and the number* μ *of linearly independent multiples of the divisor* $1/Q$, *one of which is of course a constant, are related as indicated in the following table*:

Range of q	$P_1, \cdots, P_q$ non-special	$P_1, \cdots, P_q$ special
$q \leqq p$	$\mu = 1$	$\mu > 1$
$p < q \leqq 2p - 2$	$\mu = q - p + 1$	$\mu > q - p + 1$
$2p - 2 < q$	$\mu = q - p + 1$	No case

In order to discuss the case $q \leqq p$ we may first choose an arbitrary rational function $\xi(x, y)$ and determine a divisor Q' by the equation $QQ' = Q_\xi X/D^2$. The number μ' of multiples of $1/Q'$ is the same as the number of multiples of QD^2/X, by Lemma 25·1. But from the preceding paragraphs we see that this number is $\mu' = p - q$ if the set $P_1, \cdots, P_q$ is non-special, and that $\mu' > p - q$ if it is special. Hence the first equation (25·1) of the Riemann-Roch theorem gives $\mu = 1$ for non-special sets, and $\mu > 1$ for special sets.

The proof for the second row of the table is similar except that we find $\mu' = 0$ or $\mu' > 0$, so that equation (25·1) gives the two results $\mu = q - p + 1$ or $\mu > q - p + 1$.

When $2p - 2 < q$ there are no multiples of QD^2/X since the order of this divisor is $q + 2 - 2p > 0$ and no rational function can have order greater than zero. Hence the special case does not occur and we have $\mu' = 0$, $\mu = q - p + 1$.

The number μ of the last theorem is the number of linearly independent rational functions with poles at most among the places $P_1, \cdots, P_q$ and with orders greater than or equal to those possessed by the divisor $1/P_1 \cdots P_q$. If places P_i are repeated in the product $P_1 \cdots P_q$ some of the orders of these poles may be greater than unity.

COROLLARY. *The only rational functions with poles at most among the points of a non-special set* $P_1, \cdots, P_q$ *and orders greater than or equal to those possessed by the divisor* $1/P_1 \cdots P_q$ *are constants when* $q \leqq p$. *If* $p < q$ *then the number of linearly independent functions of this sort is* $\mu = q - p + 1$, *and such a function will in general be determined to a constant factor if* $q - p$ *zeros are prescribed for it*.

The first row of the table of Theorem 26·2 shows that when $q \leqq p$ all functions with the properties described in the corollary are linearly dependent upon one of them, and we know that 1 is such a function.

When $p<q$ there are $\mu=q-p+1$ linearly independent functions $\eta_i(i=1,\cdots,\mu)$ with the properties of the corollary. But for every set of μ linearly independent functions there exist places P_s' ($s=1,\cdots,q-p$) such that the matrix $||\,\eta_i(P_s')\,||$ has rank $q-p$, by Lemma 26·1. Hence the ratios of the coefficients c_i in the function $\eta=c_1\eta_1+\cdots+c_\mu\eta_\mu$ will be uniquely determined by the condition that the function shall vanish at the points P_s', as indicated in the last sentence of the corollary.

The result stated in the corollary should be contrasted with the analogous theorem for the plane or for algebraic functions for which $p=0$. In these cases the number of zeros which can be chosen arbitrarily for a rational function is equal to the number of the poles.

THEOREM 26·3. *If a rational function $\eta(x,y)$ is a multiple of a divisor $1/P_1\cdots P_q$, and if there exists an integrand function ψ of an integral of the first kind which is a multiple of the divisor $P_1\cdots P_q D^2/X$, then $\eta(x,y)$ is expressible as a quotient $\eta=\psi_1/\psi$ of two integrand functions of the first kind. In particular every special rational function is so expressible.*

For under the hypotheses of the theorem the product $\psi_1=\eta\psi$ is evidently also a multiple of the divisor D^2/X and hence an integrand function of an integral of the first kind. Since every special rational function is by definition a multiple of a divisor $1/P_1\cdots P_q$ for which there exists a multiple ψ of the divisor $P_1\cdots P_q D^2/X$, the last statement of the theorem is also true.

THEOREM 26·4. *If there exists a rational function $\eta(x,y)$ with a single simple pole then the value of the genus p must be zero. If $p=0$ then for every place P there exists a rational function $\eta(x,y)$ with a single simple pole at P.*

If $\eta(x,y)$ has a single simple pole then for every constant α the difference $\eta(x,y)-\alpha$ has a single simple zero. The expansion of η at a place where it is finite has the form $\eta=\eta_0+ct+\cdots$, and the constant c is different from zero, since otherwise $\eta(x,y)-\eta_0$ would have a double zero. At the pole of η we have $\eta=(d/t)+\cdots$, with $d\neq0$. Hence for the function η the numbers described on page 63 have the values $w_\eta=0$, $n_\eta=1$ and the genus is $p=w_\eta/2-n_\eta+1=0$.

The last statement of the theorem is a consequence of Theorem 26·2 for the case $p=0$, $q=1$. The third row of the table of the theorem gives $\mu=2$. Hence there must be at least one function not a constant with a pole at the place P.

Consider now a divisor $Q=1/P_1\cdots P_q$ for which $2p+2<q$. By the third row of the table in Theorem 26·2 there are $\mu=q-p+1$

linearly independent rational functions $\sigma_1, \cdots, \sigma_\mu$ which are multiples of Q. At an arbitrary place P the expansion of such a multiple has the form

$$\sigma = ct^\nu + dt^{\nu+1} + \cdots$$

where ν is the smallest exponent permitted by Q at P. The coefficients c, d may be called the *leading coefficients* of σ at P. For the functions $\sigma_1, \cdots, \sigma_\mu$ and places P', P'', P''', they may be designated by suitable subscripts and primes. In a later chapter we shall need the following lemma and its corollary.

LEMMA 26·2. *If $2p+2<q$ then the $\mu=q-p+1$ linearly independent multiples $\sigma_1, \cdots, \sigma_\mu$ of a divisor $1/P_1 \cdots P_q$ have a matrix of leading coefficients*

$$(26\cdot 2) \qquad \left\| \begin{array}{ccc} c_1 & \cdots & c_\mu \\ c_1' & \cdots & c_\mu' \\ c_1'' & \cdots & c_\mu'' \\ c_1''' & \cdots & c_\mu''' \end{array} \right\|$$

at four arbitrarily selected places P, P', P'', P''' which is of rank 4. If P coincides with P' the same conclusion holds provided that the second row in the matrix is replaced by $d_1, \cdots, d_\mu$.

Suppose that this were not true for a set of places P, P', P'', P'''. Then there would be at least $\mu-3$ linearly independent functions of the form $u_1\sigma_1 + \cdots + u_\mu\sigma_\mu$ with $u_1, \cdots, u_\mu$ constants and with leading coefficients zero at P, P', P'', P'''. These functions would be multiples of the divisor $1/Q_1 = PP'P''P'''/(P_1 \cdots P_q)$, which is impossible since the number of linearly independent multiples of $1/Q_1$ can be shown to be $\mu-4$. To prove this consider the divisor Q_2 defined by the equation $Q_1Q_2 = X/D^2$. Its reciprocal $1/Q_2$ has no multiples since the order of $1/Q_2$ is $q-4+2n-w = q-2p-2>0$. Hence by the Riemann-Roch theorem the number μ_1 of multiples of $1/Q_1$ is $\mu_1 = (q-4)-p+1 = \mu-4$.

COROLLARY. *The matrix corresponding to $(26\cdot 2)$ for $k<4$ places has always rank k. In particular the leading coefficients $c_1, \cdots, c_\mu$ at each place P are not all zero, and the same is true of the second coefficients $d_1, \cdots, d_\mu$.*

These results follow readily from Lemma 26·2.

REFERENCES FOR CHAPTER III

References for the various sections of Chapter III above, in the list at the end of this book, are the following: 9; 28, Vorlesungen IX-XX; 42, Chapters IV, VI-IX; 44.

CHAPTER IV

THE RIEMANN SURFACE OF AN
ALGEBRAIC FUNCTION

27. **Introduction.** In the theory of elementary analytic geometry methods are given for determining a curve in the real xy-plane whose points are in one-to-one correspondence with the pairs of real values (x, y) satisfying a given algebraic equation $f(x, y) = 0$ of the kind described in the last chapter but with real coefficients. In the theory of algebraic functions the coefficients are allowed to be complex numbers as well as real, and the totality of real or complex number pairs (x, y) which satisfy the equation $f(x, y) = 0$ is the subject of study. These number pairs cannot be represented on a real curve in the plane, but a surface can be constructed whose places are in one-to-one continuous correspondence with the branches of the form $(13 \cdot 2)$, described in Theorem $13 \cdot 1$, which satisfy $f(x, y) = 0$. This surface is called a *Riemann surface* for the algebraic function $y(x)$ defined by the equation $f(x, y) = 0$. If the places on the surface corresponding to singular values of x are excluded the remainder of the surface is in one-to-one correspondence with the pairs (x, y) which satisfy $f = 0$ and belong to ordinary values of x.

In this chapter a method for constructing a Riemann surface is described, and some of the more elementary properties of such a surface and of single-valued holomorphic functions on it are deduced.

28. **The construction of the Riemann surface T.** In the finite part of the x-plane the singular values of x for an algebraic function are finite in number, since they are the roots of the polynomials $f_0(x)$ and $D(x)$. Let us denote them by $a_1, \cdots, a_s$ and suppose a polygon drawn through them and to infinity, as illustrated in Figure $28 \cdot 1$. The remaining part of the x-plane is a simply connected region R in which the values of the algebraic function $y(x)$ form n distinct holomorphic functions $y_k(x)$ $(k = 1, \cdots, n)$, according to Theorem $12 \cdot 3$.

In order to construct a surface which shall represent the algebraic function we may take n planes, one over the other, each cut as shown by the heavy lines in the figure. With the point in the k-th sheet over a value x in the region R we associate the pair of values $[x, y_k(x)]$. In this way a one-to-one correspondence is set up between the places on the n

75

sheets and the pairs of values (x, y) which satisfy the equation $f(x, y) = 0$ over the region R.

In order to make the correspondence continuous along the cuts exclusive of their ends, let two regions R', R'' be defined in a neighborhood of each cut, as indicated in Figure $28 \cdot 1$ for the cut $a_5 a_6$. In the region formed by R', R'' and the cut between them exclusive of its

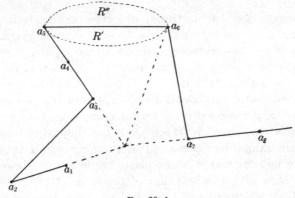

FIG. $28 \cdot 1$

ends, the values of the algebraic function $y(x)$ form again n distinct holomorphic functions $Y_l(x)$ $(l = 1, \cdots, n)$, and these can be so numbered that $y_k(x) = Y_k(x)$ in R'. In the region R'' the functions $y_k(x)$ are the functions of the set $Y_l(x)$ but possibly in a different order. We join the edge of the cut bounding R' in the k-th sheet to the edge bounding R'' in the l-th sheet, where l is so determined that $y_k(x) = Y_l(x)$ in R''. The continuous Riemann surface so formed has the property that its places over non-singular values of x are in one-to-one continuous correspondence with the non-singular pairs of values (x, y) which satisfy the equation $f(x, y) = 0$.

Over a small circle in the x-plane with center at a singular point $x = a$ the sheets of the Riemann surface are associated into cycles of one or more sheets like those shown in Figure $13 \cdot 2$. The sheets of a cycle are supposed to be joined over the singular point at a single point called the vertex of the cycle, but the vertices of different cycles are distinct over $x = a$. If C is a circle with center at $x = 0$ and so large that it has all of the finite singular values of x in its interior, then the sheets of the surface over the exterior of C similarly form cycles for $x = \infty$ which by the transformation $x = 1/x'$ go into cycles for $x' = 0$. The points of the Riemann surface, including those at $x = \infty$, are all vertices of cycles of one or more sheets, and are called *places* to distinguish them from the *points* of the x-plane corresponding to them. It is understood of course that each point where the surface intersects itself is to be regarded as consisting of two distinct points, one for each of the sheets passing through it. The complete Riemann surface which has thus been described, including the vertices of cycles at $x = \infty$, will be designated hereafter by the symbol T.

THEOREM 28·1. *By the process described in the preceding paragraphs an n-sheeted closed Riemann surface T is constructed such that to every place P of T there corresponds a pair of values $x(P)$, $y(P)$ which satisfy the equation $f(x, y) = 0$.*

Every place P_0 on the surface has a neighborhood N which is in one-to-one correspondence with a circle in the t-plane with center at the point $t = 0$. In this circle the values $x(P)$, $y(P)$ are given by a primitive branch of the form

$$(28·1) \qquad x = a + t^r, \qquad y = bt^\mu + b't^{\mu'} + \cdots ,$$

or of this form with $x = a + t^r$ replaced by $x = 1/t^r$.

The correspondence between the places P_0 on T and the primitive branches satisfying $f(x, y) = 0$ is one-to-one in the sense that every branch has one and but one place near which it represents $x(P)$, $y(P)$, and conversely.

The places of the surface T which have non-singular values $x(P)$ are in one-to-one correspondence with the pairs (x, y) which satisfy $f(x, y) = 0$ and have non-singular values x.

It is understood that in the pair $x(P)$, $y(P)$ one or both of the coordinates may be infinite. By a branch is meant a set of r primitive expansions of the type $(28·1)$ which are equivalent to each other by transformations of the type $t = \omega t'$, where ω is an r-th root of unity. The r different expansions of such a set all define the same r values y corresponding to a given x.

The arguments preceding Theorem 13·1 justify the statement that each place P_0 has a unique branch giving the values $x(P)$, $y(P)$ at places P near to P_0. Every branch $(28·1)$ satisfying $f(x, y) = 0$ must similarly belong in this way to one and but one place P_0. For as we have seen in Section 13 every branch $(28·1)$ satisfying $f(x, y) = 0$ must be equivalent to one of the set of non-equivalent branches defining the n distinct values of y near $x = a$.

The correspondence between places and pairs (x, y) having non-singular values x is one-to-one because for each non-singular value $x = a$

the correspondence between the pairs (a, b_i) satisfying $f(x, y) = 0$ and the branches satisfying this equation near $x = a$ is one-to-one.

Riemann surfaces with the properties described in the theorem may be constructed in many different ways. In forming the region R in which the values of the algebraic function $y(x)$ form n distinct holomorphic functions $y_k(x)$ $(k = 1, 2, \cdots, n)$ it is sometimes more convenient to join each singular point a_i to infinity by a straight line, as indicated in Figure 28·2. The point O should be chosen not collinear with any pair of the singular points. The rest of the argument justifying the construction of the Riemann surface is the same as before.

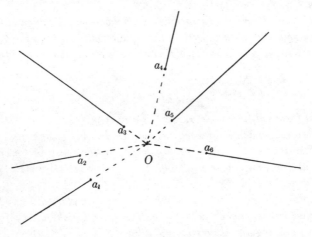

FIG. 28·2

It is clear that every surface T_1 whose places P_1 are in one-to-one continuous correspondence with the places P of T can also be regarded as a Riemann surface for the algebraic function $y(x)$ with the properties described in Theorem 28·1. Thus any surface T_1 into which T can be continuously deformed is a Riemann surface for $y(x)$. The properties of an algebraic function characterized by the Riemann surface of the function are thus properties which one studies in Analysis Situs.

It is important to notice here a property of the Riemann surface of an equation $f(x, y) = 0$ for which the polynomial $f(x, y)$ is irreducible. The Riemann surface of such an equation consists of a single connected piece, as stated in the following theorem:

THEOREM 28·2. *Let $f(x, y)$ be a polynomial having $D(x) \not\equiv 0$ and no factor $x - a$. Then a necessary and sufficient condition that $f(x, y)$ be irreducible is that its Riemann surface T consists of a single connected piece.*

We may first prove the condition necessary. For let T consist of more than one connected piece. Without loss of generality we may suppose that one of these pieces is made up of the sheets corresponding to $y_1(x)$, $\cdots$, $y_q(x)$ $(q < n)$. Every symmetric polynomial $S[y_1(x)$, $\cdots$, $y_q(x)]$ in y_1, $\cdots$, y_q is single-valued and holomorphic in the portion of the x-plane remaining after the cuts used to form the Riemann surface are made. Furthermore S has the same properties on the cuts exclusive of the singular points. For in the region $R'+R''$ of Figure 28·1, including the cut between R' and R'' exclusive of its ends, the roots of $f(x, y) = 0$ which are equal to $y_1(x)$, $\cdots$, $y_q(x)$ in R' form a set of holomorphic functions $Y_1(x)$, $\cdots$, $Y_q(x)$. These are identical with $y_1(x)$, $\cdots$, $y_q(x)$ in some order in R'' also, since the first q sheets of the Riemann surface are connected with each other across the cuts. Then in either R' or R'', on account of the symmetry of S,

$$S[y_1(x), \cdots, y_q(x)] \equiv S[Y_1(x), \cdots, Y_q(x)],$$

and we see that S is holomorphic in the whole x-plane except possibly at singular points of $y(x)$. For each singular point $x = a$ there is a factor $(x-a)^p$ such that all the products $(x-a)^p y_k(x)$ are bounded near $x = a$, by Lemma 13·1, and hence there is a similar product $(x-a)^s S$ which is also bounded near $x = a$. The function S has therefore only poles as singularities and is rational.

Consider now the polynomial

$$P = y^q + S_1 y^{q-1} + \cdots + S_q = (y - y_1) \cdots (y - y_q)$$

whose coefficients are except for signs the elementary symmetric functions of y_1, $\cdots$, y_q and therefore rational in x according to the argument in the preceding paragraph. When we divide this polynomial into f we find

$$f = PQ + R(x, y),$$

where Q and R are polynomials in y with coefficients rational in x, and the degree of R in y is at most $q-1$. At every non-singular value of x at which the coefficients of the powers of y in Q and R are finite the polynomial R must vanish for all of the roots $y = y_1$, $\cdots$, y_q, and hence it vanishes identically. When the equation $f = PQ$ is multiplied through by the lowest common denominator of the coefficients of y in P and Q it follows from Lemma 9·1 that the factors of the coefficient of f are factors in the coefficients of the powers of y in the polynomials of the second member of the equation, and hence f is reducible.

The sufficiency of the condition of the theorem is evident from the fact that when $f = P_1 \cdots P_k$ is reducible the continuations of the roots $y_1(x), \cdots, y_q(x)$ of P_1, say, are always roots of $P_1 = 0$. Hence this set of roots permutes into itself across the cuts, and the Riemann surface consists of k connected pieces, one for each of the factors $P_1, \cdots, P_k$.

From this section on we shall always understand that the polynomial $f(x, y)$ defining the algebraic function $y(x)$ under consideration is irreducible, so that its Riemann surface T consists of a single connected piece.

29. Holomorphic functions on a Riemann surface.

We have seen in Section 28 that every place P_0 on a Riemann surface T has a neighborhood N whose places are in one-to-one correspondence with the points of a circle Γ in the t-plane with center at $t = 0$. A function $g(P)$ of the places on T is said to be *analytic at a place P_0* if there is a neighborhood N of P_0 in which $g(P)$ is single-valued and defines a function $G(t) = g(P)$ which is analytic at $t = 0$ in the t-plane. A function $g(P)$ is *holomorphic on a portion S of the surface T* if $g(P)$ is single-valued and analytic at each place on S. Such functions have many properties analogous to those of functions holomorphic in a region of the x-plane. Some of these will be deduced in this section.

A function $g(P)$ holomorphic in a neighborhood N of a place P_0 except possibly at P_0 itself has by definition at P_0 an *ordinary place*, a *removable singularity*, a *pole*, or an *isolated essential singularity* according as the function $G(t) = g(P)$ in Γ has such points at $t = 0$.

If it is agreed beforehand that all removable singular places of a function $g(P)$ have been removed, then the value of $g(P)$ at an arbitrary place P_0 near which it is holomorphic is completely determined by the values of $g(P)$ in a neighborhood of P_0, since the coefficients of the Laurent expansion for $G(t) = g(P)$ in powers of t are so determined. Since the places on T over non-singular values of x are in one-to-one correspondence with the non-singular pairs (x, y) satisfying $f(x, y) = 0$ it is clear that when the values of $g(P)$ are given at all such non-singular places its values at all points near which $g(P)$ is holomorphic are well defined. Hence it is customary to represent a function $g(P)$ by the notation $g(x, y)$ and we shall use this notation from now on.

A *regular arc C on the Riemann surface T* is one whose projection $x = x(u)$ $(u_1 \leqq u \leqq u_2)$ in the x-plane is regular. If the projection does not pass through any singular point in the x-plane then C will have associated with it a regular continuation function $y(u)$ such that the pair

$$x = x(u), \qquad y = y(u) \qquad (u_1 \leqq u \leqq u_2)$$

satisfies the equation $f(x, y) = 0$ identically in u. In the sequel we shall consider only arcs C on T which have these properties unless expressly stipulated otherwise. If a function $g(x, y)$ is holomorphic on an arc C then the integral

$$\int_C g(x, y)dx = \int_{u_1}^{u_2} g[x(u), y(u)]x'(u)du$$

is well defined.

The *residue at a place* P_0 of a function $g(x, y)$ holomorphic in a neighborhood of P_0 except possibly at P_0 itself is by definition

$$R_{P_0} = \frac{1}{2\pi i} \int_C g(x, y)dx$$

where C is a simply closed arc on T bounding a neighborhood N of the place P_0 in which $g(x, y)$ is holomorphic except possibly at P_0. The value of this residue is also expressible in the forms

$$(29 \cdot 1) \qquad R_{P_0} = \frac{1}{2\pi i} \int_{C_t} G(t)(dx/dt)dt$$

$$= \frac{1}{2\pi i} \int_{C_x} \{g(x, y_1) + \cdots + g(x, y_r)\}dx$$

where $G(t) = g(P)$ near P_0, C_t is the image of C in the t-plane for the place P_0, C_x is the projection of C on the x-plane, and $y_1(x), \cdots, y_r(x)$ are the continuation functions belonging to the r sheets of the cycle with vertex at P_0.

THEOREM 29·1. *The residues of a function* $g(x, y)$ *at places* P_0 *near which* $g(x, y)$ *is holomorphic are given by the following table:*

Projection of P_0	Substitution	Expansion of $g(x, y)$	Residue
$x = a$	$x = a + t^r$	$\sum\limits_{\mu=-\infty}^{+\infty} A_\mu t^\mu$	rA_{-r}
$x = \infty$	$x = 1/t^r$		$-rA_r$

These values are readily calculated with the help of the formula (29·1) for the residue in the t-plane.

30. **Cauchy's theorem.** The integration theorems of Section 2 have generalizations for integrals along curves on Riemann surfaces which are of great importance for the theory of algebraic functions. These results and some necessary auxiliary theorems concerning connected surfaces are to be explained in this section.

A *connected surface S* is one which has the property that every pair of its points can be joined by a continuous arc lying entirely on S. A *simply connected surface S* is one which is connected and which has the further property that every simply closed continuous curve C on S separates S into two connected parts one of which has C as its complete boundary. A sphere is a simply connected surface, but an anchor ring is not. Similarly the interior of a rectangle in the plane is simply connected, but the interior of a rectangle with a hole cut in it is not.

If a surface S has a boundary B then by a *cross cut* in S is meant an arc C not intersecting itself and interior to S except for its two ends which are on B. A *loop cut* in S is an arc L interior to S except for one end-point on B, and not intersecting itself except that its second end-point is on L. A loop cut is a limiting case of a cross cut as indicated by the dotted line in Figure $30 \cdot 1$. All of the cuts considered in the following pages are supposed to consist of regular arcs, and the same is true of boundary curves when such curves exist.

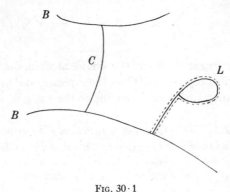

FIG. $30 \cdot 1$

THEOREM $30 \cdot 1$. *If a surface S has a boundary B and is simply connected then every cross cut C or loop cut L in S divides S into two simply connected portions.*

If S were not separated by a cross cut C then two points P, Q on opposite sides of C could be joined by a simply closed continuous arc Γ in S, as indicated schematically in Figure $30 \cdot 2$. But then the points of

S on both sides of Γ would have points of B as boundary points, which is impossible if S is simply connected.

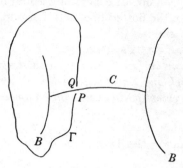

FIG. 30·2

Each of the two portions S_1, S_2 resulting from the cut along C is simply connected. For every simply closed continuous arc Γ_1 in S_1 divides S into two portions one of which has no point of B as boundary, and hence also no point of C. It is therefore entirely in S_1 and has only points of Γ_1 as boundary points.

The proof for a loop cut L is similar.

THEOREM 30·2. *A surface S whose boundary B is known to consist of simply closed curves has only one bounding curve if it has the further property that every cross cut or loop cut in S divides S into two simply connected pieces. A simply connected surface S has therefore only one bounding curve if it has bounding curves at all.*

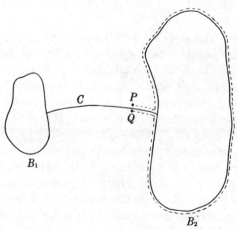

FIG. 30·3

If there were two boundary curves, B_1 and B_2, we could join them by a cross cut C since S is connected, as shown in Figure 30·3. But then two points, P and Q, on opposite sides of C could be joined by a curve in S, as indicated by the dotted line, and S would not satisfy the hypothesis of the theorem.

THEOREM 30·3. CAUCHY'S THEOREM. *If S is a simply connected portion of the Riemann surface T bounded by a simply closed regular arc B not passing through any singular places on T, and if $g(x, y)$ is holomorphic on B and S except possibly at a finite number of places interior to S, then*

$$\int_B g(x, y)dx = 2\pi i \ [\text{sum of the residues of } g(x, y) \text{ in } S],$$

where the value of the integral along B is taken in the positive sense with respect to S.

To prove this let us first cut out successively the singular places of T in S and the singularities of $g(x, y)$ in S by loop cuts L each enclosing only one singularity. Theorems 30·1 and 30·2 tell us that the part S_1 of S remaining will be simply connected and have a single bounding curve B_1. Then

$$\int_B g(x, y)dx = \int_{B_1} g(x, y)dx + \sum \int_L g(x, y)dx,$$

where the sum is taken for all the loop cuts L, and consequently

$$\int_B g(x, y)dx = \int_{B_1} g(x, y)dx + 2\pi i \ [\text{sum of residues of } g \text{ in } S]$$

since the integral along each L is $2\pi i$ times one of the residues. It is understood that the integrals along B_1 and L are taken in the positive senses with respect to S_1 and the interior of L, respectively. The value of the integral along B_1 is zero, at least if B_1 intersects the cuts used in constructing the Riemann surface T only a finite number of times. For if we cut T along these cuts the effect upon S_1 is that of a succession of a finite number of cross cuts. The result, according to Theorem 30·1, is that S_1 is separated into a finite number of simply connected pieces. Each of these pieces lies in a single one of the sheets of T and contains no singular point of T or $g(x, y)$. Hence the value of the integral taken around its boundary is zero, by Theorem 3·1, and the same is true of the value of the integral around B_1 which is the sum of the integrals around the boundaries of the pieces.

The proof has been made only for an arc B_1 which intersects the cuts used in making T only a finite number of times but a remark below will indicate how this deficiency in the proof may be removed.

It is clear that the theorem applies even to a region S of the surface T which includes places at $x = \infty$. For when these places are cut out by loop cuts simultaneously with the singularities of T and $g(x, y)$, as described above, the remaining portion S_1 of S will be bounded and simply connected.

When the region S of the theorem contains no singularities of $g(x, y)$ the value of the integral is evidently zero.

The case not covered in the proof of the theorem is taken care of by the following lemma:

LEMMA 30·1. *If S_1 is a simply connected portion of the Riemann surface T bounded by a simply closed regular curve B_1 not passing through any singular places on T, and if $g(x, y)$ is holomorphic on B_1 and S_1, then there exists a second such portion S_2 and boundary B_2 for which B_2 intersects the cuts used in making T only a finite number of times and*

$$\int_{B_1} g(x, y)dx = \int_{B_2} g(x, y)dx.$$

The truth of this lemma seems intuitive since the arc B_1 can be moved slightly without destroying any of its properties described in the theorem. But the proof of the lemma, as it occurs to the writer of these pages, is inconveniently long. Only a synopsis will be given here.

Let the curve B_1 on T be defined by functions

$$x = x(u), \qquad y = y(u) \qquad (u_1 \leq u \leq u_2).$$

The first step in the proof is to show that there exists an arc u_1u_3 of B_1 which can be replaced by an inscribed polygon forming with the remainder of B_1 a simply closed arc on T with the properties of the theorem, except possibly the one concerning intersections with the cuts used in making T. There will be a least upper bound u_4 to the values u_3 defining intervals u_1u_3 for which this is possible, and we can prove that u_4 must be at u_2 and that a polygon with the properties described can be inscribed in the whole arc B_1. By moving corners of the polygon slightly if necessary it can be changed into a new polygon B_2 with the same properties, and such furthermore that no side is parallel to one of the cuts used in making the surface T. Then B_2 will intersect these cuts in a finite number of points only.

31. **The connectivity of a Riemann surface.** If the Riemann surface T of an algebraic function is simply connected then Cauchy's theorem for a function $g(x, y)$ can be applied to every simply closed regular arc B on T which does not pass through singular places of the surface or of $g(x, y)$, since such an arc B divides T into two portions one of which has B as its complete boundary. Not every Riemann surface is simply connected, however, as one can see, for example, by examining the surface for the algebraic function defined by the equation $y^2 = (1 - x^2)(1 - k^2 x^2)$. In this section it is proposed to show that every Riemann surface can be reduced by a succession of cuts to a simply connected surface T' on which Cauchy's theorem holds for arbitrary simply closed arcs B with the properties described above. The theorems which lead to this result are theorems concerning the connectivities of two-sided surfaces in space. The Riemann surfaces described above have always two sides.

THEOREM 31·1. *A necessary and sufficient condition that a surface S having a boundary B be simply connected is that every cross cut C or loop cut L in S divides S into two simply connected pieces.*

The statement of the necessity of the condition is Theorem 30·1 proved above. To prove the sufficiency let Γ be a simply closed regular arc in S and draw the cut $P_1 P_2$ as in Figure 31·1. If Γ did not separate S then two points P_3 and P_4 on opposite sides of Γ could be joined by

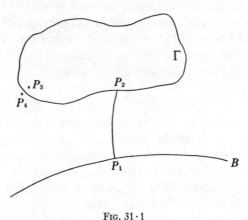

FIG. 31·1

a continuous arc in S not intersecting Γ, but that arc would necessarily touch the cut $P_1 P_2$ since by the hypothesis of the theorem every loop cut separates S. It can readily be seen, however, by following the edges of $P_1 P_2$ and Γ, that in this case P_3 and P_4 could be joined by an arc not intersecting either P_1P_2 or Γ, which is a contradiction. Hence Γ separates S into two connected parts.

The boundary B consists of a single arc, according to Theorem $30 \cdot 2$. Hence P_3 and P_4 can not both be joined to B without intersecting Γ, since otherwise by following an edge of B they could be joined to each other without intersecting Γ. It follows that one of the regions into which Γ divides S has only points of Γ as boundary points. Thus S is simply connected.

THEOREM $31 \cdot 2$. *If a system Σ of surfaces with simply closed regular curves as boundaries is decomposed by ν cross or loop cuts into α simply connected pieces, then the difference $\nu - \alpha$ is the same for every such decomposition.*

Suppose ν cuts C dividing Σ into α simply connected pieces, and ν' cuts C' dividing Σ into α' such pieces. Without loss of generality it may be supposed that the systems C and C' meet in a finite number of points only, each of which is interior to Σ and not at an intersection of the cuts C or at an intersection of the cuts C'. If this were not already so we could displace the cuts C' slightly, or compare C and C' with a third system C'' such that the pairs C and C'', C'' and C', both have these properties.

If then the cuts C have all been drawn, the cuts C' can be drawn successively. If one of the latter meets the cuts of C in k points it counts as $k+1$ new cross cuts. Let K be the total number of intersections of the cuts C and C'. Then by Theorem $30 \cdot 1$ the number of simply connected pieces resulting after superposing the cuts C' on the cuts C is $\alpha+K+\nu'$, and the number obtained by superposing the cuts C on the cuts C' is $\alpha'+K+\nu$. Since these two numbers are equal the theorem is proved.

The *connectivity of a connected surface S* is defined to be the number $N = \nu - \alpha + 2$ when by ν cross or loop cuts the surface is dividied into α simply connected pieces. If the surface has no boundary to start with we draw a simply closed curve on the surface and count it as the first cut. The proof of the last theorem then shows that for a surface without boundary the connectivity is also independent of the system of cuts used in calculating it. By Theorem $30 \cdot 1$ a simply connected surface has evidently the connectivity $N = 1$.

THEOREM $31 \cdot 3$. *If a connected surface S has connectivity N and a cross or loop cut is drawn not severing S, then the resulting surface S' has connectivity $N' = N-1$. An N-tiply connected surface can be made into a simply connected surface by $N-1$ cuts; and, conversely, if S can be made into a simply connected surface by $N-1$ cuts its connectivity is N. On a* *surface of connectivity N not more than $N-1$ cuts can be drawn without severing it.*

To prove the first statement let $N'=\nu-\alpha+2$ be the connectivity of S'. Then evidently $N=(\nu+1)-\alpha+2=N'+1$.

To prove the rest of the theorem we note that by Theorem $31\cdot1$ it is always possible to draw in a surface S of connectivity $N>1$ a cross cut or loop cut which does not sever S. Then with the help of the first statement of the theorem the rest of the theorem follows at once.

THEOREM $31\cdot4$. *If from a surface S having boundary curves a simply connected portion bounded by a simply closed curve Γ is removed, then the remaining surface S' has connectivity $N'=N+1$, where N is the connectivity of S. If S has no bounding curves then $N'=N$.*

In the surface S' remaining after the simply connected region bounded by Γ has been removed, draw the cross cut C. The resulting surface S'' has a connectivity $N''=\nu-\alpha+2$ which is related to the connectivity N' of S' by the equation $N''=N'-1$, according to Theorem $31\cdot3$. But S'' is formed from S by drawing the loop cut consisting of C and Γ, so that $N=(\nu+1)-(\alpha+1)+2=N''$ and consequently $N=N'-1$.

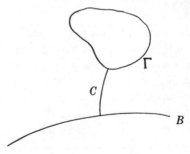

FIG. $31\cdot2$

If S has no boundary, and if for S' we have $N'=\nu-\alpha+2$, then Γ will count as a first cut in S and we find $N=(\nu+1)-(\alpha+1)+2=N'$.

THEOREM $31\cdot5$. *The connectivity of every closed surface is an odd number $N=2p+1$. The number p is called the genus of the surface.*

The connectivity N of a closed surface S is equal to the connectivity of the surface S' formed from S by removing the interior of a small simply closed curve on S, by Theorem $31\cdot4$. The surface S' has a single bounding curve, and it is transformed into a simply connected surface S'' by $N-1$ cross or loop cuts which do not sever it. Each time a cross or loop cut not severing S' is drawn the number of bounding curves is increased or decreased by unity, as may be inferred from Figure 31·3 in which the dotted lines represent new bounding curves which replace old ones after the cuts C are drawn. According to Theorem 30·2 the simply connected surface S'' has like S' a single bounding curve, and

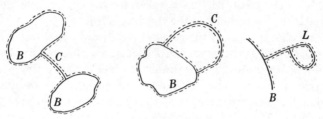

Fig. 31·3

hence the number $N-1$ of cuts necessary to reduce S' to a simply connected surface S'' is even.

THEOREM 31·6. *The connectivity of a Riemann surface T of an n-valued algebraic function is an odd number $N = 2p+1$ and the genus p has the value*

$$(31·1) \qquad p = \sum \frac{r-1}{2} - n + 1.$$

In this expression r is the number of sheets in a cycle and the sum is taken for all the cycles of the surface T.

To prove this let $a_1, \cdots, a_s$ be the values of x under the cycles of T having more than one sheet, and let the set include $x = \infty$ whether it has such cycles over it or not. The number of cycles over a_i will be denoted by n_i. If one of the vertices at $x = \infty$ is cut out by a spiral, the remainder of T has the same connectivity $N = 2p+1$ as T, by Theorem 31·4, since T has no boundary. If all of the other vertices over $a_1, \cdots, a_s$ are similarly cut out by spirals the remainder T_1 of T has, by Theorem 31·4, the connectivity

$$N_1 = N + n_1 + \cdots + n_s - 1 = 2p + n_1 + \cdots + n_s,$$

one spiral about a place over $x = \infty$ having already been drawn. But by cutting the Riemann surface by $n(s-1)$ straight lines leading from the spirals around the $s-1$ finite points of the set $a_1, \cdots, a_s$ to those at $x = \infty$, as in Figure 28·2, it is seen that T_1 falls into n simply connected pieces so that

$$N_1 = n(s - 1) - n + 2.$$

By equating the two values of N_1 so found we see that

$$2p = \sum(n - n_i) - 2n + 2$$

where the sum is taken for all the cycles over all the points a_i. But $n - n_i = \Sigma(r-1)$ where the sum is taken for the cycles over the single point a_i. Hence the formula of the theorem is true.

The number p is called the *genus of the algebraic function* defined by $f(x, y) = 0$, as well as the genus of its Riemann surface T. Evidently the value of p is determined by the branches which satisfy $f(x, y) = 0$, or by their cycles of sheets, and is therefore independent of the particular method used in constructing the Riemann surface T. The sum $\Sigma(r-1)$ in formula $(31 \cdot 1)$ is clearly always an even number.

32. Canonical systems of cuts making T simply connected. In the

preceding section it has been shown that the Riemann surface T of an algebraic function will in general be multiply connected. In order to have a surface on which Cauchy's theorem may be applicable to every simply closed regular curve it is desirable to reduce T to a simply connected surface T' by a system of cross and loop cuts. This can be done in many ways, one of which will be exhibited in this section.

In order to explain the system of cuts to be used, the following two lemmas are helpful:

LEMMA $32 \cdot 1$. *If a connected surface S is cut in such a way that its boundary becomes a single simply closed curve C, then the resulting surface S' is also connected.*

This is evident since every point of the resulting surface can be connected with the boundary by a continuous arc in S', and hence by following along the boundary every two such points can be connected with each other by a continuous arc in S'.

LEMMA $32 \cdot 2$. *If S is multiply connected and has a boundary consisting of a single arc B then it is always possible to draw a loop cut in S without severing it.*

According to Theorem $31 \cdot 1$ either a cross cut or a loop cut can be drawn in S without severing it. But every such cross cut can be made into a loop cut with the same property, as indicated by the dotted line in Figure $32 \cdot 1$.

If the connectivity $N = 2p + 1$ of the surface T is greater than one we may proceed in the following manner to draw a system of $2p$ cuts on T, none passing through a singular place, which will reduce T to a simply connected surface T'. In the first place, since T is not simply connected, there will be a simply closed cut a_1 in T which does not sever T, and which therefore provides a resulting surface with connectivity $N-1$, according to the definition in Section 31 of the connectivity of a surface without boundary. If a_1 passes through a singular place we may move part of it slightly so as to avoid the singularity. Since the new surface

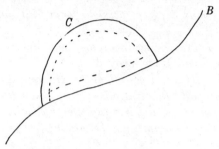

FIG. 32·1

is still connected, a cut b_1 can be drawn in it which joins two points on opposite sides of a_1, as shown in Figure 32·2. The resulting surface is connected, by Lemma 32·1, since its boundary consists of a single curve, and by Theorem 31·3 its connectivity is $N-2$. If this connectivity of the remaining surface is still greater than unity, a loop cut c_1+a_2 can be drawn which does not sever the surface, according to Lemma 32·2, and which produces a new surface with connectivity $N-3$.

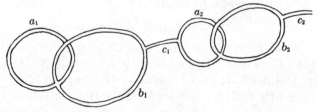

FIG. 32·2

A further cut b_2 then joins two points on opposite sides of a_2. The resulting surface is still connected, by Lemma 32·1, since its boundary consists of a single curve, as is clear from Figure 32·2. Hence b_2 also reduces the connectivity by unity. We see then that by a continuation of this process, and since cuts can always be moved slightly to avoid singular places, the following theorem is justified:

THEOREM 32·1. *The Riemann surface T of an algebraic function can always be reduced to a simply connected surface T' by a system of cuts a_1, b_1, $\cdots$, a_p, b_p joined by cuts c_1, $\cdots$, c_p, as shown in Figure 32·2, and such that none of the cuts passes through a singular place on T. Every simply closed regular arc B in T' separates T' into two parts, one of which, say S, has B as its complete boundary. Cauchy's theorem for an integrand function g(x, y) can therefore be applied to B and S provided that g(x, y) is holomorphic on B and S except possibly for a finite number of singular points in S.*

With the help of preceding theorems the following generalization of Cauchy's theorem can also be proved:

THEOREM 32·2. *If S is a portion of the Riemann surface T, not necessarily simply connected but having a boundary B consisting of one or more simply closed regular arcs, and if a function g(x, y) is holomorphic on B and S except possibly for a finite number of singular points in S, then*

$$\int_B g(x, y)\, dx = 2\pi i\, [\text{sum of residues of } g \text{ in } S],$$

where the integral along B is taken in the positive sense with respect to S.

This is easy to prove since by Theorem 31·3 it is always possible to separate S, by a finite number of cross cuts, into a number of simply connected pieces. The value of the integral of the theorem along B is the sum of its values along the boundaries of the simply connected pieces. But according to Theorem 30·3 the integral along the boundary of each piece is the sum of the residues of g(x, y) in that piece. Hence the equation of the last theorem is justified.

REFERENCES FOR CHAPTER IV

References for the various sections of Chapter IV above, in the list at the end of this book, are the following: 13, Chapter VI; 15, Chapter XIII; 16, Chapter VII; 18, Chapter IV; 24, Chapters XIV, XV; 28, Vorlesungen VII, VIII; 35, Chapter VIII; 42, Chapter III; 47, Chapter IV.

CHAPTER V

INTEGRALS OF RATIONAL FUNCTIONS

33. **Introduction.** The theory of algebraic functions seems to have been developed originally out of problems in the theory of integration. In the elementary calculus methods are exhibited for evaluating integrals of the form

$$(33 \cdot 1) \qquad\qquad I = \int \eta(x, y)dx$$

where η is a rational function of x and y, and y is a simple algebraic function of x defined by one of the equations

$$(33 \cdot 2) \qquad y^2 = ax + b, \qquad y^2 = ax^2 + bx + c.$$

For the first of these two functions the substitution $x = (y^2 - b)/a$ reduces the integral to an integral with respect to y of a rational function of y, and the result of the integration is a sum of a rational function of y and logarithms of such functions.

Another simple substitution reduces the integral $(33 \cdot 1)$ for the second function $(33 \cdot 2)$ also to the integral of a rational function. For if e_1 and e_2 are the roots of the polynomial

$$(33 \cdot 3) \qquad y^2 = ax^2 + bx + c = a(x - e_1)(x - e_2)$$

the straight line $y = t(x - e_1)$ meets the curve $(33 \cdot 3)$ in a fixed point $(x, y) = (e_1, 0)$ and in a single second point variable with t whose coordinates are

$$x = (e_1 t^2 - ae_2)/(t^2 - a), \qquad y = a(e_1 - e_2)t/(t^2 - a).$$

When these values are substituted in the integral I the result is an integral with respect to t of a rational function of t whose value is expressible as a logarithm of rational functions of $t = y/(x - e_1)$ plus logarithms of such functions.

These simple methods do not apply when y is defined as an algebraic function of x by means of an equation

$$y^2 = ax^4 + bx^3 + cx^2 + dx + e$$

93

of the third or fourth degree in x. The integrals are then called elliptic integrals, and elliptic functions and their inverses are required in order to effect the integration. The hyperelliptic cases are those for which $y^2 = R(x)$ where $R(x)$ is a polynomial of degree higher than 4.

It was Abel who first seriously attempted the study of integrals I of the form (33·1) for which y is defined as a function of x by an algebraic equation $f(x, y) = 0$ of the type described in preceding chapters. Such integrals are called Abelian integrals. In spite of the great generality of the problem many results of interest can be obtained, some of which are to be presented in the following pages.

34. **Singularities and periods of integrals.** Let the integrand $\eta(x, y)$ of the integral (33·1) be a rational function of x and y on the Riemann surface T of an algebraic function $y(x)$ defined by an irreducible equation $f(x, y) = 0$. Further let C be a regular arc on T, distinct from singular places of T or of $\eta(x, y)$, and with initial place $P_0(x_0, y_0)$ and end place $P(x, y)$. Then the integral

$$I = \int_C \eta(x, y)dx$$

has a unique finite value. If a number of these integrals are under consideration it will always be understood that their paths of integration are the same unless otherwise expressly indicated.

Near every place P' on T the values of $\eta(x, y)$ are defined by a power series in t with at most a finite number of terms with negative exponents,

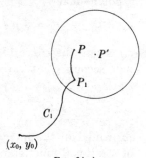

FIG. 34·1

and t is related to x by an equation of one of the forms $x = x' + t^r$, $x = 1/t^r$. Let C_1 be a path leading from P_0 to a place P_1 in a neighborhood N of P' in which the series for $\eta(x, y)$ in powers of t converges. Then the integral

$$I = \int_{C_1} \eta(x, y)dx + \int_{C} \eta(x, y)dx,$$

where C is a path in N from P_1 to P, defines a function $I(P)$ in N which may be either single or multiple valued. The values of $I(P)$ in the neighborhood N are defined by the formula

$$I(P) = \int_{C_1} \eta(x, y)dx + \int_{t_1}^{t} \eta(x, y)(dx/dt)dt$$

where the last integrand has the form

$$\eta(x, y)(dx/dt) = B_{-\mu}/t^{\mu} + \cdots + B_{-1}/t + B_0 + B_1 t + \cdots .$$

The coefficient B_{-1} is the residue of $\eta(x, y)$ at P'. The value of $I(P)$ is changed at most by a constant when the path C_1 is changed. Hence in every case the values of $I(P)$ for a fixed C_1 are defined in N by a series of the form

$$I(P) = \text{const.} + B_{-\mu}/[(1 - \mu)t^{\mu-1}] + \cdots - B_{-2}/t$$
$$+ B_{-1} \log t + B_0 t + \cdots ,$$

as was seen also in Section 24, and the character of P' as a singularity of $I(P)$ is determined by this series.

THEOREM 34·1. *If at a place P' on the Riemann surface T the integrand $\eta(x, y)$ of an integral*

$$I = \int \eta(x, y)dx$$

has its residue equal to zero then P' is either an ordinary place or a pole of I. If the residue of η at P' is different from zero then I has a logarithmic singularity at P'.

From this theorem it is evident that the only singularities of an integral I are poles and logarithmic singularities. According to the definitions already given in Section 24 an *integral of the first kind* is one which has no singularities on the surface T. An integral which has poles but no other singularities is said to be of the *second kind*, and one which has logarithmic singularities is an *integral of the third kind*.

There are only a finite number of places $\alpha_1, \cdots, \alpha_q$ at which an integrand function $\eta(x, y)$ has residues different from zero. We may cut these places out of the simply connected surface T' by loops as shown in Figure 34·2. The resulting surface T'' is also simply connected, according to Theorem 30·1. Along every simply closed integration path C on T'' the value of I is zero, since C separates T'' into two parts one of which, say S, has C as its complete boundary. The value of I along C is zero, by Cauchy's theorem, since $\eta(x, y)$ has no residues in S. By an argument like that used for the proof of Theorem 3·2 of Chapter I

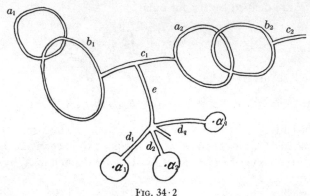

FIG. 34·2

it can be shown that the value of I is zero on every closed integration path C on T'', whether simply closed or not, and we have therefore the following theorem:

THEOREM 34·2. *Let T'' be the simply connected surface formed from T' by cutting out by means of loops the places on T' where $\eta(x, y)$ has residues different from zero, as indicated in Figure 34·2. Then the integral*

$$I(x, y) = \int_C \eta(x, y)dx$$

has the same value on every integration path C on T'' which joins a given initial place (x_0, y_0) to a given end-place (x, y). It is therefore a single-valued function $I(x, y)$ on T'' when (x_0, y_0) is fixed.

The *periods of the integral I* are by definition the numbers A_k, B_k, $H_l(k = 1, \cdots, p; l = 1, \cdots, q)$ defined by the equations

$$A_k = \int_{b_k} \eta(x, y)dx, \qquad B_k = \int_{a_k} \eta(x, y)dx,$$

$$H_l = 2\pi i \ [\text{residue of } \eta(x, y) \text{ at } \alpha_l],$$

where the integrals are taken around the cuts in the directions indicated in Figure 34·3. The directions on the cuts are chosen so that at each intersection of a pair of cuts a_k, b_k the directions on a_k and b_k are related to each other as the positive directions on the x- and y-axes.

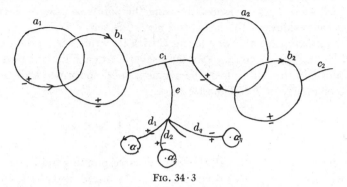

FIG. 34·3

THEOREM 34·3. *For an arbitrary path of integration C on the Riemann surface T joining (x_0, y_0) to (x, y) the value of the integral I has the form*

$$(34\cdot1) \qquad \int_C \eta(x, y)dx = I(x, y) + \sum_i (m_i A_i + n_i B_i) + \sum_k s_k H_k$$

where the coefficients m_i, n_i, s_k are positive or negative integers.

There is no loss in generality in assuming that the path C intersects the cuts used in making T'' only a finite number of times, and that at each intersection C crosses the intersecting cut. For C, and the cuts also, can be displaced slightly without changing the value of the integral along C, or its periods. We could, for example, take curves for cuts whose projections on the x-plane are polygons, and without changing the value of the integral we could replace C by a similar curve whose polygon sides are not parallel to any of the sides of the polygons belonging to the cuts.

The value of the integral I on a loop L consisting of an arc of the boundary of T'' from a point on one side of the boundary to the opposite point on the other side is always a sum of periods. One verifies readily from Figure 34·3 that the value of I thus taken from the negative side of a cut to the positive side along such a loop is that given in the following table:

Cuts	a_k	b_k	c_k	d_l	e
Values of I	$-A_i$	$-B_i$	0	$-H_l$	0

In calculating these values it must be remembered that values of I along an arc of a cut in opposite directions cancel each other, and that the sum of the values of I on the loops enclosing the points α_l is zero, since the sum of the residues of the integrand $\eta(x, y)$ is zero.

To compare the value of I along C with its value $I(x, y)$ on a curve in T'' joining (x_0, y_0) to (x, y) we may sever C at each intersection with a cut and join the two ends of the segments of C so formed by a loop L on the boundary of T''. Then we have

$$\int_C \eta(x, y)dx = I(x, y) - \sum \int_L \eta(x, y)dx$$

where the sum is taken for all the loops L corresponding to intersections of C with the cuts. This proves Theorem 34·3 and also the following corollary:

COROLLARY. *If the path of integration C intersects the boundary of T'' only a finite number of times then the integer m_k in the equation (34·1) is the difference between the number of times C crosses a_k from the $-$ to the $+$ side and the number of times it crosses a_k in the opposite direction. The other integers n_k, s_l have similar interpretations with respect to the cuts b_k and d_l.*

35. **Integrals of the first kind.** According to Theorem 24·1 there are p linearly independent integrals of the first kind. If we denote such a set by $w_1, \cdots, w_p$ then every other integral w of the first kind is expressible in the form

$$(35·1) \qquad\qquad w = c_1 w_1 + \cdots + c_p w_p$$

where $c_1, \cdots, c_p$ are constants. This relation means that the integrand functions $\psi_i(x, y)$ of the integrals w_i are related by the same equation, and equation (35·1) itself holds with the understanding that all of the integrals are taken over the same path of integration C. If the paths are different then a constant term c must be added which is a linear expression in the periods of the integrals w_k similar to the first sum in the equation (34·1). We may denote the periods of the integral w_i by the symbols A_{ik}, B_{ik} ($k = 1, \cdots, p$).

A system $w_1, \cdots, w_p$ as described above is called a *fundamental system of integrals of the first kind*. Every other such system $w_1', \cdots, w_p'$ is related to it by equations of the form

$$w_i' = c_{i1} w_1 + \cdots + c_{ip} w_p$$

where the coefficients c_{ik} are constants with determinant $|c_{ik}| \neq 0$. Conversely every system w_i' defined by such equations is a fundamental system.

LEMMA 35·1. *Let S be a simply connected portion of the Riemann surface T bounded by a simply closed regular arc B, and let $g(x, y) = u+iv$ be a function which is holomorphic on S and B. Then*

$$\int_B u\,dv > 0$$

unless $g(x, y)$ is a constant.

If $x = x_1 + ix_2$ then the real and imaginary parts of g are functions $u(x_1, x_2)$, $v(x_1, x_2)$ which satisfy the equations

$$\partial u/\partial x_1 = \partial v/\partial x_2, \qquad \partial u/\partial x_2 = -\,\partial v/\partial x_1$$

near every place on S. If we cut out the branch places and places at $x = \infty$ in S by loop cuts L, the remainder of S is a simply connected region S' bounded by a simply closed arc B', and

$$\int_B u\,dv = \int_{B'} u\,dv + \sum \int_L u\,dv$$

where the sum is taken for all the loops L. When the surface S' is cut along the cuts used originally in forming T it falls into simply connected plane pieces on each of which Green's theorem may be applied, and we find

$$
\begin{aligned}
\int_{B'} u\,dv &= \int_{B'} [u(\partial v/\partial x_1)dx_1 + u(\partial v/\partial x_2)dx_2] \\
(35\cdot 2) \qquad &= \iint_{S'} [(\partial v/\partial x_1)^2 + (\partial v/\partial x_2)^2]dx_1dx_2 \\
&= \iint_{S'} [(\partial u/\partial x_1)^2 + (\partial u/\partial x_2)^2]dx_1dx_2,
\end{aligned}
$$

which is positive unless g is constant in S'.

Let the value of g at the center P_0 of a loop L be $g_0 = u_0 + iv_0$. Then in the formula

$$\int_L u\,dv = \int_L (u - u_0)dv + \int_L u_0 dv$$

the last integral is zero, since $g = u+iv$ is holomorphic and v is therefore single valued near P_0. The first integral on the right approaches zero with the radius of the loop L, since the value of $u - u_0$ on L approaches zero. If the radii of the loops L are made to approach zero simultaneously then

$$\int_B u \, dv = \lim \int_{B'} u \, dv.$$

The integral around B' increases as the radii of the loops decrease, as is easily seen from formula (35·2), and its limit as the radii of the loops approach zero is therefore certainly positive unless the first derivatives of u and v all vanish and g is constant in S.

LEMMA 35·2. *If w is an integral of the first kind with an integrand not identically zero and with periods*

$$A_k = \alpha_k + i\alpha_k', \qquad B_k = \beta_k + i\beta_k' \qquad (k = 1, \cdots, p)$$

then

(35·3) $$\beta_k \alpha_k' - \beta_k' \alpha_k > 0,$$

where the repeated subscript indicates a sum for $k = 1, \cdots, p$ as in tensor analysis.

To prove this we note that if $w(x, y) = u + iv$ is the value of w taken from (x_0, y_0) to (x, y) along a path C in T', then at points ρ, σ and μ, ν

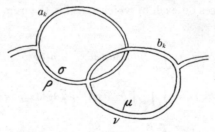

FIG. 35·1

on opposite sides of the cuts a_k and b_k, respectively, the values of u are related by the formulas

$$u(\sigma) = u(\rho) - \alpha_k, \qquad v(\sigma) = v(\rho) - \alpha_k',$$
$$u(\nu) = u(\mu) + \beta_k, \qquad v(\nu) = v(\mu) + \beta_k',$$

so that

$$\int_{a_k} [u(\sigma) - u(\rho)] \, dv = -\int_{a_k} \alpha_k \, dv = -\alpha_k \beta_k',$$

$$\int_{b_k} [u(\nu) - u(\mu)]dv = \int_{b_k} \beta_k dv = \beta_k \alpha_k',$$

where the terms on the right are this time not summed for the repeated index. But when we add these equations we find the value

$$\beta_k \alpha_k' - \beta_k' \alpha_k = \int_B u dv,$$

where the first term now represents a sum with respect to k, and this is positive, by Lemma 35·1, unless $w(x, y)$ is a constant, in which case its integrand would be identically zero.

These lemmas justify at once a succession of theorems concerning integrals of the first kind.

THEOREM 35·1. *For an integral of the first kind whose integrand is not identically zero*

(1) *the periods A_k are not all zero,*

(2) *the periods B_k are not all zero,*

(3) *the periods A_k, B_k are not all real or all pure imaginary.*

These properties follow at once from the inequality (35·3).

THEOREM 35·2. *A necessary and sufficient condition that a system $w_i(i = 1, \cdots, p)$ of integrals of the first kind with periods A_{ik}, B_{ik} be linearly independent is that the determinant $|A_{ik}|$ be different from zero, or that $|B_{ik}|$ be different from zero.*

For if the determinant $|A_{ik}|$ were zero, for example, we could find constants c_i not all zero such that the sums $c_i A_{ik}$ vanish for every k. By (1) of Theorem 35·1 the integral $c_i w_i$ would then have its integrand identically zero. A similar argument holds for $|B_{ik}|$.

THEOREM 35·3. *The integrand of an integral of the first kind is uniquely determined when one of the following sets of data are assigned:*

(1) *arbitrary values not all zero for the periods A_k;*

(2) *arbitrary values not all zero for the periods B_k;*

(3) *arbitrary values not all zero for the real parts, or for the imaginary parts, of the periods A_k, B_k.*

The proof for (1) is simple. Constants c_k not all zero are uniquely determined by the equations $A_k = c_i A_{ik}$ ($k = 1, \cdots, p$) where the A_{ik} are periods of a fundamental system w_i. The integral $w = c_i w_i$ has the desired periods. A similar proof holds for (2).

To prove (3) we see that for an integral $w = c_i w_i$ for which $c_i = \gamma_i + \gamma_i' (-1)^{1/2}$ the real parts of the periods are the sums

$$(35 \cdot 4) \qquad \gamma_i \alpha_{ik} - \gamma_i' \alpha_{ik}', \qquad \gamma_i \beta_{ik} - \gamma_i' \beta_{ik}'.$$

The determinant of coefficients of the γ_i and γ'_i in these expressions is not zero, since by (3) of Theorem 35·1 it is not possible to determine constants c_i not all zero so that the real parts of the periods of w vanish. Hence if we assign real numbers α_k, β_k not all zero arbitrarily the constants γ_i, γ'_i can be determined so that the expressions (35·4) are equal to them. A similar proof shows that one can assign arbitrarily the imaginary parts of the periods of w.

COROLLARY. *There is no linear relation*

$$m_k A_k + n_k B_k = 0,$$

with m_k, n_k *real constants, which holds for the periods* A_k, B_k *of all integrals of the first kind.*

This clearly is true since by the last theorem the real parts of A_k, B_k can be chosen arbitrarily.

36. **Expressions for an integral in terms of elementary integrals or fundamental systems.** In the theory of elliptic integrals it is proved that every elliptic integral is expressible as a sum of integrals of three simple types. The analogue of this theorem for Abelian integrals was proved in Section 24.

We shall represent as above a fundamental system of integrals of the first kind by the notations

$$w_k = \int \psi_k(x, y) dx \qquad (k = 1, \cdots, p).$$

According to Theorem 24·2 there exists for every place P on T and every integer ν an *elementary integral of the second kind*

$$\zeta_\nu(x, y ; P) = \int_C \eta_\nu(x, y ; P) dx$$

which may be denoted also by $\zeta_\nu(P)$ when no confusion results. This integral is completely determined except for an arbitrary additive integral of the first kind by the property that it has no singularity except at P and that at P its expansion has the form

$$\zeta_\nu(P) = \nu!/t^{\nu+1} + c_0 + c_1 t + \cdots .$$

Similarly for an arbitrary pair of places P_1, P_2 on T there is an *elementary integral of the third kind,*

$$\pi(x, y ; P_1, P_2) = \int_C \eta(x, y ; P_1, P_2) dx$$

which has expansions

$$\pi(P_1, P_2) = \log t + c_0 + c_1 t + \cdots \qquad at\ P_1,$$

$$\pi(P_1, P_2) = -\log t + d_0 + d_1 t + \cdots \qquad at\ P_2,$$

and no other singularities. In terms of these notations Theorem 24·4 is as follows:

THEOREM 36·1. *Let I be an arbitrary Abelian integral*

$$I = \int_C \eta(x, y)dx.$$

If I has singular places we may denote one of them by P, and the principal part of the expansion of I at P by

$$A_\nu/t^\nu + \cdots + A_1/t + A \log t.$$

Then

$$(36·1) \qquad I = \sum_P [A\pi(P, P_0) + (A_1/1!)\zeta_0(P) + \cdots + \frac{A_\nu}{(\nu-1)!}\zeta_{\nu-1}(P)] + c_k w_k$$

where the sum is taken for all the singularities P of I and P_0 is an arbitrarily chosen fixed place.

In the formula it is understood that the paths of integration are all the same. If they are different a constant term must be added which is a sum of periods of the integrals.

There are other methods of expressing an arbitrary Abelian integral *I* in terms of a finite number of others given in advance. We have seen above, for example, that every integral *w* of the first kind is expressible in the form $w = c_k w_k$ in terms of a fundamental system w_k ($k = 1, \cdots, p$). We shall see that an analogous theorem holds for integrals which have at most poles as singularities. In order to prove this we may define a *fundamental system of integrals of the first and second kinds* to be a set of $2p$ integrals $\zeta_1, \cdots, \zeta_{2p}$ having no singularities other than poles and having the determinant of its $(2p)^2$ periods different from zero.

THEOREM 36·2. *A necessary and sufficient condition that a set of integrals $\zeta_1, \cdots, \zeta_{2p}$ of the first and second kinds shall form a fundamental system is that for common paths of integration C on T' from (x_0, y_0) to (x, y) there exists no identity of the form*

$$(36·2) \qquad c_1 \zeta_1 + \cdots + c_{2p} \zeta_{2p} = \eta(x, y)$$

in which $\eta(x, y)$ is a rational function and the constants $c_1, \cdots, c_{2p}$ are not all zero.

If there were such an identity the periods A_{ik}, B_{ik} ($i=1, \cdots, 2p$; $k=1, \cdots, p$) of the integrals would satisfy the relations $c_i A_{ik} = c_i B_{ik} = 0$ since $\eta(x, y)$ is single-valued on T. Hence the determinant of the periods would be zero, and $\zeta_1, \cdots, \zeta_{2p}$ could not be a fundamental system.

If there is no such identity the determinant of periods cannot be zero. Otherwise there would be constants c_i not all zero satisfying the equations $c_i A_{ik} = c_i B_{ik} = 0$ and the function $c_1 \zeta_1 + \cdots + c_{2p} \zeta_{2p}$ would be single-valued on T as well as T' and would have only poles as singularities. Hence it would be a rational function $\eta(x, y)$, by the corollary to Theorem 19·1, which contradicts the assumption that there is no identity of the form (36·2).

THEOREM 36·3. *Every integral I having at most poles as singularities is expressible in terms of a fundamental system $\zeta_1, \cdots, \zeta_{2p}$ of integrals of the first and second kinds in the form*

$$I = c_1 \zeta_1 + \cdots + c_{2p} \zeta_{2p} + \eta(x, y)$$

where $\eta(x, y)$ is a rational function and the paths of integration are all on T'.

For $c_1, \cdots, c_{2p}$ may be selected so that the periods of the difference $I - c_1 \zeta_1 - \cdots - c_{2p} \zeta_{2p}$ are all zero. This difference is then single-valued on T as well as on T' and has only poles as singularities. Hence it is a rational function $\eta(x, y)$, by the corollary to Theorem 19·1.

THEOREM 36·4. *If $\zeta_1, \cdots, \zeta_{2p}$ is a fundamental system of integrals of the first and second kinds then every other such fundamental system $\zeta_1', \cdots, \zeta_{2p}'$ is expressible in the form*

$$(36 \cdot 3) \qquad \zeta_i' = c_{i1} \zeta_1 + \cdots + c_{i2p} \zeta_{2p} + \eta_i(x, y) \qquad (i = 1, \cdots, 2p),$$

where the coefficients c_{ij} are constants with determinant $|c_{ij}| \neq 0$ and the functions $\eta_i(x, y)$ are rational. Conversely, every system $\zeta_1, \cdots, \zeta_{2p}$ expressible in this form is a fundamental system.

Evidently each integral ζ_i' is expressible in the form (36·3), by Theorem 36·3, and the determinant $|c_{ij}|$ must be different from zero since the periods A_{ik}', B_{ik}' of ζ_i' are related to the periods A_{ik}, B_{ik} of the integrals ζ_i by the equations

$$A_{ik}' = c_{ij} A_{jk}, \qquad B_{ik}' = c_{ij} B_{jk} \qquad (i, j = 1, \cdots, 2p \,; k = 1, \cdots, p).$$

The determinant of the periods A_{ik}', B_{ik}' is therefore the product of the determinant $|c_{ij}|$ by the determinant of the periods A_{ik}, B_{ik} and is different from zero if and only if $|c_{ij}| \neq 0$.

THEOREM 36·5. *An arbitrary Abelian integral I, such as that described in Theorem* 36·1, *is expressible in the form*

$$I = \sum_P A\pi(P, P_0) + c_1\zeta_1 + \cdots + c_{2p}\zeta_{2p} + \eta(x, y)$$

where the sum is taken for all singularities P of I, P_0 is an arbitrarily chosen fixed place, the set $\zeta_1, \cdots, \zeta_{2p}$ is a fundamental system of integrals of the first and second kinds, and $\eta(x, y)$ is a rational function.

The proof of the theorem is immediate as soon as we recognize the fact that the difference $I - \Sigma A\pi(P, P_0)$ is an integral with no singularities except poles.

37. Relations between periods of integrals. There are many relations between periods of integrals of various kinds which can be deduced by the application of the following theorem:

THEOREM 37·1. *If two Abelian integrals*

$$I = \int \eta(x, y)dx, \qquad I' = \int \eta'(x, y)dx$$

have periods A_k, B_k and A_k', B_k' ($k=1, \cdots, p$), respectively, and if I has no logarithmic singularities, then

$$A_k'B_k - B_k'A_k = 2\pi i \, [sum \ of \ residues \ of \ I\eta' \ on \ T'].$$

The proof of this theorem is much like that of Lemma 35·2. From Figure 35·1 we see that

$$I(\sigma) - I(\rho) = -A_k, \qquad I(\nu) - I(\mu) = B_k,$$

from which it follows that

$$\int_{a_k} [I(\sigma) - I(\rho)]\eta'dx = -A_k \int_{a_k} \eta'dx = -A_kB_k',$$

$$\int_{b_k} [I(\nu) - I(\mu)]\eta'dx = B_k \int_{b_k} \eta'dx = B_kA_k',$$

where the terms on the right are not summed for k. The sum of these integrals for $k=1, \cdots, p$ is the value of the integral

$$\int I(x, y)\eta'(x, y)dx$$

taken around the boundary of T', and it is also $2\pi i$ times the sum of the residues of the product $I\eta'$ on T', so that the theorem is proved.

The application of Theorem 37·1 to pairs of integrals I, I' of various types gives the period relations of the following table. The results in the last column are found in each case by evaluating the sum of the residues on T' of the product of the first integral in the first column by the integrand of the second integral, and applying Theorem 37·1.

PERIOD RELATIONS FOR ELEMENTARY INTEGRALS

	Integrals I, I'	Values of $(A_k B_k' - B_k A_k')/2\pi i$	
I.	w, w'	0	
II.	$w, \zeta_\nu(P_1)$	$c_{\nu+1},$	$\psi^{(\nu)}(x_1, y_1)$
III.	$w, \pi(P_1, P_2)$	$w(P_1 C P_2)$	
IV.	$\zeta_\mu(P_1), \zeta_\nu(P_2)$	$d^\nu\eta_\mu(P_2, P_1)/dx_2^\nu - d^\mu\eta_\nu(P_1, P_2)/dx_1^\mu$	
V.	$\zeta_\mu(P_1), \pi(P_2, P_3)$	$\zeta_\mu(P_2 C P_3; P_1) - d^\mu\eta(P_1; P_2, P_3)/dx_1^\mu$	
VI.	$\pi(P_1, P_2), \pi(P_1', P_2')$	$\pi(P_1' C' P_2'; P_1, P_2) - \pi(P_1 C P_2; P_1', P_2')$	

The constant $c_{\nu+1}$ in Case II is from the coefficient of $t^{\nu+1}$ in the expansion

$$w = c_0 + (c_1/1!)t + \cdots + (c_\nu/\nu!)t^\nu + \cdots$$

of the integral w of the first kind at the singularity P_1 of the elementary integral of the second kind $\zeta_\nu(P_1)$ defined in Section 36. For the integrand $\eta_\nu(x, y; P_1)$ of this latter integral we have at P_1

$$\eta_\nu(x, y; P_1)dx/dt = - (\nu + 1)!/t^{\nu+2} + d_1 + 2d_2 t + \cdots ,$$

and hence the product $w\,\eta_\nu(x, y; P_1)$ has at P_1 the residue $-c_{\nu+1}$, which is its only residue. The result in the table has its sign changed since the period sum at the top is the negative of that evaluated in Theorem 37·1. If P_1 is a finite place $(x, y) = (x_1, y_1)$ and not a branch place then

$$c_{\nu+1} = \left[d^\nu\psi(x, y)/dx^\nu \right]^{x=x_1, y=y_1} = \psi^{(\nu)}(x_1, y_1),$$

where ψ is the integrand of w. The second value for the period sum in Case II is valid for such a place.

The proofs for the other rows of the table are similar, with the exception of Case VI which is discussed below. For simplicity it is understood that in each of Cases III–VI the places P involved are distinct from each other. The integrands $\eta_\nu(x, y; P_1)$ and $\eta(x, y; P_2, P_3)$ of $\zeta_\nu(P_1)$ and $\pi(P_2, P_3)$ are represented by $\eta_\nu(P; P_1)$ and $\eta(P; P_2, P_3)$. If some of the places P_1, P_2, P_3 in Cases IV and V are at infinity or branch places the values of some of the functions η or their derivatives must be replaced by suitable coefficients from the expansions of the products $\eta dx/dt$. In all cases where integrals occur their paths of integration are supposed to be on the simply connected surface T' unless otherwise specified. In Case VI, for example, the symbol $\pi(P_1CP_2; P_1', P_2')$ represents the value of $\pi(P_1', P_2')$ taken along a path C from P_1 to P_2, and the paths C, C' are supposed to be distinct from each other and the period cuts.

The result in Case VI requires a proof slightly different from that of Theorem 37·1. The integral of $\pi d\pi'$, where $\pi' = \pi(P_1', P_2')$, taken around the boundary of the surface T'' for π, is $2\pi i$ times the sum of

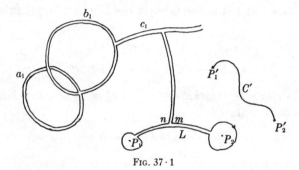

FIG. 37·1

the residues of $\pi\eta(P; P_1', P_2')$ on T''. The part of this integral arising from the cuts a_k, b_k is the period sum $B_k A_k' - A_k B_k'$, as before. The part arising from the loops L enclosing P_1 and P_2 in Figure 37·1 is

$$-\int_L \pi d\pi' = -\pi\pi'\Big|_m^n + \int_L \pi' d\pi .$$

The first term on the right vanishes since π and π' have the same values at m and n. The second is $2\pi i$ times the sum of the residues of the product $\pi'\eta(P; P_1, P_2)$ at P_1 and P_2 which is

$$\pi'(P_1) - \pi'(P_2) = - \pi(P_1CP_2; P_1', P_2').$$

The sum of the residues of $\pi\eta(P; P_1', P_2')$ on T'' is

$$\pi(P_1') - \pi(P_2') = - \pi(P_1'C'P_2'; P_1, P_2).$$

Hence the formula of Case VI is justified.

38. **Construction of fundamental systems.** There are two methods of constructing fundamental systems of integrals of the first and second kinds which will be explained here in Theorems 38·1 and 38·2.

THEOREM 38·1. *Let w_i $(i = 1, \cdots, p)$ be a fundamental system of integrals of the first kind with integrand functions $\psi_i(x, y)$, and let $P_k = (x_k, y_k)$ $(k = 1, \cdots, p)$ be a set of p finite places distinct from branch places such that the determinant $\left| \psi_i(P_k) \right|$ is different from zero. Then the system w_i, $\zeta_0(P_i)$ $(i = 1, \cdots, p)$ is a fundamental system of integrals of the first and second kinds.*

From Lemma 26·1 we know that finite non-singular places $P_k(k = 1, \cdots, p)$ can always be selected so that the determinant $\left| \psi_i(P_k) \right|$ is different from zero.

If the periods of w_i and $\zeta_0(P_i)$ are respectively A_{jl}, B_{jl} and A_{jl}', B_{jl}' then Cases I and II of the table in the last section give the period relations

$$(38 \cdot 1) \qquad \begin{aligned} A_{jl}B_{kl} - B_{jl}A_{kl} &= 0, \\ A_{jl}'B_{kl} - B_{jl}'A_{kl} &= -2\pi i\, \psi_k(P_j). \end{aligned}$$

If we could determine constants c_j, d_j not all zero and a rational function $\eta(x, y)$ such that

$$(38 \cdot 2) \qquad c_j w_j + d_j \zeta_0(P_j) = \eta(x, y)$$

then we should have

$$(38 \cdot 3) \qquad c_j A_{jl} + d_j A_{jl}' = 0, \qquad c_j B_{jl} + d_j B_{jl}' = 0,$$

and hence from the period relations $(38 \cdot 1)$

$$d_j \psi_k(P_j) = 0.$$

The constants d_j must therefore all be zero, and the constants c_j also, from equations $(38 \cdot 3)$. It follows that no relation of the form $(38 \cdot 2)$ with constants c_j, d_j not all zero is possible, so that the integrals, w_j, $\zeta_0(P_j)$ surely form a fundamental system, according to Theorem 36·2.

LEMMA 38·1. *A necessary and sufficient condition that a set of rational functions $\psi_\nu(x, y)$ $(\nu = 1, \cdots, s)$ be linearly independent on T is that the determinant*

$$D = \begin{vmatrix} \psi_1 & \cdots & \psi_s \\ \psi_1' & \cdots & \psi_s' \\ \cdot & \cdots & \cdot \\ \psi_1^{(s-1)} & \cdots & \psi_s^{(s-1)} \end{vmatrix}$$

is not identically zero on T, where $\psi_\nu^{(n)} = d^n \psi_\nu / dx^n$.

If D is not identically zero the functions ψ_ν are evidently linearly independent. If $D \equiv 0$ then at least when $s = 1$ the function ψ_1 is identically zero and satisfies a linear relation $c\psi_1 \equiv 0$ with $c \neq 0$. Suppose then that the theorem is true for $s-1$ functions. It follows that there is a linear relation between $\psi_1, \cdots, \psi_{s-1}$ if the determinant

$$\begin{vmatrix} \psi_1 & \cdots & \psi_{s-1} \\ \cdot & \cdots & \cdot \\ \psi_1^{(s-2)} & \cdots & \psi_{s-1}^{(s-2)} \end{vmatrix}$$

vanishes identically. If this last determinant does not vanish identically, then near a place where it is different from zero there are functions $\lambda_1, \cdots, \lambda_{s-1}$ satisfying the equations

$$\lambda_1\psi_1 + \cdots + \lambda_{s-1}\psi_{s-1} + \psi_s = 0,$$
$$\cdots \cdots \cdots \cdots \cdots \cdots \cdots$$
$$\lambda_1\psi_1^{(s-1)} + \cdots + \lambda_{s-1}\psi_{s-1}^{(s-1)} + \psi_s^{(s-1)} = 0,$$

since $D \equiv 0$. By differentiating these equations we find that

$$\lambda_1'\psi_1 + \cdots + \lambda_{s-1}'\psi_{s-1} = 0,$$
$$\cdots \cdots \cdots \cdots \cdots \cdots \cdots$$
$$\lambda_1'\psi_1^{(s-2)} + \cdots + \lambda_{s-1}'\psi_{s-1}^{(s-2)} = 0,$$

from which it follows that $\lambda_1, \cdots, \lambda_{s-1}$ are constants and $\psi_1, \cdots, \psi_s$ are linearly dependent.

COROLLARY. *For the integrand functions* $\psi_i(x, y)$ $(i = 1, \cdots, p)$ *of a fundamental system of integrals of the first kind the determinant D is not identically zero.*

This is evident from the lemma above since the functions ψ_i are linearly independent.

THEOREM 38·2. *Let* w_i $(i = 1, \cdots, p)$ *be a fundamental system of integrals of the first kind with integrand functions* $\psi_i(x, y)$, *and let* $P = (\xi, \eta)$ *be a finite place, distinct from the branch places, at which the determinant D for the functions ψ_i is different from zero. Then the system* w_i, $\zeta_{i-1}(P)$ $(i = 1, \cdots, p)$ *is a fundamental system of integrals of the first and second kinds.*

To prove this let the periods of w_i and ζ_{i-1} be denoted by A_{il}, B_{il} and A_{il}', B_{il}'. Then from Cases I and II of the table of Section 37 we have the period relations

$$(38 \cdot 4) \qquad A_{jl}B_{kl} - B_{jl}A_{kl} = 0,$$

$$A_{jl}B_{kl} - B_{jl}A_{kl} = -2\pi i \psi_k^{(j-1)}(\xi, \eta).$$

If there were a relation of the form $(38 \cdot 2)$ with $\zeta_0(P_i)$ replaced by $\zeta_{j-1}(P)$, we should have, from $(38 \cdot 3)$ and $(38 \cdot 4)$

$$d_j \psi_k^{(j-1)}(\xi, \eta) = 0 \qquad (j, k = 1, \cdots, p).$$

Since $D \neq 0$ at (ξ, η) this implies that the constants d_j are all zero, and from $(38 \cdot 3)$ that the same is true of the constants c_j. Hence the functions w_j, ζ_{j-1} form a fundamental system as stated in the theorem.

39. **Normal integrals.** If w_i $(i = 1, \cdots, p)$ is a fundamental system of integrals of the first kind with periods A_{ik}, B_{ik} $(i, k = 1, \cdots, p)$ then the most general such integral

$$w = c_1 w_1 + \cdots + c_p w_p$$

has periods

$$A_k = c_i A_{ik}, \qquad B_k = c_i B_{ik}.$$

Since the determinant $|A_{ik}|$ is different from zero, according to Theorem $35 \cdot 2$, the constants c_i can be determined so that the periods A_k have arbitrarily assigned values.

THEOREM $39 \cdot 1$. *There exists a fundamental system of integrals of the first kind*

$$W_i = \int \Psi_i(x, y)dx \qquad (i = 1, \cdots, p)$$

with a table of periods of the following form:

	A_1	A_2	$\cdots$	A_p	B_1	B_2	$\cdots$	B_p
W_1	$2\pi i$	0	$\cdots$	0	$2\alpha_{11}$	$2\alpha_{12}$	$\cdots$	$2\alpha_{1p}$
W_2	0	$2\pi i$	$\cdots$	0	$2\alpha_{21}$	$2\alpha_{22}$	$\cdots$	$2\alpha_{2p}$
$\cdots$	$\cdots$	$\cdots$	$\cdots$	$\cdots$	$\cdots$	$\cdots$	$\cdots$	$\cdots$
W_p	0	0	$\cdots$	$2\pi i$	$2\alpha_{p1}$	$2\alpha_{p2}$	$\cdots$	$2\alpha_{pp}$

Such a system is called a NORMAL SYSTEM OF INTEGRALS OF THE FIRST KIND. *The integrands* $\Psi_i(x, y)$ *of the integrals of a normal system are* *uniquely determined and are linearly independent. The matrix of half-periods $\alpha_{ik} = a_{ik} + a_{ik}'(-1)^{1/2}$ is symmetric and the quadratic form $a_{ik}z_iz_k$ is positive definite.*

The period relation of Case I of the table of Section 37 applied to W_i and W_j shows that the matrix α_{ik} is symmetric. The periods of $W = z_iW_j$ are $A_k = 2\pi i z_k$, $B_k = 2z_j\alpha_{jk}$. The relation $35 \cdot 3$ applied to these periods shows that for every choice of real numbers z_j not all zero the quadratic form $a_{jk}z_jz_k$ is positive.

THEOREM $39 \cdot 2$. *There exists an elementary integral of the second kind*

$$Z_\nu(P) = \int H_\nu(x, y; P) dx$$

having no other pole except one at a place P on T where it has an expansion

$$Z_\nu(P) = \nu!/t^{\nu+1} + c_0 + c_1t + \cdots$$

and having all its periods $A_k = 0$ $(k = 1, \cdots, p)$. If the singularity $P = (\xi, \eta)$ of $Z_\nu(P)$ is a finite non-singular place then the values of the periods B_k for the integral $Z_\nu(P)$ are $B_k = \Psi_k^{(\nu)}(\xi, \eta)$, where the functions Ψ_k are the integrands of a normal system of integrals of the first kind, as described in Theorem $39 \cdot 1$. Such an integral is called a NORMAL INTEGRAL OF THE SECOND KIND *with pole of order $\nu + 1$ at P. Its integrand $H_\nu(x, y; P)$ $= H_\nu(Q; P)$ is uniquely determined. Furthermore,*

(39·1) $H_0(Q; P) = H_0(P; Q)$,

(39·2) $H_\nu(Q; P) = d^\nu H_0(Q; P)/d\xi^\nu$.

From Section 24 we know that there is an elementary integral $\zeta_\nu(P)$ of the second kind with an expansion of the form

$$\zeta_\nu(P) = \nu!/t^{\nu+1} + c_0 + c_1t + \cdots$$

at the place P and no other pole. The most general such integral has the form

$$Z_\nu(P) = \zeta_\nu(P) + c_1w_1 + \cdots + c_pw_p,$$

where the constants c_i are arbitrary. If they are chosen so that the periods A_k of the sum are zero then the resulting integral $Z_\nu(P)$ has an integrand which is uniquely determined. From the period relation of Case II of the table of Section 37 applied to W_k and $Z_\nu(P)$ it follows that $B_k = \Psi_k^{(\nu)}(\xi, \eta)$, as indicated in the theorem above, when P is finite and non-singular. The symmetry of $H_0(Q; P)$ is a consequence of

Case IV of the table of Section 37 for $\mu=\nu=0$, since the periods A_k, A_k' of $Z_0(P)$, $Z_0(Q)$ are zero. The last equation of the theorem is similarly a consequence of Case IV of the table applied to $Z_0(Q)$ and $Z_\nu(P)$ with the help of the relation (39·1).

THEOREM 39·3. *There exists an elementary integral of the third kind*

$$\Pi(P_1, P_2) = \int H(x, y; P_1, P_2)\, dx$$

having expansions of the forms

$$\Pi(P_1, P_2) = \log t + c_0 + c_1 t + \cdots \qquad at\ P_1,$$

$$\Pi(P_1, P_2) = -\log t + d_0 + d_1 t + \cdots \qquad at\ P_2,$$

and no other singularities, and having periods $A_k=0$, $B_k=W_k(P_1CP_2)$, *where the path of integration C is on T'. Such an integral is called a* NORMAL INTEGRAL OF THE THIRD KIND. *Its integrand is uniquely determined and has the value*

$$(39·3) \qquad H(Q; P_1, P_2) = Z_0(P_1CP_2; Q)$$

where the path of integration C is on T'. The integrand H_ν of the integral $Z_\nu(P)$ of Theorem 39·2 is expressible in terms of $H(Q; P_1, P_2)$ in the form

$$(39·4) \qquad H_\nu(Q; P) = d^{\nu+1}H(Q; P_1, P)/d\xi^{\nu+1}.$$

The most general elementary integral of the third kind with singularities at P_1, P_2 has the form

$$\Pi(P_1, P_2) = \pi(P_1, P_2) + c_1 w_1 + \cdots + c_p w_p.$$

If the constants c_j are chosen so that the periods A_k of this sum are all zero the resulting integral $\Pi(P_1, P_2)$ has an integrand which is uniquely determined. The period relation of Case III of the table of Section 37 applied to W_k and $\Pi(P_1, P_2)$ shows that the periods B_k have the values indicated in the theorem. The formula (39·3) of the theorem is a consequence of Case V of the table of period relations applied to $Z_0(P)$ and $\Pi(P_1, P_2)$, since the periods A_k of both of these integrals are zero. Equation (39·4) for $\nu=0$ is the result of writing (39·3) in the form

$$H(Q; P_1, P) = Z_0(P_1CP; Q)$$

and differentiating with respect to the coordinate ξ of P. Equations (39·1) and (39·2) then justify (39·4) for other values of ν.

There are a number of properties of normal integrals of the third kind which should be mentioned. These are given in the following list, and the proofs are indicated below. The paths of integration of integrals in the same formula are the same unless otherwise indicated. The paths C, C' are on T' and distinct from each other. In IV the point $P = (\xi, \eta)$ is supposed to be finite and not over a branch point.

I. $\Pi(P_1, P_2) + \Pi(P_2, P_3) + \cdots + \Pi(P_k, P_1) = 0$

$\Pi(P_1, P_2) = \Pi(P_1, P) - \Pi(P_2, P)$

II. $\Pi(P_1 C P_2; P_1', P_2') = \Pi(P_1' C' P_2'; P_1, P_2)$

III. $\Pi(P_1 C P_2; P_1', P_2') = \Pi(P_1' C' P_2'; P_1, P) - \Pi(P_1' C' P_2'; P_2, P)$

IV. $Z_\nu(P_1 C P_2; P) = d^{\nu+1}\Pi(P_1 C P_2; P_3, P)/d\xi^\nu$.

The first member of the first equation in I is an integral with no singularities and periods A_k all zero. Hence it is identically zero. The second formula under I is a special case of the first. The formula II is a consequence of the sixth period relation of the table of Section 37, since for the two normal integrals of the third kind involved the periods A_k, A_k' are all zero. Formula III is readily deduced from formula II and the second formula under I. Formula IV is the result of integrating equation (39·4) along the path C from P_1 to P_2.

40. **Expressions for rational functions in terms of integrals.** Every rational function $\eta(x, y)$ is expressible as an Abelian integral of the second kind. For the algebraic function $y(x)$ defined by the equation $f(x, y) = 0$ and the derivative of $y(x)$ satisfy the equation

$$f_x(x, y) + f_y(x, y)dy/dx = 0,$$

and hence

$$d\eta(x, y)/dx = (\eta_x f_y - \eta_y f_x)/f_y.$$

Consequently

$$(40·1) \qquad \eta(x, y) = \eta(x_0, y_0) + \int_C (\eta_x f_y - \eta_y f_x)dx/f_y,$$

where C is a path of integration on T' joining (x_0, y_0) to (x, y), and the integral is of the second kind since $\eta(x, y)$ has no singularities other than poles.

THEOREM 40·1. *Every rational function $\eta(x, y)$ on the Riemann surface T is expressible by the formula (40·1) as a sum of a constant and an Abelian integral of the second kind whose periods are all zero. Conversely, every Abelian integral of the second kind whose periods are all zero is a rational function $\eta(x, y)$ on T.*

It is evident that the integral in $(40 \cdot 1)$ has periods all equal to zero since $\eta(x, y)$ is single-valued on the surface T. Conversely, an integral of the second kind whose periods vanish is rational in x, y since it is single-valued on T and has only poles as singularities, according to the corollary of Theorem $19 \cdot 1$.

THEOREM $40 \cdot 2$. *Let*

$$(40 \cdot 2) \qquad c_\nu t^{-\nu} + \cdots + c_1 t^{-1}$$

be the principal part of the expansion at a pole P of a rational function $\eta(x, y)$ on T. Then $\eta(x, y)$ is expressible in terms of normal integrals of the second kind in the form

$$(40 \cdot 3) \qquad \eta(x, y) = \sum_P \left[c_1 Z_0(P) + \cdots + \frac{c_\nu}{(\nu-1)!} Z_{\nu-1}(P) \right] + c,$$

where the sum is taken for all the singularities P of η. If these singularities occur only at finite non-singular places $P = (\xi, \eta)$ on T, then

$$(40 \cdot 4) \qquad \sum_P \left[c_1 \Psi_k(P) + \cdots + \frac{c_\nu}{(\nu-1)!} \Psi_k^{(\nu-1)}(P) \right] = 0$$

$$(k = 1, \cdots, p).$$

Conversely, if a set of such places $P = (\xi, \eta)$ and constants c satisfy the equations $(40 \cdot 4)$, then the second member of equation $(40 \cdot 3)$ is a rational function of x and y with the singularities P and principal parts $(40 \cdot 2)$.

The expression $(40 \cdot 3)$ for $\eta(x, y)$ is a consequence of Theorems $40 \cdot 1$ and $36 \cdot 1$. The period A_k of the second member of $(40 \cdot 3)$ is zero since all of the integrals $Z_{\nu-1}(P)$ involved are normal integrals. Since $\eta(x, y)$ is single-valued on T the period B_k of the second member of equation $(40 \cdot 3)$ must also be zero, and according to Theorem $39 \cdot 2$ this fact is expressed by the equation $(40 \cdot 4)$. Conversely, when the equation $(40 \cdot 4)$ is satisfied the second member of equation $(40 \cdot 3)$ is single-valued on T and has no singularities except poles, so that it is indeed a rational function of x and y.

THEOREM $40 \cdot 3$. *The logarithm of a rational function $\eta(x, y)$ on T is expressible as an Abelian integral*

$$
\begin{aligned}
\log \eta(x, y) &= \log \eta(x_0, y_0) + \int_C d\eta/\eta \\
&= \log \eta(x_0, y_0) + \int_C (\eta_x f_y - \eta_y f_x) dx/\eta f_y.
\end{aligned}
$$

$(40 \cdot 5)$

The only singularities of this integral are logarithmic singularities at the zeros and poles of $\eta(x, y)$. If at such a place

$$(40\cdot6) \qquad\qquad \eta(x, y) = ct^\nu + \cdots \qquad\qquad (c \neq 0)$$

then log η has at that place an expansion

$$(40\cdot7) \qquad\qquad \log \eta = \nu \log t + c_0 + c_1 t + \cdots .$$

The periods of the integral for log η are all integral multiples of $2\pi i$.

The first statement of this theorem is evident. At a place where $\eta(x, y)$ has the expansion $(40\cdot6)$ we see that the expansion for $d\eta/\eta dt$ has the form

$$d\eta/\eta dt = \nu/t + c_1 + c_2 t + \cdots$$

from which it follows that the integral for log η has an expansion $(40\cdot7)$. The periods for log η are integral multiples of $2\pi i$ since on opposite sides of a period cut the values of η are the same and the values of the integral in $(40\cdot5)$ therefore can differ only by integral multiples of $2\pi i$.

THEOREM $40\cdot4$. *Every rational function $\eta(x, y)$ on the Riemann surface T is expressible in the form*

$$(40\cdot8) \quad \eta(x, y) = c \operatorname{Exp} \left[\sum_P \Pi(P, P_0) - \sum_{P'} \Pi(P', P_0) + n_i W_i \right]$$

where i has the range $1, \cdots, p$, c is a constant, the symbol Exp stands for the exponential series, the sums are taken for all the zeros P and poles P' of $\eta(x, y)$, and the coefficients n_i are integers. Furthermore there exist integers m_k such that the equations

$$(40\cdot9) \qquad \sum_P W_k(P) - \sum_{P'} W_k(P') = 2m_k \pi i - 2n_j \alpha_{jk} \quad (k = 1, \cdots, p)$$

hold. Conversely, if for a set of places P and an equal number of places P' there exist integers m_k, n_j satisfying the equations $(40\cdot9)$ then the second member of equation $(40\cdot8)$ is a rational function of x and y whose zeros and poles are the places P and P' respectively.

If $\eta(x, y)$ is a rational function with zeros P and poles P' then according to Theorem $40\cdot3$ the difference

$$\log \eta - \sum_P \Pi(P, P_0) + \sum_{P'} \Pi(P', P_0)$$

has no singularities and is an integral of the first kind, say $n_j W_j$. It should be noted that the set of places P will contain a particular place

P_1 a number μ_1 of times if P_1 is a zero of order μ_1 of $\eta(x, y)$. A similar remark holds for the set P'. Hence η has the form indicated in equation (40·8). The quotient of the values of the second member of this equation at places on opposite sides of a cut a_k is Exp $[2n_k\pi i]$ and n_k must therefore be an integer since the quotient of the corresponding values of $\eta(x, y)$ is unity. Similarly with the help of Theorems 39·1 and 39·3 it is seen that for two places on opposite sides of a period cut b_k the values of the second member of (40·8) have the ratio

$$\text{Exp}\left[\sum_P W_k(P) - \sum_{P'} W_k(P') + 2n\alpha_{jjk} \right].$$

Since this ratio also must be unity it follows that there are integers m_k for which equations (40·9) are satisfied.

Conversely, if equations of the form (40·9) hold for two sets of places P and P' then one can readily see that the second member of equation (40·8) is single-valued on T and has zeros at the places P and poles at the places P' and no other singularities. It must therefore be a rational function.

COROLLARY. ABEL'S THEOREM FOR INTEGRALS OF THE FIRST KIND. *If a set of places P and an equal number of places P' are respectively the zeros and poles of a rational function $\eta(x, y)$, then for every integral w of the first kind with periods A_k, B_k there exist integers m_k, n_k such that*

$$(40\cdot 10) \qquad \sum_P w(P) - \sum_{P'} w(P') = m_k A_k + n_k B_k.$$

Conversely, if for a set of places P and an equal number of places P' and every integral w of the first kind there exist integers m_k, n_k satisfying the equation (40·10), *then the sets P and P' are the zeros and poles of a rational function.*

If the integral w is expressed in terms of the fundamental system W_k ($k = 1, \cdots, p$) in the form $w = c_k W_k$ the equation (40·10) is an immediate consequence of (40·9). Similarly (40·10) applied to an integral W_k gives (40·9).

The theorem of the corollary is a special case of a famous theorem of Abel which is to be discussed in the next chapter.

It will be interesting to study for a moment the case when the genus p is zero, and to analyze the analogies between the theorems of this section and the theorems concerning rational functions of x which were developed in Section 6 of Chapter I. When $p = 0$ the Riemann surface T is itself simply connected and needs no period cuts to make it so.

There are no integrals of the first kind, and every integral of the second kind is single-valued with no singularities except poles on T, and hence is a rational function of x and y. The integrals of the third kind have periods due to their singularities but no others. In the case $p=0$ the class of all rational functions of x and y and the class of all integrals of the second kind are evidently identical. When $p>0$ the class of integrals is the larger. In that case the integral $Z_0(P)$, for example, is a function with a single simple pole; and according to Theorem 26·4 there is no rational function of x and y with this property when $p>0$.

The complex x-plane is the Riemann surface T of the simple algebraic function $y(x)$ of genus $p=0$ defined by the equation $y-x=0$. On this surface the integral $Z_\nu(P)$ is a rational function with no singularity except a pole at the place $P=\xi$ at which it has an expansion $\nu!/(x-\xi)^{\nu+1}$ $+c_0+c_1(x-\xi)+\cdots$. The function $\nu!/(x-\xi)^{\nu+1}$ has these properties in the x-plane, and one readily sees that it can differ from $Z_\nu(P)$ by at most an additive constant. The difference $Z_\nu(P)-\nu!/(x-\xi)^{\nu+1}$ is in fact a rational function with no poles and hence a constant. We see then that in this case the expansion for $Z_\nu(P)$ at the place P has no terms with positive exponents. It is evident therefore that the expression (40·3) is a generalization of the formula (6·1), described in Theorem 6·6 of Chapter I, expressing a rational function $\eta(x)$ in terms of the principal parts of its expansions at its poles.

Similarly the formula (40·8) above is a generalization, of a somewhat more complicated sort, of the formula (6·2) described in Theorem 6·7 of Chapter I. When $p=0$ there are no integrals of the first kind and formula (40·8) can be written in the simpler form

$$(40\cdot11)\qquad \eta(x,\,y) = c\,\mathrm{Exp}\left[\ \sum_P \Pi(P,\,P_0) - \sum_{P'} \Pi(P',\,P_0)\ \right].$$

Since $p=0$ the integrals Π have as periods only integral multiples of $2\pi i$ and each of the factors $\mathrm{Exp}[\Pi(P,\,P_0)]$ is single-valued on T with a simple zero at P and a simple pole at P_0. Hence each such factor is a rational function of x and y. For the simple case $y-x=0$ one readily verifies that

$$\mathrm{Exp}\,[\Pi(P,\,P_0)] = \gamma(x-\xi)/(x-\xi_0),$$

where γ is a constant, so that formula (40·11) expresses a function $\eta(x)$ in the x-plane as the quotient of the product of the factors $(x-\xi)$ belonging to its zeros by the product of the factors $(x-\xi')$ belonging to its poles.

REFERENCES FOR CHAPTER V

References for the various sections of Chapter V above, in the list at the end of this book, are the following: 13, Chapter X; 15, Chapter XIV; 16, Chapter VII; 18, Chapters V, VII; 20, Abschnitt III; 21, Chapters II–VII; 24, Chapter XVI; 27, Chapters XI–XX; 28, Vorlesungen XIX–XXII, XXXII–XXXVII; 39, Chapter VIII; 42, Chapter XIII; 47, Chapters IV; V.

Chapter VI

ABEL'S THEOREM

41. Introduction. The theorem to be studied in this chapter is a most remarkable and extensive generalization, discovered by Abel, of the addition formulas for elliptic integrals. In the history of mathematics there have been few instances in which as great an advance has been made by one writer at one time, and the theorem is one which every mathematician should know. Its applications range from the addition formulas for elementary trigonometric functions to the most advanced theories of algebraic geometry and multiply periodic functions of several complex variables.

In the following pages two forms of the theorem are given. The first form, in Section 42 below, is more nearly the original theorem as stated and proved by Abel [1, vol. 1, pages 146–149]. The proof as given in Section 42 is relatively elementary but is based upon restrictive assumptions which are undesirable. The second and more general discussion of the theorem in Section 45 includes the preceding as a special case and affords a more satisfactory proof. In Sections 43 and 44 the applications of Abel's theorem to elementary transcendental functions and elliptic functions are given. Section 46 contains a formula for expressing a sum of $p+1$ Abelian integrals in terms of p such integrals, and the last section of the chapter is devoted to the proof of a lemma used in Section 42.

42. A first form of Abel's theorem. The theorem to be described here has to do with the intersections of a curve $f(x, y) = 0$ with a second curve $g(x, y, a_1, \cdots, a_s) = 0$ which depends upon a set of parameters a_σ $(\sigma = 1, \cdots, s)$. We shall suppose as usual that $f(x, y)$ is an irreducible polynomial, and that g is a polynomial in x and y with coefficients which are rational in the parameters a_σ. For a particular set a_σ' $(\sigma = 1, \cdots, s)$ it is assumed that the zeros of the polynomial g are all simple and at finite non-singular places (x_i, y_i) $(i = 1, \cdots, \mu)$ on the Riemann surface T of the equation $f = 0$. There will be no loss of generality in requiring further that the values x_i shall all be distinct, and similarly for the y_i, since if this is not the case it can readily be brought about by a simple linear transformation of the form $x' = ax + by$, $y' = cx + dy$ with constant

119

coefficients. When the properties just described hold for the sets (x_i, y_i) corresponding to the particular values a_σ' they will hold also in a neighborhood of these values, and it is to such a neighborhood that the following theorem will apply.

THEOREM 42·1. A FIRST FORM OF ABEL'S THEOREM. *The sum of the values of an Abelian integral*

$$I = \int \eta(x, y)dx$$

taken on the Riemann surface T of an irreducible algebraic curve $f(x, y) = 0$ from a fixed place (x_0, y_0) to the variable intersections (x_i, y_i) $(i = 1, \cdots, \mu)$ of this curve with a second curve $g(x, y, a_1, \cdots, a_s) = 0$ of the kind described above, is expressible in the form

$$(42·1) \qquad \sum_i \int_{(x_0, y_0)}^{(x_i, y_i)} \eta(x, y)dx = \rho(a_1 \cdots, a_s)$$

$$+ c_k \log r_k(a_1, \cdots, a_s) + P$$

where the functions ρ and r_k are rational in the parameters a_σ, the sum c_k $\log r_k$ contains only a finite number of terms and has constant coefficients c_k, and P is a suitably selected period of the integral.

If it is agreed that the paths of integration of the integrals in equation $(42·1)$ shall all lie on the surface T'' of the integral I then the period P can be thought of as part of the functions ρ and omitted.

To prove the theorem we note first that the values x_i are the roots of an equation

$$(42·2) \qquad \Theta(x, a_1, \cdots, a_s) = 0$$

found by eliminating y from the equations $f = 0$, $g = 0$. The function Θ is a polynomial of degree μ in x with coefficients rational in $a_1, \cdots, a_s$, and having distinct roots x_i for the parameter values which we are considering. For each of these roots x_i the greatest common factor of $f(x_i, y)$ and $g(x_i, y, a_1, \cdots, a_s)$ is linear in y. By the greatest common divisor process applied to $f(x, y)$ and $g(x, y)$ we find therefore an equation

$$y_i = \psi(x_i, a_1, \cdots, a_s)$$

which gives us the corresponding value y_i. The function ψ is rational in its arguments and is the same for all roots y_i. The sum

$$S = \sum_i \int_{(x_0, y_0)}^{(x_i, y_i)} \eta(x, y)dx,$$

when the paths of integration are on T'', is a single-valued function of the parameters $a_1, \cdots, a_s$ and has the differential

$$dS = \eta(x_i, y_i)dx_i$$

where the differentials dx_i are determined by the equations

$$\Theta_x(x_i, a_1, \cdots, a_s)dx_i + \Theta_{a_\sigma}(x_i, a_1, \cdots, a_s)da_\sigma = 0$$

in which the second term is a sum with respect to σ and the first is not a sum with respect to i. Hence

$$dS = - da_\sigma\, \eta(x_i, y_i)\, \Theta_{a_\sigma}(x_i, a)/\Theta_x(x_i, a)$$
$$= R_\sigma(a_1, \cdots, a_s)da_\sigma,$$

where the coefficients R_σ are rational in $a_1, \cdots, a_s$ since they are symmetric in the variables x_i and therefore expressible rationally in terms of the coefficients of the equation $(42 \cdot 2)$. Theorem $42 \cdot 1$ is an immediate consequence of the last form for dS since a single-valued function S whose differential has this form is expressible as a rational function of $a_1, \cdots, a_s$ plus a sum of constants times logarithms of such functions. This last statement is a theorem from integral calculus, an explicit proof of which is given in Section 47 below.

43. **Elementary applications of Abel's theorem.** The familiar addition theorems for elementary transcendental functions and elliptic functions can be proved by means of Abel's theorem. In this section a number of such proofs will be given in order to illustrate the methods which may be used in making other applications of the same sort. The following lemma will be found frequently useful.

LEMMA $43 \cdot 1$. *If $h(x)$ is a polynomial of the n-th degree with distinct roots $x_1, \cdots, x_n$, and if $g(x)$ is a polynomial of the m-th degree, then the sum*

$$g(x_i)/h'(x_i) = c$$

where c is the constant term of the quotient found by dividing $xg(x)$ by $h(x)$.

According to the theory of partial fractions

$$xg(x)/h(x) = c + c_1 x + \cdots + \sum_i x_i g(x_i)/(x - x_i)h'(x_i)$$

where the constants $c, c_1, \cdots$ are all zero unless $m+1 \geqq n$. For $x=0$ this gives the desired result at once provided that none of the roots x_i is zero. If one of them is zero the term corresponding to the root $x_i=0$ in the sum in the second member of the last equation vanishes, and for $x=0$ the equation becomes

$$g(0)/h'(0) = c - \sum_j g(x_j)/h'(x_j),$$

where the last sum is taken for the roots $x_j \neq 0$ only. But this equation gives again the conclusion of the lemma.

The addition formula for $\sin x$ is deducible from that for arc $\sin x$, and the latter is the addition formula for the integral

$$I = \int dx/y$$

on the Riemann surface of the algebraic function defined by the equation $f(x, y) = x^2 + y^2 - 1 = 0$. If we intersect this curve $f = 0$ by the straight line $g(x, y, a, b) = y - ax - b = 0$ the coordinates $x_i (i = 1, 2)$ of the points of intersection (x_i, y_i) will be roots of the equation

$$\Theta(x, a, b) = (a^2 + 1)x^2 + 2abx + b^2 - 1 = 0.$$

Their derivatives with respect to a and b are

$$\partial x_i/\partial a = - \Theta_a(x_i, a, b)/\Theta'(x_i, a, b) = - 2x_i y_i/\Theta'(x_i, a, b),$$
$$\partial x_i/\partial b = - \Theta_b(x_i, a, b)/\Theta'(x_i, a, b) = - 2y_i/\Theta'(x_i, a, b),$$

where the primes indicate derivatives with respect to x. Hence the sum

$$S(a, b) = \int_0^{x_1} dx/y + \int_0^{x_2} dx/y$$

has the derivative

$$S_a = - \sum_i 2x_i/\Theta'(x_i), \qquad S_b = - \sum_i 2/\Theta'(x_i).$$

According to Lemma 43·1 these have the values

$$S_a = - 2/(1 + a^2), \qquad S_b = 0$$

and therefore

$$S = - 2 \text{ arc tan } a = \text{arc sin } [- 2a/(1 + a^2)],$$

the additive constant of integration being zero since $a = 0$, $b = 1$ gives $x_1 = x_2 = 0$ and $S(0, 1) = 0$. From the equations

$$y_1 = ax_1 + b, \qquad y_2 = ax_2 + b, \qquad a = (y_1 - y_2)/(x_1 - x_2),$$
$$y_1 = (1 - x_1^2)^{1/2}, \qquad y_2 = (1 - x_2^2)^{1/2},$$

we find after simple calculations that

$$- 2a/(1 + a^2) = x_1 y_2 + x_2 y_1.$$

Hence

$$\int_0^{x_1} dx/y + \int_0^{x_2} dx/y = \text{arc sin } (x_1 y_2 + x_2 y_1) = \int_0^{x_1 y_2 + x_2 y_1} dx/y$$

which is the addition formula for arc sin x.

The addition formulas for

$$\log x = \int_1^x dx/x, \qquad \text{arc tan } x = \int_0^x dx/(1 + x^2)$$

can be found in a similar manner by means of the polynomials $f(x, y) = y - x$ and $g(x, y, a, b) = x^2 + ax + b$.

44. Addition formulas for elliptic integrals.[*] The addition formulas for elementary elliptic integrals can be most conveniently calculated for the algebraic function defined by the equation

$$(44 \cdot 1) \qquad y^2 - x(1 - x)(1 - k^2 x) = 0.$$

The three elementary integrals for this function have the form

$$I_1 = \int dx/y, \qquad I_2 = \int (1 - k^2 x) dx/y, \qquad I_3 = \int dx/(1 + nx)y.$$

These are readily transformable into the usual Legendre types by the substitution $x = z^2$.

If we intersect the curve $(44 \cdot 1)$ by the straight line $y - ax - b = 0$, the coordinates x_i of the three points of intersection (x_i, y_i) $(i = 1, 2, 3)$ are roots of the equation

$$(44 \cdot 2) \quad \Theta(x, a, b) = k^2 x^3 - (1 + k^2 + a^2) x^2 + (1 - 2ab)x - b^2 = 0,$$

and their derivatives with respect to a and b are

$$\partial x_i/\partial a = 2 x_i y_i/\Theta'(x_i), \qquad \partial x_i/\partial b = 2 y_i/\Theta'(x_i).$$

Hence for the integral of the first kind I_1 the sum

$$S(a, b) = \int_0^{x_1} dx/y + \int_0^{x_2} dx/y + \int_{1/k^2}^{x_3} dx/y$$

* See Barnum, *Abel's theorem and the addition formulae for elliptic integrals*, Annals of Mathematics, 2nd Series, vol. 11 (1910), pp. 103–114.

has the derivatives

$$S_a = \sum_i 2x_i/\Theta'(x_i) = 0, \qquad S_b = \sum_i 2/\Theta'(x_i) = 0,$$

according to Lemma 43·1, and we see that $S(a, b) = C$.

To eliminate the constant C we may substitute in place of x_1, x_2, x_3 a set of the special form 0, x', x_3. Then

$$\int_0^{x'} dx/y + \int_{1/k^2}^{x_3} dx/y = C,$$

and by subtracting this from the equation $S(a, b) = C$ we find

(44·3) $$\int_0^{x_1} dx/y + \int_0^{x_2} dx/y = \int_0^{x'} dx/y.$$

The relation between the coordinates x_1, x_2, x_3 of the intersections P_1, P_2, P_3 of the curve (44·1) with the straight line $y = ax + b$, and the coordinate x' of the intersection point of the line through P_3 and the origin, is shown in the accompanying figure for the case when the curve (44·1) and the line $y = ax + b$ have real graphs.

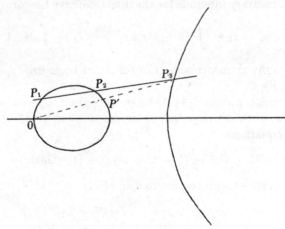

Fig. 44·1

The places $P_1 = (x_1, y_1)$ and $P_2 = (x_2, y_2)$ are supposed to be given in advance. They determine successively $P_3 = (x_3, y_3)$ and $P' = (x', y')$. The coordinates of P_1 and P_2 satisfy the equations

$$y_1^2 = x_1(1 - x_1)(1 - k^2x_1), \qquad y_2^2 = x_2(1 - x_2)(1 - k^2x_2),$$

and determine the coefficients a, b of the straight line joining them by means of the equations

$$y_1 = ax_1 + b, \qquad y_2 = ax_2 + b.$$

It turns out that only the value

$$(44\cdot4) \qquad b = (x_1y_2 - x_2y_1)/(x_1 - x_2) = x_1x_2(1 - k^2x_1x_2)/(x_1y_2 + x_2y_1)$$

is needed. From equation $(44\cdot2)$ we see that $x_3 = b^2/k^2x_1x_2$. For the straight line through the origin and (x_3, y_3) the constant b is zero, and from the coefficient of x in $(44\cdot2)$ it follows that $x'x_3 = 1/k^2$, so that with the help of $(44\cdot4)$

$$(44\cdot5) \qquad x' = x_1x_2/b^2 = [(x_1y_2 + x_2y_1)/(1 - k^2x_1x_2)]^2/x_1x_2.$$

The addition formula for integrals of the first kind is the formula $(44\cdot3)$ *with the value* $(44\cdot5)$ *for* x'.

When the substitution $x = z^2$ is made this addition formula takes the well-known Legendre form

$$\int_0^{z_1} dz/Y + \int_0^{z_2} dz/Y = \int_0^{z'} dz/Y$$

where

$$Y^2 = (1 - z^2)(1 - k^2z^2),$$
$$z' = (z_1Y_2 + z_2Y_1)/(1 - k^2z_1^2z_2^2).$$

The addition formulas for the integrals of the second and third kinds are as follows:

$$\int_0^{x_1} (1 - k^2x)dx/y + \int_0^{x_2} = \int_0^{x'} + 2k^2(x_1x_2x')^{1/2},$$

$$\int_0^{x_1} dx/(1 + nx)y + \int_0^{x_2} = \int_0^{x'} + M,$$

where the integrands not indicated are the same as the preceding ones, x' has the value $(44\cdot5)$, and M has one or the other of the values

$$M = (2/p^{1/2}) \text{ arc tan } \frac{n(px_1x_2)^{1/2}x'}{(1 + nx')x'^{1/2} - ny'(x_1x_2)^{1/2}}$$

$$= [1/(-p)^{1/2}] \log \frac{1 + nx' - bny' + bnx'(-p)^{1/2}}{1 + nx' - bny' - bnx'(-p)^{1/2}},$$

where $b = (x_1x_2/x')^{1/2}$ from $(44\cdot5)$, and $y'^2 = x'(1 - x')(1 - k^2x')$. The two forms for M are given so that when n and k are real only real expressions need occur. The first is to be used when $p = (1+n)(1+k^2/n)$ is positive, and the second when p is negative. If complex quantities are allowed arc tan u is always expressible in terms of a logarithm by means of the formula

$$\text{arc tan } u = (1/2i) \log \left[(i - u)/(i + u) \right].$$

The proof of the addition formula for the integral of the second kind is quite as simple as that for the integral of the first kind. For the integral of the third kind Lemma $43 \cdot 1$ must be applied for the function $h(x)$ $= (1+nx) \Theta(x)$. The integrations in order to find $S(a, b)$ from its derivatives S_a and S_b are more complicated, but are elementary in character.

45. Abel's theorem in more general form. The theorem to be proved in this section is the following one:

THEOREM $45 \cdot 1$. *On the Riemann surface T of an irreducible algebraic equation $f(x, y) = 0$ let*

$$I = \int \eta(x, y) dx$$

be an Abelian integral with periods A_k, B_k across the period cuts a_k, b_k ($k = 1, \cdots, p$). Suppose further that $\xi(x, y)$ is a rational function on T with zeros $P_i = (x_i, y_i)$ and poles $P_i' = (x_i', y_i')$ ($i = 1, \cdots, q$) distinct

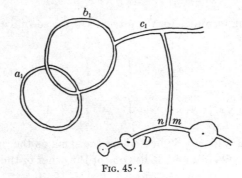

FIG. $45 \cdot 1$

from the singularities of I. Let D be a simply closed curve on T containing all of the singularities of I but no zero or pole of ξ. Then

$$(45 \cdot 1) \qquad \sum_{i=1}^{q} \left[\int_{(x_0, y_0)}^{(x_i, y_i)} \eta dx - \int_{(x_0, y_0)}^{(x_i', y_i')} \eta dx \right]$$

$$= [sum \ of \ residues \ of \ \eta \ \log \xi \ in \ D] + m_k A_k + n_k B_k$$

where x_0, y_0 is an arbitrary place on T and the coefficients m_k and n_k are integers.

To prove the theorem let I' represent the integral

$$I' = \log \xi(x, y) = \log \xi(x_0, y_0) + \int_C (\xi_x f_y - \xi_y f_x)dx/\xi f_y$$

with properties as described in Theorem $40 \cdot 3$. The surface T with the cuts indicated in Figure $45 \cdot 1$ is a surface T'' for the integral I. On its boundary $B' + D$

$$\int_{B'+D} I dI' = \int_{B'+D} I d\xi/\xi$$

(45·2)
$$= 2\pi i[sum\ of\ residues\ of\ (I/\xi)(d\xi/dx)\ on\ T'']$$

$$= 2\pi i \sum_{i=1}^{q} [I(x_i, y_i) - I(x_i', y_i')].$$

But this integral can be calculated in another way also. By an argument like that used in proving Theorem $37 \cdot 1$

(45·3) $$\int_{B'} I dI' = A_k B_k' - B_k A_k' = 2\pi i(m_k A_k + n_k B_k),$$

where the coefficients m_k and n_k are integers, since the periods A_k', B_k' of I' are all integral multiples of $2\pi i$ as stated in Theorem $40 \cdot 3$. Furthermore

(45·4) $$\int_D I dI' = I I' \Big|_m^n - \int_D I' dI,$$

where m and n are the places indicated in Figure $45 \cdot 1$. Since the sum of the residues of η in D is zero, and since D contains no zero or pole of ξ, the values of both I and I' are the same at m and n and the first term on the right side of equation $(45 \cdot 4)$ vanishes. The second has the value

(45·5) $$\int_D I' dI = -2\pi i[sum\ of\ residues\ of\ \eta \log \xi\ in\ D],$$

the negative sign being taken since in $(45 \cdot 2)$ the integral around D is taken in clockwise sense. The formulas $(45 \cdot 2)$ to $(45 \cdot 5)$ justify the statements in the theorem.

It should be remarked that the sum on the left in equation $(45 \cdot 1)$ can be written in the form

$$\sum_{i=1}^{q} \int_{(x_i',y_i')}^{(x_i,y_i)} \eta \, dx$$

for a quite arbitrary pairing of the zeros and poles of $\xi(x, y)$, provided that the paths of the integrals here and in formula $(45 \cdot 1)$ are all on the surface T''. If there is no restriction on the paths the last expression may differ by a period of the integral I from the sum in the first member of $(45 \cdot 1)$. If the path of one of the integrals in the equation $(45 \cdot 1)$ is properly modified the two sides of the equation will be equal for the values $m_k = n_k = 0$.

COROLLARY 1. *If $\xi(x, y)$ is a rational function of parameters a_1, $\cdots$, a_s as well as x, y then the bracket on the right in equation $(45 \cdot 1)$ has the form*

$$(45 \cdot 6) \qquad \rho(a_1, \cdots, a_s) + c_j \log r_j(a_1, \cdots, a_s)$$

where ρ and the function r_j in the sum $c_j \log r_j$ are rational in $a_1, \cdots, a_s$ and the coefficients c_j are constants.

This follows because the expansion of the function $\log \xi(x, y, a)$ at a place P_0 is found by substituting the branch

$$x = x_0 + t^r, \qquad y = bt^\mu + \cdots$$

in ξ and expanding the resulting function $\log \xi(t, a)$ in powers of t in the form

$$\log \xi(t, a) = \log \xi(0, a) + [\xi_t(0, a)/\xi(0, a)](t/1!) + \cdots.$$

The function $\xi(0, a)$ and the coefficients of this expansion are rational in $a_1, \cdots, a_s$ and hence the sum of the residues of the product $\eta \log \xi$ at points in the interior of D has the form described in the corollary.

Theorem $42 \cdot 1$ is a consequence of Theorem $45 \cdot 1$ and Corollary 1 since the poles of a polynomial $g(x, y, a)$ on the Riemann surface T occur only at the poles of the algebraic function $y(x)$ and are therefore fixed. Hence the sum of the integrals to the poles (x_i', y_i') in the formula $(45 \cdot 1)$ is a constant and may be taken into the function ρ of the expression $(45 \cdot 6)$. The proof of Theorem $42 \cdot 1$ thus supplied by the arguments of this section is more satisfactory than that of Section 42, since it lays no restrictions upon the positions of the zeros (x_i, y_i) on T except that they must be distinct from the singularities of the integral I.

COROLLARY 2. *If the integral I has no logarithmic singularity then there are no logarithmic terms in the expression $(45 \cdot 6)$.*

For in this case the product $\eta \, dx/dt$ has no expansion with a term of the form A/t, and consequently the function $\eta \log \xi \, dx/dt$ has no expansion with a term in t^{-1} having a coefficient of the form $\log \xi(0, a)$.

COROLLARY 3. *For an integral w of the first kind, an elementary integral $\zeta_\nu(P)$ of the second kind, and an elementary integral $\pi(P_1, P_2)$ of the third kind, the formula (45·1) of Abel's theorem has respectively the forms*

$$\sum_{i=1}^{q} [w(x_i, y_i) - w(x_i', y_i')] = m_k A_k + n_k B_k,$$

$$\sum_{i=1}^{q} [\zeta_\nu(x_i, y_i; P) - \zeta_\nu(x_i', y_i'; P)] = -(d^{\nu+1} \log \xi/dt^{\nu+1})_P + m_k A_k + n_k B_k,$$

$$\sum_{i=1}^{q} [\pi(x_i, y_i; P_1, P_2) - \pi(x_i', y_i'; P_1, P_2)]$$

$$= \log [\xi(P_1)/\xi(P_2)] + m_k A_k + n_k B_k.$$

The first of these formulas is evident since the product $\psi \log \xi \, dx/dt$, where ψ is the integrand of w, has no expansions with negative powers of t at places distinct from the zeros and poles of ξ. The first formula of the corollary is also formula (40·10).

For the integrand $\eta(x, y; P)$ of $\zeta_\nu(P)$ the only residue of $\eta \log \xi \, dx/dt$, except at the zeros and poles of ξ, is at the place P, where

$$\eta dx/dt = -(\nu + 1)! t^{-\nu-2} + c_0 + c_1 t + \cdots ,$$

$$\log \xi = \log \xi(P) + (d \log \xi/dt)_P(t/1!) + \cdots ,$$

and the residue is therefore as indicated in the second formula of the corollary.

The required residues of $\eta \log \xi$ for the integrand $\eta(x, y; P_1, P_2)$ of $\pi(P_1, P_2)$ occur at the places P_1 and P_2, where

$$\eta dx/dt = \quad t^{-1} + c_0 + c_1 t + \cdots , \quad \log \xi = \log \xi(P_1) + \cdots ,$$

$$\eta dx/dt = -t^{-1} + d_0 + d_1 t + \cdots , \quad \log \xi = \log \xi(P_2) + \cdots .$$

The sum of the residues of $\eta \log \xi \, dx/dt$ at P_1 and P_2 is therefore in this case $\log [\xi(P_1)/\xi(P_2)]$.

46. **An expression for $p+1$ integrals in terms of p integrals.** For the theorem to be proved in this section the following lemma is important.

LEMMA 46·1. *If $p+1$ places P_k ($k=1, \cdots, p+1$) are selected arbitrarily on the Riemann surface T the matrix $\|\psi_i(P_k)\|$ of values of the integrands $\psi_i(i=1, \cdots, p)$ of a set of linearly independent integrals of* *the first kind will in general have every one of its determinants of order p different from zero.*

It has been shown in Lemma 26·1 that the determinant $|\psi_i(P_j)|$ for p places $P_j (j = 1, \cdots, p)$ will be different from zero unless the p places are special. To adjoin a place P_{p+1} with the properties described in the lemma let $c_{i1}, \cdots, c_{ip}$ be solutions of the linear equations whose coefficients are the rows of $|\psi_i(P_j)|$ except the i-th. If P_{p+1} is not a solution of any of the equations

$$c_{i1}\psi_1(P) + \cdots + c_{ip}\psi_p(P) = 0 \qquad (i = 1, \cdots, p)$$

then the matrix $||\psi_i(P_k)||$ will have the properties described in the lemma.

THEOREM 46·1. *If a set of places $P_k = (x_k, y_k)$ $(k = 1, \cdots, p+1)$ is such that the matrix $||\psi_i(P_k)||$ $(i = 1, \cdots, p; k = 1, \cdots, p+1)$ has all of its determinants of order p different from zero, then there is a rational function $\xi(x, y)$, uniquely determined except for a constant factor, which has simple poles at each of the places P_k. If the set of places (x_i', y_i') $(i = 1, \cdots, p)$ are the zeros of the function $\xi(x, y) - \xi(x_0, y_0)$ other than (x_0, y_0), then for an arbitrary Abelian integral*

$$I = \int \eta(x, y) dx$$

the equation

$$(46·1) \quad \sum_{k=1}^{p+1} \int_{(x_0, y_0)}^{(x_k, y_k)} \eta dx = \sum_{i=1}^{p} \int_{(x_0, y_0)}^{(x_i', y_i')} \eta dx + \rho$$
$$+ c_l \log r_l + m_i A_i + n_i B_i$$

holds, where ρ and the functions r_l are rational in the coordinates (x_k, y_k), the coefficients c_l are constants, and the coefficients m_i, n_i are integers.

Since the places $P_k (k = 1, \cdots, p+1)$ are non-special we know by Theorem 26·2 that there are exactly $\mu = 2$ linearly independent multiples of $1/P_1 \cdots P_{p+1}$, and there will be one of these $\xi(x, y)$ which is not a constant. If we set up a basis for the divisor $Q = 1$ and then transform it into a basis for $1/P_1 \cdots P_{p+1}$ normal at $x = \infty$ by the processes described in the proofs of Theorems 20·2 and 21·2 we see that the resulting functions will be rational in the coordinates (x_k, y_k) of the places P_k. Hence $\xi(x, y)$ will also have this property, since it is a linear combination of products of functions of the basis by powers of x, as described in the proof of Theorem 21·3. The function $\xi(x, y)$ must have a pole at each point P_k since otherwise ξ would be a rational function not constant with poles among the points of a non-special subset of $r \leqq p$ of the points P_k, which is impossible by the corollary to Theorem 26·2.

Equation (46·1) of the last theorem is equation (45·1) of Abel's theorem applied to the integral I and the function $\xi(x, y) - \xi(x_0, y_0)$. The residues of the product $\eta \log (\xi - \xi_0)$ are rational in the coordinates (x_k, y_k) of the places P_k, since $\xi(x, y)$ has this property, and the sum of these residues has the form $\rho + c_l \log r_l$ as indicated in Corollary 1 of Theorem 45·1.

The formula (46·1) is an expression for the values of I at $p+1$ places P_k in terms of its values at the p places P_i'.

47. **Proof of a lemma.** In the proof of the first form of Abel's theorem in Section 42 use was made of the following lemma which was not proved.

LEMMA 47·1. *If a function $S(x_1, \cdots, x_n)$ has a differential of the form*

$$dS = R_i(x_1, \cdots, x_n)dx_i \qquad (i = 1, \cdots, n)$$

where each R_i is rational in $x_1, \cdots, x_n$, then S is itself expressible in the form

$$S = \rho(x_1, \cdots, x_n) + c_k \log r_k(x_1, \cdots, x_n),$$

where ρ and r_k are rational in $x_1, \cdots, x_n$, the sum $c_k \log r_k$ contains a finite number of terms, and the coefficients c_k are constants.

We know that the lemma is true for $n=1$. Suppose it is true for $n-1$ and let us prove it for n. We have

$$\partial S/\partial x_1 = R_1(x_1, \cdots, x_n)$$

where R_1 is expressible by the theory of partial fractions in the form

$$(47·1) \qquad R_1 = P(x_1, x_2, \cdots, x_n) + \sum N/D^\mu.$$

In this expression P is a polynomial in x_1 with coefficients rational in $x_2, \cdots, x_n$; D is one of the irreducible polynomial factors in the denominator of R_1; N is a polynomial in x_1 of degree lower than the degree of D in x_1 with coefficients rational in $x_2, \cdots, x_n$; and the sum is taken for all the factors D and exponents μ less than or equal to that with which D occurs in the denominator of R_1.* We may denote the roots of D as a polynomial in x_1 by $\alpha, \alpha', \alpha'', \cdots$. We consider them near a set of values of $x_2, \cdots, x_n$ for which they are distinct. Then

---

* See, for example, Goursat-Hedrick, A course in Mathematical Analysis, vol. I, p. 211.

$$(47 \cdot 2) \quad N/D^{\mu} = \sum_{\alpha} [a_1/(x_1 - \alpha) + a_2/(x_1 - \alpha)^2 + \cdots + a_{\mu}/(x_1 - \alpha)^{\mu}]$$

where $a_1, \cdots, a_n$ are rational in $\alpha, x_2, \cdots, x_n$. The sum is taken for all the roots $\alpha, \alpha', \cdots$ of D, and the coefficients a_k for the different roots are found by permuting the roots $\alpha, \alpha', \cdots$ in the expressions giving them for α. It follows by an integration of $(47 \cdot 1)$ with respect to x_1 that

$$S = (rational \ function \ of \ x_1, \cdots, x_n) + \sum_{\alpha} a_1 \log (x_1 - \alpha)$$
$$+ C(x_2, \cdots, x_n)$$

since the integral of the sum of the terms after the first in $(47 \cdot 2)$ is symmetric in the roots α and therefore rational in $x_2, \cdots, x_n$ as well as x_1. The coefficients a_1 are constants since they are functions of x_2, $\cdots, x_n$ explicitly and in the roots α, and since the last equation when differentiated with respect to one of these variables, say x_i, gives for

$$\sum_{\alpha} (\partial a_1/\partial x_i) \log (x_1 - \alpha)$$

a rational function of x_1. This is impossible unless $\partial a_1/\partial x_i = 0$. The constants a_1 are all equal for the different roots α, since a rational equation $a_1(\alpha, x_2, \cdots, x_n) = c$, when satisfied by one of the roots α of an irreducible polynomial D, will necessarily have a factor in common with D and therefore have D itself as a factor. The equation will therefore be satisfied by all the roots of D. Hence we see that

$$\sum_{\alpha} a_1 \log (x_1 - \alpha) = c \log D,$$

where c is the common value of the coefficients a_1. But from the equations $\partial S/\partial x_i = R_i (i = 2, \cdots, n)$ we now know that C is expressible in terms of $x_2, \cdots, x_n$ in the form described in the theorem, which completes the proof.

REFERENCES FOR CHAPTER VI

References for the various sections of Chapter VI above, in the list at the end of this book, are the following: 1, Memoire XII; 13, Chapter X; 18, Chapter IX; 20, Abschnitt III; 21, Chapter VIII; 24, Chapter XVIII; 27, Chapter XXI; 28, Vorlesung XXXVII; 39, Chapter IX; 47, Chapters V, VI.

Chapter VII

BIRATIONAL TRANSFORMATIONS

48. Introduction. Two algebraic curves $f(x, y) = 0$ and $\phi(\xi, \eta) = 0$, defined by irreducible polynomials f and ϕ, are said to be equivalent by a birational transformation provided that there is a one-to-one correspondence between their branches and that this correspondence is defined by equations of the form

$$(48 \cdot 1) \qquad \xi = \xi(x, y), \qquad \eta = \eta(x, y),$$

with inverses of the form

$$(48 \cdot 2) \qquad x = x(\xi, \eta), \qquad y = y(\xi, \eta),$$

where the four functions on the right are rational in their arguments. This is equivalent to saying that there is a one-to-one correspondence between the places on the Riemann surfaces of the two curves, defined by equations of the form $(48 \cdot 1)$ and $(48 \cdot 2)$.

A Cremona transformation is a transformation of the complex xy-plane into the complex $\xi\eta$-plane which is one-to-one except possibly for certain exceptional loci in the two planes and which is also defined by equations of the form $(48 \cdot 1)$ and $(48 \cdot 2)$. A simple example of such a transformation is afforded by the equations $\xi = x$, $\eta = x/y$ and their inverses $x = \xi$, $y = \xi/\eta$. The correspondence in this special case is one-to-one between the portions of the planes which are not on the coordinate axes. It is evident that a Cremona transformation will in general take an algebraic curve in the xy-plane into one birationally equivalent to it in the $\xi\eta$-plane. But not every birational transformation of one curve into another is a Cremona transformation of one plane into another, as can readily be shown in special cases. The curves

$$y^2 - x(x - 1) = 0, \qquad \eta - \xi = 0,$$

for example, are equivalent under the transformation $\xi = y/x$, $\eta = y/x$ and its inverse $x = 1/(1 - \xi^2)$, $y = \xi/(1 - \xi^2)$, but this is not a Cremona transformation of the xy-plane into the $\xi\eta$-plane.

In Section 49 below the structure and first properties of birational transformations are discussed. In Section 50 it is shown how birational transformations may be used to reduce algebraic curves of special types to normal forms. Thus every irreducible algebraic curve $f(x, y) = 0$ of genus $p = 0$ can be transformed birationally into the straight line $\eta - \xi = 0$. Such curves are called unicursal curves. Similarly every curve with genus $p = 1$ can be transformed into the curve

$$\eta^2 = (1 - \xi^2)(1 - k^2\xi^2)$$

usually associated with the theory of elliptic integrals. Normal forms are also deduced for curves of genus $p = 2$ and the so-called hyper-elliptic curves.

Projective transformations are among the most important of the Cremona transformations. Simplifications which can be effected by projective transformations are discussed in Section 51, and the next three sections are devoted to the application of these results to the determination of a second formula for the genus, the number of projective intersections of two curves, and a further formula for the integrands of integrals of the first kind.

49. Birational transformations. In this section a number of theorems applicable to the study of birational transformations will be deduced, the first of which is the following one:

THEOREM 49·1. *On the Riemann surface T of an irreducible algebraic equation $f(x, y) = 0$ the values of a pair of rational functions $\xi(x, y)$, $\eta(x, y)$, for which ξ is not constant, satisfy an irreducible algebraic equation $\phi(\xi, \eta) = 0$ in which the polynomial ϕ is unique except for a constant factor and has a degree in η which is a divisor of the sum ν of the orders of the zeros of $\xi(x, y)$ on T.*

To prove this one may first show that every cycle of the algebraic equation $f(x, y) = 0$ defines a similar cycle for the variables ξ, η. At a cycle of $f(x, y) = 0$ at which $\xi(x, y)$ has a finite value α, for example, we have expansions for ξ and η of the form

$$(49\cdot1) \qquad \xi = \alpha + \gamma t^\rho + \cdots, \qquad \eta = \delta t^\sigma + \cdots \qquad (\gamma \neq 0, \rho \geqq 1).$$

The first of these equations has a solution

$$(49\cdot2) \qquad t = \gamma^{-1/\rho}(\xi - \alpha)^{1/\rho} + \cdots,$$

and when this expression for t is substituted in the second a cycle for ξ, η is found with the equations

$$(49\cdot3) \qquad \xi = \alpha + \tau^\rho, \qquad \eta = \beta\tau^\sigma + \cdots.$$

For a cycle of $f(x, y) = 0$ at which ξ has a pole instead of a finite value α the result is similar, except that the first equation (49·3) is replaced by $\xi = 1/\tau^\rho$.

For a given constant α the sum of the orders of the zeros of the difference $\xi(x, y) - \alpha$ on T is ν, since the sum of the orders of the poles of $\xi(x, y)$ is $-\nu$. Hence for the expansions (49·1) having the same constant α the sum of the exponents ρ is ν. For every value ξ near α the corresponding expansions (49·3) define ν values $\eta_1, \cdots, \eta_\nu$, and the pairs (ξ, η_i) $(i = 1, \cdots, \nu)$ so determined are the totality of pairs of values of the functions $\xi(x, y)$, $\eta(x, y)$ on T having this value of ξ. A nonsingular value $\xi = \alpha$ or $\xi = \infty$ is by definition one for which the exponents ρ in (49·3) are all unity and the exponents σ not negative. With the help of Theorem 23·1 we see that the number of singular values of ξ is finite, since by that theorem the sum w_ξ of the values $\rho - 1$ for the branch places of ξ is finite.

The expansions (49·3) satisfy an algebraic equation $\psi(\xi, \eta) = 0$. For if $\eta_1, \cdots, \eta_\nu$ are the values of η on T corresponding to a non-singular value ξ the product

$$(49·4) \qquad\qquad (\eta - \eta_1) \cdots (\eta - \eta_\nu)$$

is a polynomial in η with coefficients which are symmetric in $\eta_1, \cdots, \eta_\nu$ and uniquely determined by the value ξ. With the help of the expansions (49·3) one readily sees that these coefficients are holomorphic at nonsingular values $\xi = \alpha$, and that at other values they have at most poles, by Theorem 5·2. Hence they are rational functions of ξ. If the polynomial (49·4) is multiplied by the lowest common denominator of the coefficients of its powers of η, a polynomial $\psi(\xi, \eta)$ is found which vanishes for all pairs of values of the functions $\xi(x, y)$, $\eta(x, y)$ on the surface T, and hence for all of the expansions (49·3).

Each irreducible factor $\phi(\xi, \eta)$ of $\psi(\xi, \eta)$ vanishes for an infinity of values of $\xi(x, y)$, $\eta(x, y)$ at pairs of values (x, y) satisfying the equation $f(x, y) = 0$. Hence the rational function $\phi[\xi(x, y), \eta(x, y)]$ has roots y in common with $f(x, y)$ for an infinity of distinct values x, and we see with the help of the corollary to Lemma 9·1 that its numerator must be divisible by $f(x, y)$. Thus all of the pairs of values ξ, η on T satisfy the equation $\phi = 0$. Since the same is true of every other irreducible factor of ψ it is evident, by the corollary to Lemma 9·1 again, that these factors can differ by constant multipliers only. The polynomial ψ is therefore expressible as a power of an irreducible polynomial ϕ and the degree of ϕ in η must then be a divisor of ν. The same argument which shows that the irreducible factors of ψ are identical except for constant multipliers shows also that the polynomial ϕ of the theorem is unique except for a constant factor.

COROLLARY 1. *A necessary and sufficient condition for the curves* $f(x, y) = 0$ *and* $\phi(\xi, \eta) = 0$ *to be birationally equivalent is that the degree of* ϕ *in* η *be exactly equal to the sum* ν *of the orders of the zeros of* $\xi(x, y)$, *or that there exists a value* $\xi = \alpha$ *for which the* ν *corresponding values of* $\eta(x, y)$ *on* T *are all distinct. If the curves* $f = 0$ *and* $\phi = 0$ *are not birationally equivalent then the genus of* $\phi = 0$ *is less than that of* $f = 0$.

If the degree of ϕ in η is less than ν then the polynomial ψ constructed above is a power higher than the first of ϕ, and for every value ξ some of the corresponding values $\eta_1, \cdots, \eta_\nu$ will be equal. To a place (ξ, η) on the Riemann surface of $\phi = 0$ there correspond therefore more than one place (x, y), and x and y cannot be expressible as rational functions of ξ and η. Thus the relation between the curves $f = 0$ and $\phi = 0$ is not bi-rational.

On the other hand, if the degree of ϕ in η is ν, so that ϕ and ψ coincide except possibly for a constant factor, then for all except a finite number of values of ξ the corresponding roots $\eta_1, \cdots, \eta_\nu$ of $\phi = 0$ will be distinct. Each branch $(49 \cdot 3)$ must provide precisely ρ distinct values of η for values of ξ near to α, and must be primitive, by Theorem $13 \cdot 1$. The totality of branches $(49 \cdot 3)$, obtained as described from the cycles of the equation $f(x, y) = 0$, is therefore the totality of non-equivalent primitive branches of the curve $\phi(\xi, \eta) = 0$. We have thus a one-to-one correspondence between the cycles of $\phi = 0$ and those of $f = 0$ defined by the equations

$$(49 \cdot 5) \qquad \xi = \xi(x, y), \qquad \eta = \eta(x, y).$$

The vertices of corresponding cycles are also transformed into each other by these equations when their coordinates are finite. To each place (ξ, η) near the vertex of a cycle $(49 \cdot 3)$ the corresponding solution (x, y) of equations $(49 \cdot 5)$ is found by substituting the series

$$(49 \cdot 6) \qquad t = \gamma^{-1/\rho} \tau + \cdots ,$$

from $(49 \cdot 2)$, in the expansions for x and y at the cycle of $f = 0$ from which $(49 \cdot 3)$ was deduced. Hence x and y are holomorphic functions except for poles on the Riemann surface of the equation $\phi = 0$ and are rationally expressible in terms of ξ and η, so that the relation between $f = 0$ and $\phi = 0$ is birational.

If $f = 0$ and $\phi = 0$ are not birationally equivalent then the polynomial

ψ used in the proof of Theorem 49·1 is a power of its irreducible factor ϕ. If $\psi = \phi^k$ then the set of values $\eta_1, \cdots, \eta_\nu$ corresponding to a given value of ξ is composed of ν_1 groups of k equal values, where ν_1 is the degree of ϕ in η. The cycles

$$\eta = \beta(\xi - \alpha)^{\sigma/\rho} + \cdots$$

from (49·3) may not all be primitive, but each will provide a primitive cycle when the exponents of $(\xi - \alpha)$ are reduced to a suitable common denominator ρ_1 which is a factor of ρ. The sum of the exponents ρ corresponding to a given value $\xi = \alpha$ is k times the sum of the exponents ρ_1. The values of the genus p for the curves $f = 0$ and $\phi = 0$ are now

$$p = \sum(\rho - 1)/2 - \nu + 1 = k(\sum\rho_1/2 - \nu_1) - N/2 + 1,$$
$$p_1 = \sum(\rho_1 - 1)/2 - \nu_1 + 1 = \sum\rho_1/2 - \nu_1 - N/2 + 1,$$

where N is the number of cycles with exponents $\rho > 1$. The sum in the formula for p_1 should be taken for all cycles arising from cycles (49·3) with $\rho > 1$, even though for some of them $\rho_1 = 1$. It is evident then that $p > p_1$ when $k > 1$.

COROLLARY 2. *When two irreducible algebraic curves $f(x, y) = 0$ and $\phi(\xi, \eta) = 0$ are equivalent by a birational transformation the parameters t and τ of corresponding places on two corresponding branches are related by an equation of the form*

(49·7) $$t = c_1\tau + c_2\tau^2 + \cdots \qquad (c_1 \neq 0).$$

The equation of the corollary is equation (49·6) in slightly different notation.

COROLLARY 3. *If two irreducible algebraic curves $f(x, y) = 0$ and $\phi(\xi, \eta) = 0$ are equivalent under a birational transformation then the transformation takes every rational function $g(x, y)$ on the Riemann surface T of $f = 0$ into a rational function $\gamma(\xi, \eta)$ on the Riemann surface T_1 of $\phi = 0$. At corresponding places on T and T_1 the orders of $g(x, y)$ and $\gamma(\xi, \eta)$ are the same. The genus of $f = 0$ is equal to the genus of $\phi = 0$.*

If the equations relating x, y and ξ, η are

$$\xi = \xi(x, y), \qquad \eta = \eta(x, y)$$

then

$$g(x, y) = \gamma[\xi(x, y), \ \eta(x, y)].$$

The expansion for $g(x, y)$ in powers of t at a place P of T goes over into the corresponding expansion for $\gamma(\xi, \eta)$ in powers of τ by means of the transformation (49·7). Hence the orders of g and γ at corresponding places are the same. The genus of the curve $f=0$, from Section 23, is

$$p = w_\xi/2 - n_\xi + 1$$

where w_ξ is the sum of the numbers $\rho-1$ for the expansions (49·3) for $\xi(x, y)$, and n_ξ is the negative of the sum of the orders of the poles of ξ. Since these numbers for ξ have the same values when calculated on the Riemann surface T_1 of $\phi=0$ as when calculated on T it follows that the genus of T_1 is also p.

We could also see that the genus of T is the same as that of T_1 by drawing on T_1 the images of the cuts a_k, b_k on T. A cut which does not sever T has an image on T_1 which does not sever T_1, and conversely. It is evident then that the number of cuts necessary to reduce T_1 to a simply connected surface T_1' is the same as that required to transform T into T'.

COROLLARY 4. *Every Abelian integral on the surface T is transformed into an Abelian integral of the same kind on the surface T_1 and the new integral has the same periods as the original one.*

By a birational transformation

(49·8) $x = x(\xi, \eta), \qquad y = y(\xi, \eta)$

an Abelian integral I on the Riemann surface T is transformed into one on T_1 by the formula

(49·9) $$I = \int_C R(x, y)dx = \int_{C_1} R_1(\xi, \eta)d\xi,$$

where C_1 is the path on T_1 corresponding to C on T and

$$R_1(\xi, \eta) = R[x(\xi, \eta), y(\xi, \eta)](x_\xi + x_\eta d\eta/d\xi)$$
$$= R[x(\xi, \eta), y(\xi, \eta)](x_\xi\phi_\eta - x_\eta\phi_\xi)/\phi_\eta.$$

The last form is valid since along every path C_1 on T_1 the values of ξ and η satisfy the equation $\phi=0$ and their differentials along the path satisfy $\phi_\xi d\xi + \phi_\eta d\eta = 0$. The expansion for the former of the integrals (49·9) in powers of t at a place P on T is transformed into the expansion in powers of τ for the latter at the corresponding place P_1 of T_1 by the formula (49·7), since this formula relates places (x, y) and (ξ, η) satisfying equations (49·8) on the cycles with vertices at P and P_1, and since the function R_1 was so defined that for paths or cycles which satisfy (49.8) we have always $Rdx = R_1d\xi$. Hence we see that the singularities of the two integrals at corresponding places have the same character, and the orders of the principal parts are the same. The periods of the two integrals are the same since the period cuts on T_1 can be taken as the images of the cuts on T.

As a consequence of the equivalence of the expansions of an integral at corresponding places on T and T_1 by means of equation (49·7), one verifies readily that an elementary integral of the first kind is transformed by a birational transformation into one of the same kind; an elementary integral $\zeta_0(P)$ with a single simple pole is transformed into a new integral of the same kind except for a constant factor; an elementary integral $\zeta_\nu(P)$ goes into an integral with a single pole of order $\nu+1$ but with a principal part for its expansion at the pole which is possibly different from that of $\zeta_\nu(P)$; and an elementary integral of the third kind is transformed into a similar integral except for a constant factor.

50. Curves of genus $p=0$ or $p=1$, and hyperelliptic curves. A *unicursal curve* is by definition one which is representable in the parametric form

$$(50·1) \qquad\qquad x = R_1(\zeta), \qquad y = R_2(\zeta),$$

where R_1 and R_2 are rational functions of a parameter ζ such that each point (x, y) on the curve is determined by one and but one value of ζ. By means of the theory of birational transformations developed in the last section it can be shown that every algebraic curve of genus $p=0$ is representable as a unicursal curve and is birationally equivalent to the straight line $\eta - \xi = 0$. Curves of genus $p=1$ may be called *elliptic curves* since they are always transformable birationally into the simple curves usually associated with the theory of elliptic integrals. *Hyperelliptic curves* are related curves of genus $p>1$, and curves of genus $p=2$ are always of hyperelliptic type. These are the results which are established in the theorems of this section.

THEOREM 50·1. *Every irreducible algebraic curve $f(x, y) = 0$ of genus $p = 0$ is representable as a unicursal curve, and conversely.*

We have seen in Theorem 26·4 that when an irreducible algebraic curve $f(x, y) = 0$ has genus $p = 0$ there always exists a rational function $\zeta(x, y)$ with a single simple pole. According to Theorem 49·1 the rational functions

$$(50·2) \qquad\qquad \xi = \zeta(x, y), \qquad \eta = \zeta(x, y)$$

on the Riemann surface of the curve $f(x, y) = 0$ satisfy an irreducible algebraic equation, and we see by inspection that this equation is

$\phi = \eta - \xi = 0$. Since the degree of ϕ in η is the sum of the orders of the zeros of $\zeta(x, y)$, which is unity, it follows by Corollary 1 of the last section that the curves $f = 0$ and $\eta - \xi = 0$ are birationally related by the equations (50·2). Hence the coordinates x and y of places on the curve $f = 0$ are expressible rationally in terms of ζ, in the form (50·1). To each place on $f = 0$ there corresponds one and but one place on the line $\eta - \xi = 0$, and therefore one and but one value ζ, so that the representation (50·1) is unicursal according to the definition given above.

When a unicursal curve is given the functions (50·1) defining it may be regarded as a pair of rational functions of the coordinates of the place $(\xi, \eta) = (\zeta, \zeta)$ on the straight line $\phi = \eta - \xi = 0$. According to Theorem 49·1 these functions will satisfy an irreducible algebraic equation $f(x, y) = 0$. The correspondence between $\phi = 0$ and $f = 0$ defined by the equations (50·1) is birational, by Corollary 1 of Theorem 49·1, because for every value x at which the ν roots of the first equation (50·1) are distinct the second of these equations defines ν distinct values of y since the curve (50·1) is now by hypothesis unicursal. We can see in a number of ways that there are such non-singular values x, for example by the remarks at the end of the second paragraph of the proof of Theorem 49·1. Since the straight line $\eta - \xi = 0$ has genus $p = 0$ it follows that the birationally equivalent curve $f = 0$ has the same property, according to Corollary 3 of Theorem 49·1, and Theorem 50·1 is therefore proved completely.

COROLLARY 1. *A necessary and sufficient condition that an irreducible algebraic curve $f(x, y) = 0$ shall have genus $p = 0$ is that it be birationally equivalent to the straight line $\eta - \xi = 0$.*

This is evident from the arguments in the preceding paragraphs.

COROLLARY 2. *A necessary and sufficient condition that the equations*

$$(50·3) \qquad x = N_1(\zeta)/D_1(\zeta), \qquad y = N_2(\zeta)/D_2(\zeta),$$

shall define a unicursal curve, where N_1 and D_1 are polynomials without common factor, and similarly for N_2 and D_2, is that the resultant with respect to ζ of the two polynomials

$$(50·4) \qquad N_1(\zeta) - xD_1(\zeta), \qquad N_2(\zeta) - yD_2(\zeta)$$

is an irreducible polynomial $f(x, y)$.

The resultant of the polynomials (50·4), formed as indicated in Section 8, is a polynomial $f(x, y)$ in x and y. It has no factor in x alone, since otherwise there would be a value x for which the two polynomials (50·4) would have a common root ζ for every value of y. This is clearly impossible, because for a fixed value of x the first polynomial (50·4) has only a finite number of roots, and we can always select y so that none of them is a root of the second. Since the resultant has no factor involving x alone, and with the help of formula (8·4), it follows that except for a constant factor the resultant $f(x, y)$ is the product

$$\Pi\left[y - N_2(\zeta_i)/D_2(\zeta_i)\right]$$

taken for all the roots of the first polynomial (50·4) and multiplied by the lowest common denominator of the coefficients of its powers of y when expressed in terms of x. This is, however, precisely the polynomial in x and y, analogous to ψ in the proof of Theorem 49·1, which is satisfied identically by the functions (50·3) when we think of them as rational functions of the places $(\xi, \eta) = (\zeta, \zeta)$ on the line $\eta - \xi = 0$. From Corollary 1 of Theorem 49·1 it follows that the line $\eta - \xi = 0$ and the curve $f(x, y) = 0$ are birationally related by the equations (50·3) if and only if $f(x, y)$ is irreducible. From the second paragraph of the proof of Theorem 50·1 it follows further that the curve (50·3) is unicursal if and only if the curves $f(x, y) = 0$ and $\eta - \xi = 0$ are birationally related, and therefore if and only if $f(x, y)$ is irreducible. The corollary is therefore proved.

COROLLARY 3. *For every unicursal representation* (50·1) *of an irreducible algebraic curve* $f(x, y) = 0$ *of genus* $p = 0$ *the value of the parameter* ζ *corresponding to a place* (x, y) *on* $f = 0$ *is expressible as the value of a rational function* $\zeta(x, y)$ *with a single simple pole. The most general representation* (50·1) *is found from a particular one by a bilinear transformation* $\zeta = (a\zeta_1 + b)/(c\zeta_1 + d)$.

It has been shown in the proof of Theorem 50·1 that the equations (50·1) of a unicursal curve relate birationally the line $\eta - \xi = 0$ and the curve $f = 0$. Hence the coordinates $\xi = \eta = \zeta$ of a place on the line are determined by a rational function $\zeta(x, y)$. This function can have but a single pole, since otherwise there would be more than one place (x, y) corresponding to each value $\zeta = \alpha$.

For two unicursal representations of the curve $f = 0$ in terms of parameters ζ and ζ_1 the corresponding functions $\zeta(x, y)$ and $\zeta_1(x, y)$ satisfy an irreducible equation $\phi(\zeta, \zeta_1) = 0$ which is linear in each of them, by Theorem 49·1, since each of them has but a simple pole. Hence ζ and ζ_1 are bilinearly related, as stated in the corollary.

THEOREM 50·2. *Every irreducible algebraic curve* $f(x, y) = 0$ *of genus* $p = 1$ *can be transformed birationally into a curve of the form*

(50·5) $$\eta^2 - (1 - \xi^2)(1 - k^2\xi^2) = 0$$

where k is a constant.

To prove this we note first that if two places P_1, P_2 on the Riemann surface T of $f=0$ are selected arbitrarily there is always a rational function $\xi(x, y)$ which has a simple pole at each of them and no other singularities. For according to the third row of the table of Theorem 26·2 there are $\mu = 2$ linearly independent functions with no poles except at P_1 and P_2. One of these functions is not a constant, and must have poles at both P_1 and P_2 since if it had a pole at only one of them the genus of $f=0$ would be $p=0$, by Theorem 26·4. If we select for P_1 and P_2 ordinary places at which the values of y are distinct then the functions $\xi(x, y)$, $\eta(x, y) = y$ will satisfy an irreducible equation $\phi(\xi, \eta) = 0$ of degree 2 in η. For according to Theorem 49·1 the degree of ϕ in η is a divisor of the sum of the orders of the zeros of ξ, and it must be exactly 2, by Corollary 1 of Theorem 49·1, since at two places on T where ξ takes a value near $\xi = \infty$ the corresponding values of $\eta = y$ are near to those belonging to P_1 and P_2 and are therefore distinct. The curves $f=0$ and $\phi=0$ are consequently birationally equivalent by a transformation of the form

$$(50·6) \qquad\qquad \xi = \xi(x, y), \qquad \eta = y.$$

Since the equation $\phi=0$ satisfied by the functions (50·6) is of the second degree in y it has a solution which can be given the form

$$(50·7) \qquad\qquad \eta = P(\xi) + Q(\xi)[R(\xi)]^{1/2},$$

where P and Q are rational in ξ and R is a polynomial in ξ having no squared factors. Consequently the birational transformation

$$(50·8) \qquad\qquad \xi = \xi_1, \qquad \eta = P(\xi) + Q(\xi)\eta_1$$

following the transformation (50·6) takes the curve $f=0$ into the curve

$$(50·9) \qquad\qquad \eta_1^2 - R(\xi_1) = 0.$$

The genus of the last equation must be $p=1$, since it is birationally equivalent to $f=0$. By examination of its two-sheeted Riemann surface, which has no cycles except at $\xi_1 = \infty$ or at the roots of $R(\xi_1)$, it is found that the genus can be unity only if the degree of $R(\xi_1)$ is 3 or 4. If we determine a constant k so that an anharmonic ratio of the numbers ± 1, $\pm 1/k$ is equal to one of the anharmonic ratios of the four roots of $R(\xi_1)$, or of its three roots and $\xi_1 = \infty$, then a bilinear transformation $\xi_1 = (a\xi_2+b)/(c\xi_2+d)$ can be determined which will take the four roots, or the three roots and $\xi_1 = \infty$, into ± 1, $\pm 1/k$ in suitable order. A simple transformation of the form

$$\xi_1 = (a\xi_2 + b)/(c\xi_2 + d), \qquad \eta_1 = e\eta_2/(c\xi_2 + d)^2$$

will then take $(50 \cdot 9)$ into a curve of the form $(50 \cdot 5)$.

THEOREM $50 \cdot 3$. *If on the Riemann surface T of an irreducible algebraic equation $f(x, y) = 0$ of genus p there exists a rational function $\xi(x, y)$ with the sum of the orders of its poles equal to 2, then the curve $f = 0$ is transformable birationally into a curve of the form*

$$(50 \cdot 10) \qquad\qquad \eta^2 - R(\xi) = 0$$

where $R(\xi)$ is a polynomial in ξ with no multiple roots and of degree $2p+1$ or $2p+2$. A curve $f(x, y)$ with this property is called an elliptic curve if $p = 1$, or a hyperelliptic curve if $p > 1$.

The proof is similar to that of the preceding theorem provided that we can prove, as in the next paragraph, that there exists a rational function $\eta(x, y)$ on T which for some constant value α takes distinct values at the two places on T where $\xi(x, y) - \alpha = 0$. For then, by Corollary 1 of Theorem $49 \cdot 1$, the irreducible equation $\phi(\xi, \eta) = 0$ satisfied by ξ and η must be of degree 2 in η and therefore birationally equivalent to $f = 0$. It has a solution of the form $(50 \cdot 7)$ which goes into a curve of the form $(50 \cdot 9)$ by a transformation $(50 \cdot 8)$. The genus of the curve $(50 \cdot 9)$ must now be p, which can be true only if $R(\xi_1)$ is of degree $2p+1$ or $2p+2$.

To show the existence of a function η which has two distinct values at two places where ξ has the same value α, we may first select α distinct from the branch values of ξ, so that the two places P, P' on T where $\xi(x, y) - \alpha = 0$ are distinct. If we select $q > 2p+2$ other places $P_1, \cdots,$ P_q then according to Theorem $26 \cdot 2$ and the corollary to Lemma $26 \cdot 2$ the $\mu = q - p + 1$ linearly independent multiples $\sigma_1, \cdots, \sigma_\mu$ of the divisor $1/P_1 \cdots P_q$ will have a matrix of leading coefficients at P and P' of rank 2. Hence in the linear combination

$$\eta = u_1\sigma_1 + \cdots + u_\mu\sigma_\mu$$

the constant coefficients u can be chosen so that the values of η at P and P' are distinct.

THEOREM $50 \cdot 4$. *On the Riemann surface of every irreducible algebraic curve $f(x, y) = 0$ of genus $p = 2$ there is a rational function with the sum of the orders of its poles equal to 2. According to the last theorem every such curve is therefore transformable birationally into a curve of the form $(50 \cdot 10)$ for which the polynomial $R(\xi)$ has degree 5 or 6.*

When $p = 2$ an integrand function $\psi(x, y)$ of an integral of the first kind has a divisor of the form $Q_\psi = P_1 P_2 D^2 / X$, since every such function ψ must be a multiple of the divisor D^2/X which has the order $2 - 2p = -2$, and since Q_ψ has order zero. Furthermore if ψ is one such function, then according to Theorem 26·1 there is a second, ψ', with places P_1', P_2' in its divisor $Q_{\psi'} = P_1' P_2' D^2 / X$ distinct from P_1. The places P_1', P_2' are also distinct from P_2 since otherwise the quotient ψ'/ψ would have but a single pole and the genus p could not be equal to 2. The quotient ψ'/ψ is therefore a special rational function with two poles, and the theorem is proved.

51. **Projective transformations.** A projective transformation is one of the form

$$(51\cdot1) \qquad \xi = u/w, \qquad \eta = v/w,$$

where

$$u = a_1 x + b_1 y + c_1, \quad v = a_2 x + b_2 y + c_2, \quad w = a_3 x + b_3 y + c_3$$

and the determinant $|\, a_1 b_2 c_3 \,|$ of the constant coefficients in these expressions is different from zero. It is one of the most important of the special cases of a Cremona transformation and may be used to simplify an algebraic equation $f(x, y) = 0$, as indicated in the following theorems.

THEOREM 51·1. *By a projective transformation an irreducible algebraic curve can be transformed into one with the following properties:*

I. *If the terms of degree k in x and y are denoted by $(x, y)_k$ so that*

$$f(x, y) = (x, y)_0 + (x, y)_1 + \cdots + (x, y)_\nu,$$

then $(x, y)_\nu$ has ν distinct linear factors and contains terms in x^ν and y^ν with coefficients different from zero.

II. *The polynomial $f(a, y)$ has a multiple root b of order q only when the curve $f(x, y) = 0$ has at $(x, y) = (a, b)$ a multiple point of order q, or an ordinary point with a vertical tangent at which $f_x(a, b) \neq 0$, $f_y^{(a,b)=0}$, $f_{yy}(a, b) \neq 0$. The latter case occurs only when $q = 2$.*

We shall first see that the equation

$$f(x, y) = (x, y)_0 + (x, y)_1 + \cdots + (x, y)_\nu = 0$$

can be transformed into an equation

$$\phi(\xi, \eta) = [\xi, \eta]_0 + [\xi, \eta]_1 + \cdots + [\xi, \eta]_\nu = 0$$

which has the property I. For this purpose we select a line

$$w = cx - y + d = 0$$

for which the equation $f(x, cx+d) = 0$ defining its intersections with $f(x, y) = 0$ has ν distinct finite roots x. To have such a line it is only necessary to select numerical values for c, d such that the coefficient $(1, c)_\nu$ of x^ν in the polynomial $f(x, cx+d)$ is different from zero, and furthermore such that the discriminant of $f(x, cx+d)$ as a polynomial in x is different from zero. The latter selection is possible since $f(x, cx+d)$ as a polynomial in x, c, d is irreducible when $f(x, y)$ is irreducible. We may then select the lines $u = 0$ and $v = 0$ not intersecting on $w = 0$ and so that they do not pass through any intersection of $w = 0$ and $f = 0$. The relation between f and its transform ϕ, by the transformation $\xi = u/w$, $\eta = v/w$, is

$$f(x, y) = w^\nu \phi(\xi, \eta) = [u, v]_0 w^\nu + [u, v]_1 w^{\nu-1} + \cdots + [u, v]_\nu,$$

and we readily see that the roots of $[u, v]_\nu$ must be distinct and that u^ν and v^ν occur in $[u, v]_\nu$, on account of the properties of u, v, w as chosen above.

If a polynomial $f(x, y)$ has the property I then a transformation

(51·2) $$x = A\xi + B\eta, \qquad y = C\xi + D\eta$$

can be selected which will take it into a new polynomial $\phi(\xi, \eta)$ having the property II as well as I. To see this we note first that the polynomial

$$\psi(x, y) = f_{xx}f_y^2 - 2f_{xy}f_xf_y + f_{yy}f_x^2,$$

in which the subscripts indicate partial derivatives of f, does not vanish identically on the Riemann surface of $f(x, y) = 0$ unless $f(x, y)$ is linear in x and y. If $\psi(x, y)$ were identically zero then for the branch $y(x)$ through a non-singular place (x_0, y_0) where $f_y \neq 0$ the equations

$$f_x + f_y y' = 0, \qquad f_{xx} + 2f_{xy}y' + f_{yy}y'^2 + f_y y'' = 0,$$

satisfied by the branch, would imply $y'' \equiv 0$, and this would mean that $f(x, y) = 0$ would be of the first degree or else have a linear factor. In the former case the properties I and II are easily attainable, and the latter case is impossible since $f(x, y)$ is irreducible. We therefore can assume $\psi(x, y) \not\equiv 0$.

The property II will be attained if we can find a transformation (51·2) taking $f = 0$ into a new curve $\phi(\xi, \eta)$ on which $\partial^q \phi / \partial \eta^q \neq 0$ at every multiple point of order q, and on which ϕ_η and $\phi_{\eta\eta}$ vanish simultaneously only when ϕ_ξ also vanishes. At a multiple point (a, b) of order q the polynomial $f(x, y)$ has an expansion of the form

$$f(x, y) = \{x - a, y - b\}_q + \cdots + \{x - a, y - b\}_\nu.$$

For the transformation (51·2) we select the coefficients A, B, C, D with determinant different from zero so that $(A, C)_\nu \neq 0$, $(B, D)_\nu \neq 0$, $\{B, D\}_q \neq 0$ for every multiple point (a, b), and furthermore so that $f_x B + f_y D \neq 0$ at every finite zero of the polynomial $\psi(x, y)$ on T. The first two restrictions on the coefficients insure the preservation of the properties I after the transformation. If $(x, y) = (a, b)$ and $(\xi, \eta) = (\alpha, \beta)$ are corresponding points under (51·2) the transformation may also be written in the form

$$x - a = A(\xi - \alpha) + B(\eta - \beta),$$
$$y - b = C(\xi - \alpha) + D(\eta - \beta).$$

It is evident then that

$$\phi(\xi, \eta) = f(A\xi + B\eta, C\xi + D\eta)$$

has a multiple point of order q at the image (α, β) of each multiple point (a, b) of order q of $f = 0$, and in the terms $\{\xi - \alpha, \eta - \beta\}_q$ the coefficient of $(\eta - \beta)^q$ is $\{B, D\}_q \neq 0$. Furthermore if the functions

$$(51·3) \qquad \phi_\eta = f_x B + f_y D, \qquad \phi_{\eta\eta} = f_{xx} B^2 + 2f_{xy} BD + f_{yy} D^2$$

vanish at a point (ξ, η) of $\phi = 0$ then $\phi_\xi = f_x A + f_y C$ also vanishes. Otherwise the image of (ξ, η) would be a point where

$$(f_x, f_y) \neq (0, 0), \qquad f_x B + f_y D = 0,$$
$$f_{xx} f_y^2 - 2f_{xy} f_x f_y + f_{yy} f_x^2 = 0,$$

and the last two equations are not compatible on account of the way in which the coefficients A, B, C, D were selected above.

THEOREM 51·2. *An irreducible algebraic curve* $f(x, y) = 0$ *with the property* I *of Theorem* 51·1 *has at* $x = \infty$ *expansions of the form*

$$(51·4) \qquad y = \alpha_k x + \beta_k + \gamma_k x^{-1} + \cdots \qquad (k = 1, 2, \cdots, \nu)$$

for which the constants α_k *are the distinct finite roots of the polynomial* $(1, \alpha)_\nu = 0$. *These places at* $x = \infty$ *are the only poles of the algebraic function* $y(x)$ *defined by the equation* $f = 0$. *If* $f = 0$ *has further the property* II *then it has branch places only at multiple points* (a, b) *of order* q *at which* $f(a, y)$ *has a multiple root* $y = b$ *of order exactly* q, *or at points* (a, b) *at which* $f_x(a, b) \neq 0$ *and* $f(a, y)$ *has* $y = b$ *as a double root. At places of the latter type the branches have the form*

$$(51·5) \qquad x = a + t^2, \qquad y = b + \alpha t + \cdots.$$

The expansions at $x = \infty$ may be found in the manner described in Section 14, or more directly by substituting $y = vx$ in $f(x, y) = 0$ and writing this equation in the form

$$f(x, y) = x^{\nu}\{(1, v)_0/x^{\nu} + (1, v)_1 x^{\nu-1} + \cdots + (1, v)_{\nu}\} = 0.$$

From Theorem $7 \cdot 1$ it follows then that v has expansions

$$v = \alpha_k + \beta_k x^{-1} + \gamma_k x^{-2} + \cdots \qquad (k = 1, \cdots, \nu),$$

and the expansions for y are therefore of the form given in the theorem.

From the property II we see that every point (a, b) at which $f(a, y)$ has a multiple root $y = b$ of order q is a multiple point of order q, or possibly a point with a simple vertical tangent when $q = 2$. At a point of the latter type we have $f_x(a, b) \neq 0, f_y(a, b) = 0, f_{yy}(a, b) \neq 0$, and Theorem $16 \cdot 1$ shows that the expansion for y has the form $(51 \cdot 5)$.

52. A second formula for the genus. With the help of the properties I and II described in the last section it is possible to deduce for the genus p of an algebraic curve an expression in terms of the degree ν of $f(x, y)$ in x and y, the orders of multiple points with distinct tangents, and the number of cusps. This is deduced from the formula $(31 \cdot 1)$ and supplements it.

THEOREM $52 \cdot 1$. *If the order of a multiple point of an irreducible algebraic curve $f(x, y) = 0$ of degree ν in x and y is designated by q then the genus of the curve has the value*

$$(52 \cdot 1) \qquad p = (\nu - 1)(\nu - 2)/2 - \sum q(q - 1)/2 - R - I$$

where the sum is taken for all multiple points with distinct tangents of the curve, R is the number of simple cusps, and I is a non-negative integer which is zero in case the curve $f = 0$ has no multiple points of other types.

To prove this we may first suppose the curve to have been transformed by a projective transformation into one having the properties I and II of Theorem $51 \cdot 1$. According to formula $(8 \cdot 6)$ the discriminant of $f(x, y)$ with respect to y differs from the product

$$D(x) = f_y(x, y_1) \cdots f_y(x, y_{\nu})$$

by a constant factor only, since the coefficient of y^{ν} in f is a constant, by property I. This product is therefore a polynomial in x, as one may also see because it is rational in x and as a result of property I has no poles in the finite part of the x-plane. The formula $(52 \cdot 1)$ is to be proved by calculating the degree of the polynomial $D(x)$ in two different ways.

On account of the property I it is readily seen with the help of the expansions (51·4) that each factor $f_y(x, y)$ has a pole of order $\nu - 1$ at $x = \infty$, and hence that $D(x)$ has a pole of order $\nu(\nu - 1)$ and is a polynomial in x of degree $\nu(\nu - 1)$.

The zeros of $D(x)$ occur only at finite places (a, b) where one of the factors $f_y(x, y_i)$ vanishes. Such places are ordinary points with simple vertical tangents or multiple points (a, b) of order q for which $f(a, y)$ has a multiple root $y = b$ of order exactly q, as described in Theorem 51·2. We may further classify the multiple points as those with distinct tangents, simple cusps, and those of other types.

At an ordinary point (a, b) with a simple vertical tangent the expansions for y and $f_y(x, y)$ in the notations of Theorem 16·1 are

$$y - b = c_1(x - a)^{1/2} + \cdots \qquad [c_1 = -(A_{10}/A_{02})^{1/2}],$$
$$f_y(x, y) = 2A_{02}c_1(x - a)^{1/2} + \cdots .$$

Since there are two such factors $f_y(x, y_i)$ in the product $D(x)$, corresponding to the values of y on the two sheets of the cycle, it follows that $D(x)$ has a factor $(x - a)$ for each point (a, b) with a vertical tangent.

For each multiple point (a, b) of order q with distinct tangents we have

$$f(x, y) = \{x - a, y - b\}_q + \cdots$$

and q cycles

$$y - b = \mu_i(x - a) + \cdots \qquad (i = 1, \cdots, q)$$

for which the constants μ_i are the roots of $\{1, \mu\}_q$, according to Theorem 16·2. Hence there are q corresponding expansions

$$f_y(x, y) = \{1, \mu_i\}_{qy}(x - a)^{q-1} + \cdots$$

and $D(x)$ has the factor $(x - a)^{q(q-1)}$.

In the notations of Theorem 16·3 we have at a simple cusp (a, b) the expansions

$$f(x, y) = \{x - a, y - b\}_2 + \{x - a, y - b\}_3 + \cdots ,$$
$$y - b = \mu(x - a) + \nu(x - a)^{3/2} + \cdots ,$$

where μ is the double root of $\{1, m\}_2$ and $\nu \neq 0$. Hence

$$f_y(x, y) = 2A_{02}\nu(x - a)^{3/2} + \cdots .$$

Since there are two such factors $f_y(x, y_i)$ corresponding to the cycle it follows that $D(x)$ has a factor $(x - a)^3$ for each simple cusp.

These results give for the degree of $D(x)$ the value

$$(52 \cdot 2) \qquad \nu(\nu - 1) = N + \sum q(q - 1) + 3R + I_1$$

where N is the number of vertical tangents, the sum is taken for all multiple points with distinct tangents, R is the number of simple cusps, and I_1 is a positive integer which is zero if there are no multiple points of other types. The formula $(31 \cdot 1)$ gives

$$(52 \cdot 3) \quad p = \sum (r - 1)/2 - n + 1 = (N + R + I_2)/2 - \nu + 1,$$

where I_2 is the sum of the numbers $r-1$ taken for all cycles not arising from vertical tangents or cusps, i.e., all cycles of more than one sheet arising from multiple points. It is zero if all the multiple points are simple cusps or have distinct tangents. By combining the last two equations we see that

$$p = (\nu - 1)(\nu - 2)/2 - \sum q(q - 1)/2 - R - (I_1 - I_2)/2.$$

It is evident from this formula that $(I_1 - I_2)/2$ is an integer I, and we have seen that it vanishes if the curve $f = 0$ has no singular points other than multiple points with distinct tangents and simple cusps. We can prove that in every other case it is positive. For the only factors of $D(x)$ not accounted for in the above paragraphs are those arising from cycles at multiple points (a, b) whose tangents are not all distinct. At such a point

$$(52 \cdot 4) \qquad \begin{aligned} f(x, y) &= A_{\alpha\beta}(x - a)^{\alpha}(y - b)^{\beta}, \\ f_y(x, y) &= \beta A_{\alpha\beta}(x - a)^{\alpha}(y - b)^{\beta-1}, \end{aligned}$$

and a cycle arising from such a point has the form

$$(52 \cdot 5) \qquad y - b = c(x - a)^{s/r} + \cdots .$$

Hence the lowest power of $x-a$ in the r factors $f_y(x, y)$ belonging to such a cycle has an exponent of the form $[\alpha r + (\beta - 1)s]/r$, and the contribution of the whole cycle to the integer I_1 in $(52 \cdot 2)$ is at least $\alpha r + (\beta - 1)s$. On the other hand the contribution of the cycle to the integer I_2 in formula $(52 \cdot 3)$ is $r - 1$, and the difference of these contributions is at least $(\alpha - 1)r + (\beta - 1)s + 1$. This difference is surely positive since for a multiple point (a, b) every term in the expression $(52 \cdot 4)$ has its point (α, β) in the $\alpha\beta$-plane not on the same side of the line $(\alpha - 1)r + (\beta - 1)s = 0$ with the origin, because this line is parallel to the polygon side giving rise to the expansion $(52 \cdot 5)$ and passes through the point $(1, 1)$. Hence the difference $I_1 - I_2$ is also positive in case there are multiple points other than those with distinct tangents and simple cusps.

The following corollary has an important application in succeeding paragraphs:

COROLLARY. *For every irreducible algebraic curve* $f(x, y) = 0$ *of degree* ν *in* x *and* y *we have the inequality*

$$\sum q(q - 1)/2 + R \leqq (\nu - 1)(\nu - 2)/2$$

where the sum is taken for the orders q *of all multiple points with distinct tangents and* R *is the number of simple cusps.*

This formula is an immediate consequence of formula $(52 \cdot 1)$ since p is always a positive number.

53. The number of projective intersections of two curves. Let $f(x, y)$ and $g(x, y)$ be two irreducible polynomials not differing by a constant and of degrees ν and ρ, respectively, in x and y, and let $w = a_3 x + b_3 y + c_3$ be a straight line intersecting $f = 0$ and $g = 0$ in $\nu + \rho$ distinct finite points. Such a line can be determined by the argument in Section 51 above. Furthermore let

$$u = a_1 x + b_1 y + c_1, \qquad v = a_2 x + b_2 y + c_2$$

be selected so that $u \neq 0$, $v \neq 0$ at the $\nu + \rho$ intersection points and so that the determinant of coefficients in u, v, w is different from zero. The transformation $\xi = u/w$, $\eta = v/w$ then takes $f = 0$ and $g = 0$ into two curves $\phi(\xi, \eta) = 0$ and $\psi(\xi, \eta) = 0$ whose intersections are all in the finite $\xi\eta$-plane since none of them are on the line $w = 0$ in the xy-plane. The old and the new polynomials are related by the formulas

$$f(x, y)/w^\nu = \phi(\xi, \eta), \qquad g(x, y)/w^\rho = \psi(\xi, \eta).$$

The *number of projective intersections* of the two curves $f = 0$ and $g = 0$ is by definition the sum of the orders of the zeros of the function $\psi(\xi, \eta)$ on the Riemann surface of the equation $\phi(\xi, \eta) = 0$, or what is the same thing the sum of the orders of the zeros of $g(x, y)/w^\rho$ on the Riemann surface of $f(x, y) = 0$.

THEOREM $53 \cdot 1$. *The number of projective intersections of two irreducible algebraic curves* $f(x, y) = 0$ *and* $g(x, y) = 0$ *is the product* $\nu\rho$ *of their degrees in* x *and* y.

To prove this we see first that $\phi(\xi, \eta)$ has the property I of Theorem $51 \cdot 1$ and hence that the algebraic function $\eta(\xi)$ defined by the equation $\phi = 0$ has no poles in the finite part of the ξ-plane. At $\xi = \infty$ its expansions have the form

$$(53 \cdot 1) \qquad \eta = \alpha_k \xi + \beta_k + \gamma_k \xi^{-1} + \cdots \qquad (k = 1, \cdots, \nu)$$

where the numbers α_k are the distinct roots of the polynomial $(1, \alpha)_\nu$ defined by the terms $(\xi, \eta)_\nu$ of highest degree in the polynomial ϕ. Furthermore the terms $[\xi, \eta]_\rho$ of highest degree in $\psi(\xi, \eta)$ are such that for each α_k the expression $[1, \alpha_k]_\rho$ is different from zero, on account of the manner in which the line $w = 0$ was selected. It follows readily then that $\psi(\xi, \eta)$ has no poles at finite places on the Riemann surface T_1 of $\phi = 0$, and at $\xi = \infty$ it has poles the sum of whose orders is $\nu\rho$, as one sees by substituting the expansions $(53 \cdot 1)$ in the polynomial ψ. But the sum of the orders of the zeros of ψ on T_1 is then $\nu\rho$.

54. A formula for integrand functions ψ of integrals of the first kind. A projective transformation $\xi = u/w$, $\eta = v/w$ takes an integral

$$I = \int \psi(x, y)dx$$

of the first kind for an irreducible algebraic curve $f(x, y) = 0$ into a second such integral for the transformed curve $\phi(\xi, \eta) = 0$, with an integrand function which may be designated by $\Psi(\xi, \eta)$. If we make the transformation in such a way that $\phi = 0$ has the property I of Section 51 then we can prove that Ψ and also ψ have the property described in the following theorem.

THEOREM 54·1. *An integrand function $\psi(x, y)$ of an integral of the first kind for an irreducible algebraic curve $f(x,y) = 0$ can always be expressed in the form*

$$\psi(x, y) = Q(x, y)/f_v(x, y)$$

where $Q(x,y)$ is a polynomial of degree at most $\nu - 3$ in x and y, ν being the degree of $f(x, y)$ in x and y.

Let us prove the theorem first for a curve $f = 0$ which has the property I of Theorem 51·1. We can infer that the sum

$$(54 \cdot 1) \qquad P_{k-2}(x) = y_1^k \psi(x, y_1) + \cdots + y_\nu^k \psi(x, y_\nu),$$

where k is a positive integer, is a polynomial in x of degree at most $k - 2$. It is clearly rational in x since it is symmetric in $y_1, \cdots, y_\nu$. At a finite non-singular point x it has no pole since the algebraic function $y(x)$ and the integrand $\psi(x, y)$ have no poles over such a value x. At a singular point $x = a$ it is possible that ψ has a pole of order $r - 1$ and that some of the terms in $(54 \cdot 1)$ may have expansions of the form

$$c_r(x - a)^{-(r-1)/r} + \cdots + c_1(x - a)^{-1/r} + c_0 + \cdots.$$

But since the sum $(54 \cdot 1)$ of these terms has an expansion in powers of $x - a$ which are not fractional, it follows that in the sum the terms with negative exponents cancel. Hence $P_{k-2}(x)$ has no pole at any finite value x whatsoever and is a polynomial. At a place over $x = \infty$ the expansions for y and ψ have the form

$$y = \alpha x + \beta + \gamma x^{-1} + \cdots, \qquad \psi(x, y) = c x^{-2} + d x^{-3} + \cdots,$$

since every integrand function ψ of an integral of the first kind has a zero of order at least 2 at each place over $x = \infty$. Consequently each term of the sum $(54 \cdot 1)$, and therefore $P_{k-2}(x)$ itself, has a pole of order at most $k - 2$ at $x = \infty$, and the degree of $P_{k-2}(x)$ in x is at most $k - 2$. In particular we see that $P_{-2} \equiv P_{-1} \equiv 0$.

The equations $(54 \cdot 1)$ for $k = 0, 1, \cdots, \nu - 1$ can be solved for the values $\psi(x, y_i)$ by a special device. Let

$$f(x, y) = f_0 y^\nu + f_1 y^{\nu-1} + \cdots + f_\nu$$
$$= (y - y_1)(B_0 y^{\nu-1} + \cdots + B_{\nu-1})$$

so that

$$f_y(x, y_1) = B_0 y_1^{\nu-1} + \cdots + B_{\nu-1}.$$

By comparison of coefficients in the next to last equation

$$B_k = f_0 y_1^k + f_1 y_1^{k-1} + \cdots + f_k.$$

Each B_k is of degree at most k in x and y_1 since each f_k is of degree at most k in x. By multiplying the equation $(54 \cdot 1)$ by $B_{\nu-k-1}$ and summing for $k = 0, 1, \cdots, \nu - 1$ we find

$$f_y(x, y_1) \psi(x, y_1) = B_0 P_{\nu-3} + B_1 P_{\nu-4} + \cdots + B_{\nu-3} P_0,$$

and the polynomial on the right is of degree at most $\nu - 3$ in x and y_1. Since (x, y_1) is a quite arbitrary place on T the conclusion of the theorem is established.

If the equation $f(x, y) = 0$ has not the property I we may transform it by a projective transformation $\xi = u/w, \eta = v/w$ into a curve $\phi(\xi, \eta) = 0$ which does have this property. Then on the Riemann surface T_1 of $\phi = 0$ an integral of the first kind has an integrand of the form $Q_1(\xi, \eta)/\phi_\eta(\xi, \eta)$ where Q_1 is a polynomial of degree at most $\nu - 3$. Under the projective transformation we have the following relations on the Riemann surface T between Q_1, ϕ and their transforms Q, f:

$$(54 \cdot 2) \qquad \begin{aligned} f(x, y) &= w^\nu \phi(\xi, \eta), & Q(x, y) &= w^{\nu-3} Q_1(\xi, \eta), \\ \phi_\xi \xi_y + \phi_\eta \eta_y &= f_y/w^\nu, & \phi_\xi \xi' + \phi_\eta \eta' &= 0, \end{aligned}$$

where $\xi' = \xi_x + \xi_y y'$, $\eta' = \eta_x + \eta_y y'$, and y' is the derivative of the algebraic function $y(x)$ defined by the equation $f = 0$. The last two equations (54·2) give the value

$$\phi_\eta = \xi' f_y / w^\nu (\xi' \eta_y - \xi_y \eta') = \xi' f_y / w^{\nu-3} \Delta,$$

where Δ is the determinant of the coefficients of u, v, w. Hence we find

$$\int \frac{Q_1(\xi, \eta)}{\phi_\eta(\xi, \eta)} \, d\xi = \int \frac{Q(x, y)}{f_y(x, y)} \Delta \, dx.$$

Since Q is of degree at most $\nu - 3$ and every integral of the first kind on T is the transform of one on T_1 it follows that the conclusion of the theorem is true for an arbitrary irreducible curve $f(x, y) = 0$.

The polynomials $Q(x, y)$ which occur in the numerators of the integrands $\psi = Q(x, y)/f_y(x, y)$ of integrals of the first kind are called *adjoined polynomials of degree $\nu - 3$*. There are evidently p linearly independent polynomials of this kind such that every adjoined polynomial of degree $\nu - 3$ is expressible linearly in terms of them.

THEOREM 54·2. *If an irreducible algebraic curve $f(x, y) = 0$ of degree ν in x and y has the properties* I *and* II *of Theorem* 51·1, *and if in the projective xy-plane it has no singularities other than multiple points with distinct tangents and simple cusps, then its adjoined polynomials of degree $\nu - 3$ are characterized by the properties that they vanish at each cusp and have multiple points of order at least $q - 1$ at each multiple point of order q of $f = 0$.*

If $Q(x, y)$ is a polynomial of degree $\nu - 3$ in x and y the integral

$$(54·3) \qquad \int \frac{Q(x, y)}{f_y(x, y)} \, dx$$

has no singularity at a place over $x = \infty$. For at such places the expansions of Q and f_y are found with the help of the formula (51·4) to have the forms

$$Q(x, y) = x^{\nu-3}(c_0 + c_1/x + c_2/x^2 + \cdots),$$
$$f_y(x, y) = x^{\nu-1}(d_0 + d_1/x + d_2/x^2 + \cdots) \qquad (d_0 \neq 0).$$

The constant d_0 is different from zero since it is the value $(1, \alpha)_{\nu y}$ of the derivative with respect to y of the polynomial $(x, y)_\nu$ of Theorems 51·1 and 51·2 at one of the distinct roots α of $(1, \alpha)_\nu$. Hence the integrand of the integral (54·3) has a zero of order at least 2 at each place over $x = \infty$ and is finite.

The only other places where the integral could have singularities are finite places at which the derivative f_y vanishes. These places arise from points (a, b) at which the curve $f = 0$ has a vertical tangent, a multiple point with distinct tangents, or a simple cusp. It is easy to see by an examination of the expansions used in the proof of Theorem 52·1 that the quotient $(dx/dt)/f_y$ has no singularity at a cycle of two sheets corresponding to a vertical tangent, and that it has a pole of order $q - 1$ at each cycle corresponding to a multiple point of order q, and a pole of order 1 at a cycle corresponding to a cusp. It follows then that $Q(x, y)$ must have the properties of the theorem if the integral (54·3) is to remain finite everywhere, and conversely.

The number of coefficients in a polynomial $Q(x, y)$ of degree $\nu - 3$ is

$$1 + 2 + \cdots + \nu - 2 = (\nu - 1)(\nu - 2)/2.$$

The condition that $Q(x, y)$ shall have a multiple point of order $q - 1$ at a point (a, b) imposes

$$1 + 2 + \cdots + q - 1 = q(q - 1)/2$$

linear relations on these coefficients, and the condition that Q shall vanish at a cusp imposes one such linear relation. Hence the number of arbitrary constants remaining in an adjoined polynomial of degree $\nu - 3$ is

$$(54·4) \qquad (\nu - 1)(\nu - 2)/2 - \sum q(q - 1)/2 - R,$$

where the sum is taken for all the multiple points with distinct tangents of the curve $f = 0$, and R is the number of simple cusps. But the expression (54·4) is precisely the value of the genus p given by formula (52·1), as it should be since there are exactly p linearly independent adjoined polynomials of degree $\nu - 3$, as we have seen above.

REFERENCES FOR CHAPTER VII

References for the various sections of Chapter VII above, in the list at the end of this book, are the following: 13, Chapter VI; 18, Chapter VI; 24, Chapter XVIII; 28, Vorlesungen XVI, XXIV; 39, Chapter II; 42, Chapter V.

Chapter VIII

THE REDUCTION OF SINGULARITIES
BY TRANSFORMATION

55. Introduction. There are two famous transformation theorems in the literature of the theory of algebraic curves. The first of these states that every irreducible algebraic curve can be transformed by a Cremona transformation into another algebraic curve which has no singularities other than multiple points with distinct tangents. The second theorem asserts that every irreducible algebraic curve can be transformed by a birational transformation into another such curve having no singularities other than double points with distinct tangents. For convenience we may designate these theorems in this chapter as Theorems A and B.

Theorem A has been with universal agreement ascribed to Noether.[*] In 1871 he stated the theorem and indicated a proof which has since been perfected and modified by many writers. The proof in Section 56 below is one which was published by Picard and ascribed by him to Simart. Theorem A has frequently been made a starting point for the theory of algebraic functions. For if the curve $f=0$ has no singularities other than multiple points with distinct tangents many of the proofs of theorems concerning the algebraic function $y(x)$ associated with it can be greatly simplified. An example in the preceding pages of such a discussion is the determination of the properties of adjoined polynomials of degree $\nu - 3$ in Theorem 54·2.

The precise origin of Theorem B is much less easy to determine. The first published statement and proof of the theorem seems to be one by Halphen in 1884. But Halphen ascribed the theorem to Noether; Klein states that he first heard of it from Kronecker in 1869; and other writers before 1891 seem to have regarded it as familiar material. Since 1891 the literature concerning the theorem has been greatly extended. Many of the published proofs have, however, been criticized, and none of them has apparently been adopted with universal or even with widespread approval. In the reference cited above the writer has called at-

[*] For the literature and a discussion of the various methods of proof of Theorems A and B see the paper [43] by Bliss.

tention to the fact that there are really two Theorems B, one for the projective xy-plane, and one for the function-theoretic plane consisting of all the pairs of values (x, y) for which x and y themselves range over two complex planes. The distinction between the theorems in the two cases has not been clearly made in the literature, though they do not seem to be easy consequences of each other. If a curve has only double points with distinct tangents in the projective plane it will in general have singularities of a much more complicated sort in the function-theoretic plane, and vice versa.

The proofs of the two Theorems B in the following pages are based upon a most interesting memoir of Kronecker concerning the discriminant of an algebraic function, published in 1881. Hensel and Landsberg extended Kronecker's results to secure a proof of Theorem B in the function-theoretic plane. Their proof is given, with some modifications by the writer, in Sections 59 and 60 below. A similar extension has been made by the writer in order to secure Theorem B in the projective plane, which seems considerably more difficult to prove. These methods are described in Sections 57 and 58. There are many other proofs in the literature, but the ones based upon the results of Kronecker are perhaps the most interesting from the standpoint of the theory of algebraic functions because of the information, important in itself, which they give concerning the structure of the discriminant. It should be noted that the proofs of Theorem B in the following sections are purely analytic in character, dependent only upon the expansion theorems of Chapter II and the theory of rational functions in Chapter III.

56. Reduction of singularities to multiple points with distinct tangents. The theorem to be proved in this section is the following one:

THEOREM 56·1. *By a succession of projective and Cremona transformations of the form*

$$(56·1) \qquad \xi = x - a, \qquad \eta = (x - a)/(y - b)$$

every irreducible algebraic curve $f(x, y) = 0$ can be transformed into one having no singular points in the projective plane other than multiple points with distinct tangents. This property will be designated as property III *of $f = 0$.*

First let us suppose a projective transformation to have been applied so that $f = 0$ is a curve having the properties I and II of Theorem 51·1. The intersections of such a curve with the line at infinity are all distinct, as one readily verifies, and hence all of its multiple points are finite.

Consider then a finite multiple point (a, b) of order q with tangents not distinct, and suppose that the x- and y-axes have been rotated so that each of the lines $x = a$ and $y = b$ has exactly q intersections with the curve at (a, b) and all of its other intersections with the curve finite and distinct from each other and those at (a, b). If we apply the transformation (56·1) the original and transformed curves are

$$(56\cdot2) \quad f(x, y) = (x - a, y - b)_q + \cdots + (x - a, y - b)_\nu,$$

$$(56\cdot3) \quad \phi(\xi, \eta) = (\eta, 1)_q \eta^{\nu-q} + \xi (\eta, 1)_{q+1} \eta^{\nu-q-1} + \cdots + \xi^{\nu-q}(\eta, 1)_\nu.$$

The latter is of degree $2\nu - q$ and in homogeneous coordinates ξ, η, ζ has the form

$$(56\cdot4) \quad (\eta, \zeta)_q \eta^{\nu-q}\zeta^{\nu-q} + \xi(\eta, \zeta)_{q+1} \eta^{\nu-q-1}\zeta^{\nu-q-1} + \cdots + \xi^{\nu-q}(\eta, \zeta)_\nu.$$

At the vertices of the coordinate triangle in the $\xi\eta\zeta$-plane we find multiple points of $\phi = 0$ determined by the initial terms

$$(\eta, \zeta)_\nu,$$
$$(1, 0)_q \zeta^{\nu-q} + \xi (1, 0)_{q+1} \zeta^{\nu-q-1} + \cdots + \xi^{\nu-q}(1, 0)_\nu,$$
$$(0, 1)_q \eta^{\nu-q} + \xi (0, 1)_{q+1} \eta^{\nu-q-1} + \cdots + \xi^{\nu-q}(0, 1)_\nu.$$

On account of the property I and the choice of axes these have distinct tangents. On the lines $\zeta = 0$ and $\eta = 0$ there are no other intersections. On the line $\xi = 0$ there are q other intersections which may lie in multiple points the sum of whose orders is at most q.

A second multiple point (a', b') of $f = 0$ is transformed by (56·1) into a point (α', β') not on the coordinate axes in the $\xi\eta$-plane, since the lines $x - a = 0$, $y - b = 0$ do not pass through it. If we write the transformation (56·1) in the equivalent form

$$x - a' = \xi - \alpha', \qquad y - b' = [(\xi - \alpha')\beta' - (\eta - \beta')\alpha']/\beta'\eta$$

we can verify readily the fact that a multiple point (a', b') of (56·2) transforms into a multiple point of (56·3) or (56·4) not on a side of the coordinate triangle in the $\xi\eta\zeta$-plane, and the new multiple point has the same order as before and has distinct tangents if the tangents at (a', b') are distinct.

The accompanying figures show schematically the results of transforming the multiple points. The lines $z = 0$ and $\zeta = 0$ are the lines at infinity. The letters at the corners indicate the orders of the multiple points. The multiple points at the corners in the $\xi\eta\zeta$-plane have distinct tangents. The sum of the orders of those on the line $\xi = 0$ and not surely having distinct tangents is at most q, and hence each of them has multiplicity less than q unless there is only one.

If there is only one multiple point on the line $\xi = 0$ aside from those at the vertices of the coordinate triangle the same process may be applied again to that multiple point. It will be shown in the next paragraph that after a finite number of such steps the original multiple point

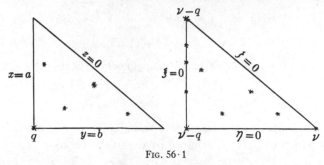

FIG. 56·1

of order q will surely be replaced by multiple points with distinct tangents and possibly by a number of others each with multiplicity less than q and with the sum of their multiplicities less than or equal to q. It is evident then that after a finite number of such transformations it can be brought about that all of the multiple points remaining have distinct tangents.

To prove that after a finite number of projective and Cremona transformations like those described above there will surely be more than one multiple point distinct from the corners on the side $\xi = 0$ of the coordinate triangle, let us assume that the contrary were true. Let C and C_1 denote, respectively, the curve $f = 0$ and the curve deduced from it by a first projective transformation and transformation of the form (56·1). The degree of C_1 would be $\nu_1 = 2\nu - q = 2(\nu - q) + q$, and C_1 would have, in place of the original multiple point (a, b) of order q, three new multiple points with distinct tangents of orders $\nu - q, \nu - q, \nu$ at the vertices of the new coordinate triangle, and one of order q on the axis $\xi = 0$ which would possibly have tangents not distinct. We could then repeat the process on C_1 and the multiple point of order q. If the same result were always attained after successive transformations we should find a succession of curves C_k of degrees $\nu_k = 2^k(\nu - q) + q$ and the multiple points with distinct tangents introduced after transforming C_k would have orders $\nu_k - q, \nu_k - q, \nu_k$. For the curve C_k, however, we must have

$$\sum q(q - 1)/2 \le (\nu_k - 1)(\nu_k - 2)/2,$$

according to the corollary to Theorem 52·1, where the sum is taken for all multiple points with distinct tangents of C_k. In particular for those introduced for C_k by the successive transformations we would have

$$\sum_{i=0}^{k-1}[(\nu_i - q)(\nu_i - q - 1) + \nu_i(\nu_i - 1)/2] = (3/2)(\nu - q)^2 \frac{2^{2k} - 1}{2^2 - 1}$$

$$+ (\nu - q)\frac{2q - 3}{2}(2^k - 1) + \frac{kq(q - 1)}{2} \leqq (\nu_k - 1)(\nu_k - 2)/2,$$

where it is understood that $\nu_0 = \nu$. The second form for the first member of this inequality is found by substituting the value $\nu_k = 2^k(\nu - q) + q$ and summing the coefficients of the powers of $\nu - q$. By the same substitution in the second member this would reduce to

$$(\nu - q)^2/2 + (\nu - q)(2q - 3)/2 + (q - 1)(q - 2)/2 - kq(q - 1)2 \geqq 0$$

which is impossible if k is sufficiently large. Hence at some stage there must be a curve C_k for which the original multiple point of order q of C is replaced by multiple points with distinct tangents and multiple points of orders less than q.

57. **Curves in the projective plane with double points only.** If the substitution $x = x_1/x_3$, $y = x_2/x_3$ is made in an irreducible algebraic equation $f(x, y) = 0$ this equation will take the form

$$g(x_1, x_2, x_3) = x_3^\nu f(x_1/x_3, x_2/x_3) = 0$$

where g is a homogeneous polynomial in x_1, x_2, x_3 with the degree ν which f has in x and y. The equation $g = 0$ defines a curve in the totality of points (x_1, x_2, x_3) which constitute the projective plane.

Each primitive branch of one of the two forms

$$(57 \cdot 1) \qquad \begin{aligned} x &= t^{-r}, & y &= bt^\mu + b't^{\mu'} + \cdots, \\ x &= a + t^r, & y &= bt^\mu + b't^{\mu'} + \cdots, \end{aligned}$$

which satisfies the equation $f = 0$, defines a branch satisfying $g = 0$ of the form

$$(57 \cdot 2) \qquad\qquad x_i = a_i + \alpha_i t + \cdots \qquad\qquad (i = 1, 2, 3)$$

with $(a_1, a_2, a_3) \neq (0, 0, 0)$. It can be readily verified that every point (x_1, x_2, x_3) in a neighborhood of (a_1, a_2, a_3) on one of these branches corresponds to one and but one value of t near $t = 0$, since the branches $(57 \cdot 1)$ are primitive and have a similar property. A branch $(57 \cdot 2)$ which has this property is also called *primitive*.

A *linear branch* (57·2) *is one for which the matrix*

$$\left\| \begin{array}{ccc} a_1 & a_2 & a_3 \\ \alpha_1 & \alpha_2 & \alpha_3 \end{array} \right\|$$

has rank 2. If the coordinate a_3 is different from zero, for example, equations (57·2) give

$$x = x_1/x_3 = a_1/a_3 + (a_3\alpha_1 - a_1\alpha_3)t/a_3^2 + \cdots ,$$
$$y = x_2/x_3 = a_2/a_3 + (a_3\alpha_2 - a_2\alpha_3)t/a_3^2 + \cdots .$$

Since the determinants in the coefficients of t cannot both vanish when the matrix above has rank 2, it follows that in terms of x and y the branch has one of the forms

$$(57·3) \qquad \begin{array}{l} y - b = c_1(x - a) + \cdots , \\ x - a = d_1(y - b) + \cdots , \end{array}$$

where $a = a_1/a_3$, $b = a_2/a_3$, $c_1 = (a_3\alpha_2 - a_2\alpha_3)/(a_3\alpha_1 - a_1\alpha_3)$ and d_1 is the reciprocal of c_1. Hence a linear branch is one on which $y - b$ is expressible in positive integral powers of $x - a$, or vice versa.

Two linear branches with the same vertex $a_1 : a_2 : a_3$ have *distinct tangents* provided that the determinant

$$\left| \begin{array}{ccc} a_1 & a_2 & a_3 \\ \alpha_1 & \alpha_2 & \alpha_3 \\ \alpha_1' & \alpha_2' & \alpha_3' \end{array} \right|$$

is different from zero, the constants α_i' being the coefficients of t in the second branch. This can be readily verified by comparing the values of the constants c_1 for the two branches.

If two curves $g = 0$ and $g_1 = 0$ are equivalent under a projective transformation of the form

$$\rho y_i = a_{i1}x_1 + a_{i2}x_2 + a_{i3}x_3 \qquad (i = 1, 2, 3)$$

with determinant $|a_{ik}| \neq 0$, then this same transformation takes the totality of primitive branches satisfying the equation $g = 0$ into the similar totality for $g_1 = 0$. Furthermore a linear branch is transformed into a linear branch, and two branches with the same center but distinct tangents are transformed into two other branches with the same property.

A curve $g = 0$ is said to have no singularities other than double points with distinct tangents if all of its branches are linear, if the same center

(a_1, a_2, a_3) is never shared by more than two branches, and if every pair of branches with a common center has distinct tangents.

THEOREM 57·1. *The following conditions* A *and* B *are sufficient to insure that an irreducible curve* $f(x, y) = 0$ *of degree n in y has no singularities other than double points with distinct tangents in the projective plane:*

A. *At* $x = \infty$ *the n values of the algebraic function* $y(x)$ *defined by the equation* $f(x, y) = 0$ *are given by expansions*

$$(57·4) \qquad\qquad y = x(b_k + b_k' x^{-1} + \cdots) \qquad\qquad (k = 1, \cdots, n)$$

with distinct constants b_k, *and* $y(x)$ *has no other poles.*

B. *The discriminant of* $y(x)$ *has the form*

$$D(x) = V(x)^2 \Delta(x)$$

where $\Delta(x)$ *is the product of the factors* $(x - a)^{r-1}$ *belonging to cycles of r sheets, and* $V(x)$ *is a polynomial with roots distinct from each other and those of* $\Delta(x)$.

The most convenient formula for the discriminant for the proof of this theorem is

$$(57·5) \qquad\qquad D(x) = f_0^{2n-2} \prod_{i<k} (y_i - y_k)^2 \qquad (i, k = 1, \cdots, n),$$

where f_0 is the coefficient of y^n in the polynomial $f(x, y)$ and $y_1, \cdots, y_n$ are the roots of $f(x, y)$. It is the formula $(8·5)$ except for an unessential constant factor.

To prove the theorem let $f(x, y)$ be expressed in the form

$$f(x, y) = (x, y)_0 + \cdots + (x, y)_\nu$$

where $(x, y)_k$ is homogeneous and of degree k in x and y. From the assumption that the series $(57·4)$ satisfy the equation $f = 0$ it follows readily that $(1, b_k)_\nu = 0$ for every value of k, and hence that $(x, y)_\nu$ is of degree exactly n in y since by the hypothesis of the theorem it is of degree at most n in y. Furthermore the degree ν of $(x, y)_\nu$ in x and y together is equal to n since otherwise $(x, y)_\nu$ would have a term in y^n multiplied by a power of x and the coefficient of y^n in f would be a polynomial in x. The function $y(x)$ would then have poles at finite values of x as well as $x = \infty$, contrary to the property A of the theorem. The n intersections of $f = 0$ with the line at infinity are defined by the equation $(x, y)_n = 0$ and are distinct. None of them is a multiple point of the curve. Since the term y^n actually occurs in $(x, y)_n$ it follows that f_0 is a constant different from zero.

For a root $x = a$ of $\Delta(x)$ the n values of y are given by one or more expansions of the form

$$(57 \cdot 6) \qquad y = b + b'(x - a)^{1/r} + \cdots .$$

Each of these series furnishes r values of y and $r(r-1)/2$ differences $y_i - y_k$ in the expression $(57 \cdot 5)$, each with a factor $(x-a)^{1/r}$ at least. Hence if $D(x)$ contains at most a factor $(x-a)^{r-1}$ for each cycle, as indicated in assumption B, it follows that no two of the series $(57 \cdot 6)$ defining different cycles over $x = a$ can have the same constant term b, and for each of these series the coefficient b' is different from zero. The value $y = b$ is therefore exactly an r-tuple root of $f(a, y)$, by Theorem $13 \cdot 2$, and $(y-b)^r$ is the lowest power of $(y-b)$ alone occurring in the expansion

$$(57 \cdot 7) \qquad f(x, y) = (x - a, y - b)_1 + \cdots + (x - a, y - b)_n$$

at $(x, y) = (a, b)$. It can readily be verified that the series $(57 \cdot 6)$ will satisfy $f = 0$ identically only if the term in $x - a$ is present in $(x - a, y - b)_1$. Hence none of the points (a, b) corresponding to a root $x = a$ of $\Delta(x)$ is a multiple point of the curve $f = 0$.

At a root $x = a$ of $V(x)$ the series $(57 \cdot 6)$ for $y(x)$ all have $r = 1$ since by the assumption B no such root is a branch value of x. Since $D(x)$ has exactly the factor $(x-a)^2$ it follows that only one of the differences $y_i - y_k$ vanishes at $x = a$, and that for this difference the expansions are

$$(57 \cdot 8) \qquad \begin{aligned} y_i &= b + c_1(x - a) + \cdots , \\ y_k &= b + c_2(x - a) + \cdots , \end{aligned}$$

with $c_1 \neq c_2$. The polynomial $f(a, y)$ has no multiple root except the double root $y = b$, and $(y-b)^2$ is the lowest power of $y - b$ alone occurring in the expression $(57 \cdot 7)$. The two series $(57 \cdot 8)$ can satisfy $f = 0$ identically only if the terms of the first degree in $(57 \cdot 7)$ are absent, and if $(1, c_1)_2 = (1, c_2)_2 = 0$. Hence the point (a, b) is a double point of the curve $f = 0$ with distinct tangents.

At every point $x = a$ not a root of $D(x)$ the roots $y = b$ of $f(a, y)$ are distinct and the corresponding points (a, b) are ordinary points of the curve $f = 0$.

It is easy to verify that the projective branches $(57 \cdot 2)$ for the curve $f = 0$ corresponding to the branches $(57 \cdot 4)$, $(57 \cdot 6)$ and $(57 \cdot 8)$, and to the non-singular branches satisfying $f = 0$ as well, have the properties required in the definition of a curve with no singularities in the projective plane other than double points with distinct tangents.

58. Reduction of singularities in the projective plane to double points with distinct tangents. In this section it is proposed to prove the following theorem:

THEOREM 58·1. *An irreducible algebraic curve $f(x, y) = 0$ can always be transformed by a birational transformation into a second such curve $\phi(\xi, \eta) = 0$ having no singularities in the projective $\xi\eta$-plane except double points with distinct tangents.*

Let us consider first a divisor $Q = P_1^{-1} \cdots P_q^{-1}$ containing $q > 2p + 2$ distinct places on the Riemann surface T of $f = 0$. Such a divisor has $\mu = q - p + 1$ linearly independent multiples $\sigma_i(x, y)$ $(i = 1, \cdots, \mu)$, according to the third row of the table of Theorem 26·2. The theorem of this section is to be established by constructing two multiples

$$\xi(x, y) = u_1\sigma_1 + \cdots + u_\mu\sigma_\mu,$$

$$\eta(x, y) = v_1\sigma_1 + \cdots + v_\mu\sigma_\mu$$

of the divisor Q having constant coefficients u_i, v_i and satisfying an irreducible equation $\phi(\xi, \eta) = 0$ birationally related to $f(x, y) = 0$ and having the properties A and B of Theorem 57·1.

Since by the corollary to Lemma 26·2 the leading coefficients in the expansions of the functions σ_i at each of the planes P_k $(k = 1, \cdots, q)$ are not all zero we know that the constants u_i can be selected once for all so that the function $\xi(x, y)$ has a simple pole at each of these places. If at one of the places P_k

$$\xi = c_k t^{-1} + \cdots, \qquad \sigma_i = c_{ik} t^{-1} + \cdots$$

then η has a corresponding expansion in powers of $1/\xi$ of the form

$$(58·1) \qquad \eta = \xi(\beta_k + \beta_k' \xi^{-1} + \cdots),$$

where $\beta_k = v_i c_{ik}/c_k$, this expression being summed for i but not for k. According to the corollary to Lemma 26·2 the matrix of coefficients c_{1k}, $\cdots$, $c_{\mu k}$ for two of the places P_k has rank 2, and it is evident that no two of the linear expressions β_k in $v_1, \cdots, v_\mu$ have coefficients which are proportional. It follows then that if in selecting numerical values for $v_1, \cdots, v_\mu$ we avoid solutions of a certain system L of linear equations the values β_k will all be distinct. Corresponding to a value ξ in a neighborhood of $\xi = \infty$ the q values η defined by the series $(58·1)$ will be distinct, and according to Corollary 1 of Theorem 49·1 the irreducible equation satisfied by ξ and η will therefore be of degree q and will be birationally related to $f(x, y) = 0$.

If we denote by $\eta_1, \cdots, \eta_q$ the values of the function $\eta(x, y)$ corresponding to a fixed value of $\xi(x, y)$ then the product

$$(58 \cdot 2) \qquad \phi(v_1, \cdots, v_\mu, \xi, \eta) = (\eta - \eta_1) \cdots (\eta - \eta_q)$$

is a polynomial in $v_1, \cdots, v_\mu, \xi, \eta$. We see this because the coefficients of its powers of η are symmetric in $\eta_1, \cdots, \eta_q$ and therefore polynomials in $v_1, \cdots, v_\mu$ and rational in ξ, and they are polynomials in ξ since they have no poles except at $\xi = \infty$. This is due to the fact that $\eta(x, y)$ has no poles except at those of $\xi(x, y)$. The discriminant of the polynomial (58·2) with respect to η,

$$D(v_1, \cdots, v_\mu, \xi) = \prod_{k<l}(\eta_k - \eta_l)^2 \qquad (k, l = 1, \cdots, q),$$

is also a polynomial in the variables $v_1, \cdots, v_\mu, \xi$. It may be written in the form $W(v_1, \cdots, v_\mu, \xi)\Delta(\xi)$ where $\Delta(\xi)$ is the product of its irreducible factors containing ξ alone.

Near every place P distinct from the poles of $\xi(x, y)$ on the Riemann surface T of $f=0$ we have expansions

$$\xi = \alpha + \alpha' t^\rho + \cdots, \qquad \sigma_i = \alpha_i + \alpha_i' t + \cdots$$

and a corresponding expansion

$$(58 \cdot 3) \qquad \eta = \gamma + \gamma'(\xi - \alpha)^{1/\rho} + \cdots$$

where $\gamma = v_i \alpha_i$, $\gamma' = v_i \alpha_i' (\alpha')^{-1/\rho}$. The values η_k corresponding to a value ξ near $\xi = \alpha$ are given by a number of expansions (58·3). Each of them contributes a number ρ of the values η_k, and the corresponding $\rho(\rho-1)/2$ differences $\eta_k - \eta_l$ contribute a factor $(\xi - \alpha)^{\rho-1}$ to D when the coefficients v_i are indeterminates. The polynomial $\Delta(\xi)$ therefore contains the factor $\Pi(\xi - \alpha)^{\rho-1}$ where the product is taken for all of the expansions of the form (58·3) corresponding to $\xi = \alpha$. It can contain no more factors $\xi - \alpha$ since from the corollary to Lemma 26·2 it follows that when the variables v_i do not satisfy a certain system of linear equations the constant terms γ in the expansions (58·3) corresponding to $\xi = \alpha$ are all distinct, and the coefficients γ' are all different from zero. Hence for such a particular selection of the v_i the discriminant D contains only the factor $\Pi(\xi - \alpha)^{\rho-1}$, and D can evidently not contain more factors $\xi - \alpha$ when the coefficients v_i are indeterminates.

The factor W of the discriminant is the product of a number of irreducible polynomials in the variables $v_1, \cdots, v_\mu, \xi$. Each of these irreducible factors must occur at least twice in W. Otherwise we could select special values for the coefficients v_i such that the roots ξ of the distinct irreducible factors of W would all be distinct and distinct from the roots of $\Delta(\xi)$. A zero ξ_0 of a simple irreducible factor of W would then be a simple root of D distinct from the branch values of ξ. But this is impossible since ξ_0 must be a zero of one of the factors $\eta_k - \eta_l$ when expanded in powers of $\xi - \xi_0$, and each such factor occurs twice in D. No irreducible factor of W can occur more than twice in W. For when we substitute a value ξ_0 distinct from the branch values of ξ the polynomial W becomes the square of a product of factors $\eta_k - \eta_l$ which are linear in $v_1, \cdots, v_\mu$, and such that no one is a constant times another, as one can see with the help of Lemma 26·2 and its corollary. Hence no one of these factors can occur three times in D. It follows that $D = V(v_1, \cdots, v_\mu, \xi)^2 \Delta(\xi)$ where V is a product of distinct irreducible factors no one of which contains ξ alone.

It is a simple matter now to see that the coefficients $v_1, \cdots, v_\mu$ can always be selected numerically so that the polynomial $\phi(\xi, \eta)$ has the properties A and B of Theorem 57·1. We may select them not satisfying a certain system L of linear equations, described in a preceding paragraph, in order that the coefficients β_k in the expansions (58·1) shall all be distinct; and we may furthermore select them so that the roots ξ of the irreducible factors of $V(v_1, \cdots, v_\mu, \xi)$ are all distinct from each other and from the roots of $\Delta(\xi)$. Then the properties A and B are assured. The curve $\phi(\xi, \eta) = 0$ is birationally related to $f(x, y) = 0$ and has no singularities in the projective plane other than double points with distinct tangents.

59. **Curves in the function-theoretic plane with double points only.** When homogeneous coordinates x_1, x_2 and y_1, y_2 are introduced in the equation $f(x, y) = 0$ by means of the relations $x = x_1/x_2$, $y = y_1/y_2$ an equation of the form

$$h(x_1, x_2; y_1, y_2) = x_2^m y_2^n f(x_1/x_2, y_1/y_2) = 0$$

is obtained, m and n being the degrees of f in x and y respectively. The polynomial h is homogeneous and of degree m in x_1 and x_2, and homogeneous and of degree n in y_1 and y_2. When set equal to zero it defines a curve in the function-theoretic plane of points $(x_1, x_2; y_1, y_2)$.

The primitive branches (57·1) which satisfy the equation $f = 0$ are transformed into branches of the form

$$(59·1) \qquad x_i = a_i + \alpha_i t + \cdots, \qquad y_i = b_i + \beta_i t + \cdots. \qquad (i = 1, 2)$$

satisfying the equation $h = 0$ and having $(a_1, a_2) \neq (0, 0)$, $(b_1, b_2) \neq (0, 0)$, and furthermore such that each point $(x_1, x_2; y_1, y_2)$ on the branch and sufficiently near the center $(a_1, a_2; b_1, b_2)$ is defined by only one value of t near $t = 0$. A branch with this property is said to be *primitive*, and it is furthermore said to be *linear* if the determinants $a_1\alpha_2 - a_2\alpha_1$ and $b_1\beta_2 - b_2\beta_1$ are not both zero. Two such branches with the same vertex are said to have *distinct tangents* if the expression

$$(a_1\alpha_2' - a_2\alpha_1')(b_1'\beta_2 - b_2'\beta_1) - (a_1'\alpha_2 - a_2'\alpha_1)(b_1\beta_2' - b_2\beta_1')$$

is different from zero, where the primes designate coefficients of the second branch, and it is understood that $(a_1', a_2') = (ka_1, ka_2)$ and $(b_1', b_2') = (lb_1, lb_2)$ for two branches with the same vertex. A linear branch is always representable in one of the forms $(57 \cdot 3)$, as one readily verifies.

If two curves $h = 0$ and $h_1 = 0$ are equivalent under a bilinear transformation of the form

$$\rho x_i' = \alpha_{i1}x_1 + \alpha_{i2}x_2, \qquad \sigma y_i' = \beta_{i1}y_1 + \beta_{i2}y_2 \qquad (i = 1, 2)$$

with determinants $| \alpha_{ik} |$ and $| \beta_{ik} |$ different from zero the totality of primitive branches satisfying $h = 0$ will transform into the similar totality for $h_1 = 0$, and the properties of linearity, and distinctness of tangents for two branches with the same center, are preserved.

A curve $h = 0$ with no singularities other than double points with distinct tangents is now defined to be one whose primitive branches are all linear and such that no vertex is shared by more than two of them, and furthermore such that every pair of branches with a common vertex has distinct tangents.

THEOREM $59 \cdot 1$. *An irreducible algebraic curve $f(x, y) = 0$ of degree n in y has no singularities except double points with distinct tangents in the function-theoretic plane, provided that the algebraic function $y(x)$ defined by the equation $f = 0$ has the following properties*:

A_1. *At $x = \infty$ the function $y(x)$ has distinct finite values.*

A_2. *The poles of $y(x)$ are simple and at values $x = a$ distinct from each other and from the branch values of x.*

B. *The discriminant of $y(x)$ has the property B of Theorem $57 \cdot 1$.*

From the property A_1 it follows that the branches giving the values of $y(x)$ at $x = \infty$ have the form

$$x = 1/t, \qquad y = b_i + c_it + \cdots \qquad (i = 1, \cdots, n)$$

where the constants b_i are distinct. These define branches $(59 \cdot 1)$ which are linear and have vertices distinct from each other and those of other branches which satisfy $f = 0$. Similarly at the poles of $y(x)$ we have branches

$$x = a_k + t, \qquad y = b_k t^{-1} + c_k + d_k t + \cdots$$

with distinct values a_k, and those branches define branches (59·1) which are linear and have vertices distinct from each other and those of other branches. The remainder of the proof is similar to that of Theorem 57·1.

60. **Reduction of singularities in the function-theoretic plane to double points with distinct tangents.** The theorem to be proved in this section is similar to that of Section 58 but a simpler birational transformation can be used, as indicated in the following theorem:

THEOREM 60·1. *An irreducible algebraic curve* $f(x, y) = 0$ *can always be transformed by a birational transformation of the form*

$$(60·1) \qquad\qquad \xi = x, \qquad \eta = \eta(x, y)$$

into a second such curve $\phi(x, \eta) = 0$ *having no singularities in the function theoretic plane except double points with distinct tangents.*

To prove this we start from a divisor $Q = P_1^{-1} \cdots P_q^{-1}$ with $q > 2p+2$, as in Section 58, whose places P_k $(k = 1, \cdots, q)$ have values x_k which are distinct from each other and from the values of x at branch places on the Riemann surface T of $f(x, y) = 0$. With the help of the corollary to Lemma 26·2 we see that the function

$$\eta(x, y) = v_1 \sigma_1 + \cdots + v_\mu \sigma_\mu$$

will take q distinct finite values at $x = \infty$ and have a simple pole at each place P_k provided that the coefficients v_i do not satisfy a certain system L_1 of linear equations. It follows then, by Corollary 1 of Theorem 49·1, that the degree of the irreducible equation $\phi(x, \eta) = 0$ satisfied by x and η is exactly q, and that this equation is birationally equivalent to $f = 0$ by the transformation (60·1). The curve $\phi = 0$ has evidently the property A_1 of Theorem 59·1, and the property A_2 is an immediate consequence of the way in which the places P_k in the divisor Q were chosen.

To show that the coefficients v_i can be chosen numerically so that $\phi(x, \eta)$ has the property B we may consider the discriminant

$$(60·2) \qquad D(v_1, \cdots, v_\mu, x) = \phi_0^{2q-2} \prod_{k<l} (\eta_k - \eta_l)^2 \qquad (k, l = 1, \cdots, q)$$

of the algebraic function $\eta(x)$ defined by the equation $\phi = 0$. The factor ϕ_0 is the coefficient of η^q in the polynomial $\phi(x, \eta)$ and must contain a factor $x - x_k$ for each of the places P_k where $\eta(x)$ has a simple pole. At each such place P_k one only of the values η_i has a simple pole, and the product in equation (60·2) has a pole of order $2q-2$ which is canceled by the factor preceding the product. Since the places P_k are the only finite places where D could become infinite it follows that D is a polynomial in x as well as $v_1, \cdots, v_\mu$. It may now be proved as in Section 58 that D is a product of the form $D = V(v_1, \cdots, v_\mu, x)^2 \Delta(x)$ where V has distinct irreducible factors all containing the variables $v_1, \cdots, v_\mu$ and $\Delta(x)$ is the product $\Pi(x-a)^{r-1}$ formed for all branch places on T. If we select numerical values $v_1, \cdots, v_\mu$ not satisfying the system L_1 of linear equations mentioned above, and so that the roots x of the irreducible factors of V are distinct from each other and those of $\Delta(x)$, then the curve $\phi(x, \eta) = 0$ will be birationally related to $f(x, y) = 0$ and will have the properties A_1, A_2, B of Theorem 59·1. It will therefore have no singularities except double points with distinct tangents in the function-theoretic plane.

REFERENCES FOR CHAPTER VIII

The literature concerning the reduction of singularities by birational transformation is extensive. It has been listed by the author in the reference numbered 43 in the list at the end of this book. For the special methods of this chapter see 28. pages 402–409, and 41.

CHAPTER IX

INVERSION OF ABELIAN INTEGRALS

61. Introduction. The importance of the problem of the inversion of an Abelian integral, to be discussed in this chapter, will be understood from the fact that all of the elementary transcendental functions, and many other such functions besides, can be defined as Abelian integrals or as inverses of such integrals in the manner described in the following paragraphs. The function log x, for example, may be defined by the first of the equations

$$u = \int_1^x dx/x = \log x, \qquad x = \text{Exp } u,$$

and the exponential function e^u, which will be denoted here by Exp u, is then the solution of this equation as a function of u, the so-called inverse of the function defined by the integral. The functions arc sin x and sin u are related in a similar manner, as indicated by the equations

$$u = \int_0^x dx/(1 - x^2)^{1/2} = \text{arc sin } x, \qquad x = \sin u,$$

and the other trigonometric functions and their inverses can be defined in analogous ways.

These definitions of elementary transcendental functions suggest the desirability of studying the possibility of the determination of inverse functions $x(u)$, $y(u)$ by means of an equation of the form

$$(61 \cdot 1) \qquad u = \int_{(x_0, y_0)}^{(x, y)} \eta(x, y)dx,$$

where the integral on the right is an arbitrarily selected Abelian integral on the Riemann surface of an irreducible algebraic equation $f(x, y) = 0$. It turns out, however, that the integrals u which define single-valued inverses $x(u)$, $y(u)$ are very special ones relative to the total class of such integrals. In the following pages these special cases are analyzed, and it is shown that for them the inverse functions defined are rational functions of u, or rational functions of a simple exponential of the form Exp (u/a), or the so-called elliptic functions.

169

62. **Integrals which define single-valued inverses.** It is quite easy to discover the types of integrals which have single-valued inverses, with the help of the theory of rational functions and their divisors developed in Chapter III. Suppose that the integral (61·1) has such inverses $x(u)$, $y(u)$. At one of its ordinary places P on the Riemann surface T its expansion

$$(62\cdot1) \qquad u = \int_{(x_0, y_0)}^{(x, y)} \eta(x, y)dx = u_1 + ct^\rho + \cdots \qquad (c \neq 0),$$

must have the exponent ρ equal to unity. Otherwise the equation $(62\cdot1)$ would define a solution series for t in powers of $(u - u_1)^{1/\rho}$ of the form

$$t = c^{-1/\rho}(u - u_1)^{1/\rho} + \cdots,$$

and to each value of u near to u_1 there would correspond by this equation ρ values of t and consequently ρ places (x, y) on T near P for each of which equation $(62\cdot1)$ would be satisfied. The equation has a single-valued inverse only when $\rho = 1$.

Since when $\rho = 1$ the value of c in the expansion $(62\cdot1)$ is the value of the product $\eta dx/dt$ at the place P, it follows that this product can have no zeros on the surface T. The divisor of the product has therefore the form $Q_\eta X/D^2 = 1/I$, where Q_η is the divisor of η, X/D^2 is the divisor of dx/dt, and I is an integral divisor. The order q of I is $q = 2 - 2p$ since the orders of Q_η and X/D^2 are zero and $w - 2n = 2p - 2$, respectively, in accordance with Corollary 2 of Theorem 21·4. Since $q = 2 - 2p$ is necessarily positive or zero it follows that the only possible values for the genus p when the integral $(62\cdot1)$ defines single-valued inverses are $p = 0$ and $p = 1$.

In the case $p = 1$ the value of q is zero and the product $\eta dx/dt$ has the divisor $Q_\eta X/D^2 = 1$ and has no zeros or poles on the surface T. The integral $(62\cdot1)$ is then an integral of the first kind. When $p = 0$ we have $q = 2$, and the divisor of $\eta dx/dt$ has the form $Q_\eta X/D^2 = 1/P_1 P_2$. If the places P_1 and P_2 are coincident the integral $(62\cdot1)$ is an integral of the second kind with a simple pole, and if P_1 and P_2 are distinct it is an integral of the third kind with two simple logarithmic places and no other singularities. These results may be summarized in the following theorem:

THEOREM 62·1. *If an Abelian integral*

$$(62\cdot2) \qquad u = \int_{(x_0, y_0)}^{(x, y)|} \eta(x, y)dx$$

on the Riemann surface T of an irreducible algebraic equation $f(x, y) = 0$ defines single-valued inverse functions $x(u)$, $y(u)$, then the genus of the curve $f = 0$ must be either $p = 0$ or $p = 1$. In the case $p = 0$ the integral is either of the second kind with a single simple pole, or of the third kind with two simple logarithmic places and no other singularities. In case $p = 1$ the integral is of the first kind.

The integrals which may have single-valued inverses are thus of relatively simple kinds, but the functions which they define and their inverses are some of the most useful ones known to mathematicians, as we shall see in the following sections.

63. **Inverse functions for the case $p = 0$.** It has been seen on page 117 that when $p = 0$ all integrals of the second kind are single-valued on the Riemann surface T and are expressible as rational functions of x and y. An integral $(62 \cdot 2)$ of the second kind which has a single-valued inverse is therefore a rational function $\xi(x, y)$ with a single simple pole. The equation $u = \xi(x, y)$ with the equation $f(x, y) = 0$ consequently define x and y as rational functions of u, as shown in the proof of Theorem $50 \cdot 1$. The inverse functions $x(u)$, $y(u)$ for the integral $(62 \cdot 2)$ are therefore in this case rational functions of u.

When the integral $(62 \cdot 2)$ is of the third kind with two simple logarithmic singularities at places P_1 and P_2 we can always construct a rational function $\xi(x, y)$ with a simple pole at P_2 and a simple zero at P_1. For by the third row of the table of Theorem $26 \cdot 2$ for the case $p = 0$, $q = 1$ there are $\mu = 2$ linearly independent functions with no singularities other than a simple pole at P_2, and a linear combination of them can be selected which vanishes at P_1. According to Theorem $40 \cdot 3$ the function $\log \left[\xi(x, y) / \xi(x_0, y_0) \right]$ is expressible as an Abelian integral with simple logarithmic singularities at P_1 and P_2, and the difference $u - a \log \left[\xi(x, y) / \xi(x_0, y_0) \right]$ will be an integral with no singularities provided that a is the residue of the integrand η of the integral $(62 \cdot 2)$ at the place P_1. The integral expressing the difference $u - a \log (\xi / \xi_0)$ must have its integrand identically zero since when $p = 0$ there is no integral of the first kind. Hence we have

$$\xi(x, y) = \xi(x_0, y_0) \ \text{Exp} \ (u/a).$$

The argument applied in the last paragraph now shows that x and y are expressible as rational functions of $\text{Exp} \ (u/a)$.

THEOREM $63 \cdot 1$. *When $p = 0$ an integral $(62 \cdot 2)$ of the second kind with a single simple pole defines single-valued inverse functions $x(u)$, $y(u)$ which* *are rational in u, an integral of the third kind with two simple logarithmic places and no other singularities defines single-valued inverse functions $x(u)$ and $y(u)$ which are expressible rationally in terms of $Exp(u/a)$, where a is a residue of the integrand $\eta(x, y)$ of the integral.*

The integral of the third kind for the case $p = 0$ is single-valued for integration paths on a surface T'' formed from T by joining the logarithmic singularities P_1 and P_2 by a cut. The period of the integral across this cut is $2\pi i a$, where a is the residue described in the theorem, and the values of the integral corresponding to arbitrary paths on T from (x_0, y_0) to (x, y) differ by integral multiples of this period, since when $p = 0$ there are no other periods. It is evident, therefore, that if a value u corresponds to a place (x, y) then all of the values $u + m2\pi i a$, where m is an integer, will correspond to the same place. The inverse functions $x(u)$, $y(u)$ must consequently be periodic with the period $2\pi i a$, as indicated also by the fact that they are expressible rationally in terms of the function $\mathrm{Exp}\,(u/a)$ which has the same period.

64. Inverse functions when $p = 1$. Every integral $(62 \cdot 2)$ of the first kind defines single-valued inverse functions $x(u)$, $y(u)$ when $p = 1$. To prove this we may notice in the first place that equation $(62 \cdot 2)$ has at most one solution (x, y) for each value of u. If it were satisfied by two places $P_1 = (x_1, y_1)$, $P_2 = (x_2, y_2)$ and the same value u there would be a

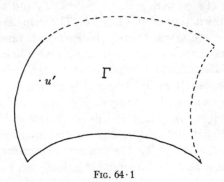

FIG. 64·1

rational function $\xi(x, y)$ with a simple zero at P_1 and a simple pole at P_2, according to the corollary to Theorem $40 \cdot 4$. But this is impossible when $p = 1$, by Theorem $26 \cdot 4$.

We can also prove that equation $(62 \cdot 2)$ has at least one solution $x(u)$, $y(u)$ for every finite value u. To do this let us consider the curve Γ in the u-plane which corresponds to the boundary B' of the simply

connected Riemann surface T' by means of equation (62·2) in which
the path of the integral is supposed not to cross the boundary of T'. It
is a curvilinear polygon, as shown in Figure 64·1, whose opposite sides
are congruent under the translations $u_1 = u + 2\omega_1$ and $u_1 = u + 2\omega_2$, where
$2\omega_1$ and $2\omega_2$ are the periods of the integral (62·2) across the cuts a_1 and
b_1. If u' is a value in the interior of Γ the first integral in the equation

$$\int_\Gamma du/(u - u') = \int_{B'} \eta dx/(u - u')$$

has the value $2\pi i$, and since the product $\eta dx/dt$ has no singularities on
T' it follows that in the second integral the denominator $u(x, y) - u'$
must vanish at one place $P' = (x', y')$ at least on the interior of T'. The
same reasoning applied to the two integrals in opposite order shows that
every value u' of $u(x, y)$ at a place P' interior to T' must be interior to
Γ. Hence equation (62·2) defines a one-to-one correspondence between
the surface T' and the parallelogram Γ when the paths of integration
of the integral do not cross the boundary of T'. Equation (62·2) has
further a solution $x(u)$, $y(u)$ for every finite value u, whether on the
parallelogram Γ or not, provided that the path of integration of the
integral is properly chosen. This follows from the fact that every such
value u is expressible in the form $u = u' + 2m_1\omega_1 + 2m_2\omega_2$ where m_1 and
m_2 are integers and u' is on Γ or its interior. Hence if values x', y' correspond to u' by means of equation (62·2) with a path of integration
on T', they will also correspond to u by the same equation with a path
on T which crosses the period cuts a proper number of times. The functions $x(u)$, $y(u)$ thus defined on the entire u-plane are therefore single-
valued and doubly periodic with the periods $2\omega_1$ and $2\omega_2$.

It is easy to see that $x(u)$ and $y(u)$ have no singularities in the finite
u-plane other than poles. To prove this we may show first that the
product $\eta dx/dt$ has no zeros on the Riemann surface T. Its divisor
$Q_\eta X/D^2$ has in fact the order zero when $p = 1$, as was seen in Section 62,
and this shows that $\eta dx/dt$ has no zeros, since for an integral of the first
kind it can have no poles. The expansion for the integral (62·2) at an
arbitrary place P on T has therefore the form

(64·1) $$u = \int_{(x_0, y_0)}^{(x,y)} \eta(x, y)dx = u_1 + ct + \cdots ,$$

where u_1 and c are the values of the integral and its derivative $\eta dx/dt$
at P, and c is different from zero. For values of u near to u_1 the places

$P = (x, y)$ on T where equation $(64 \cdot 1)$ is satisfied are consequently defined by a series

$(64 \cdot 2)$ $\qquad\qquad t = c^{-1}(u - u_1) + \cdots$

in positive integral powers of $u - u_1$. The corresponding values of $x(u)$, $y(u)$ are found by substituting the value of t from $(64 \cdot 2)$ in the expansions of the branch satisfying $f = 0$ with vertex at P. It is evident then that $x(u)$ and $y(u)$ have no singularities except poles. Hence we have the following theorem:

THEOREM $64 \cdot 1$. *When $p = 1$ an Abelian integral $(62 \cdot 2)$ of the first kind defines single-valued inverse functions $x(u)$, $y(u)$ which are holomorphic except for poles in the finite u-plane and which are doubly periodic. The periods of $x(u)$ and $y(u)$ are the periods $2\omega_1$ and $2\omega_2$ of the integral $(62 \cdot 2)$ on the cuts a_1 and b_1.*

According to the corollary to Theorem $35 \cdot 3$ the periods $2\omega_1$ and $2\omega_2$ do not satisfy any linear relation of the form $a\omega_1 + b\omega_2 = 0$, where a and b are real constants. Two periods of this sort are said to be independent. An *elliptic function* $g(u)$ is by definition one which is holomorphic except for poles in the finite u-plane and which has two independent periods $2\omega_1$, $2\omega_2$. The inverse functions $x(u)$, $y(u)$ in Theorem $64 \cdot 1$ are evidently elliptic functions.

COROLLARY. *Every irreducible algebraic curve $f(x, y) = 0$ of genus $p = 1$ is representable parametrically in the form $x = x(u)$, $y = y(u)$ where $x(u)$ and $y(u)$ are elliptic functions with periods $2\omega_1$ and $2\omega_2$ equal to those of an integral $(62 \cdot 2)$ of the first kind associated with the curve.*

This representation of a curve of genus $p = 1$ is analogous to that for a unicursal curve of genus $p = 0$ in equation $(50 \cdot 1)$.

65. Analogies between elliptic functions and rational functions of x and y. The following theorem describes a correspondence between rational functions on the Riemann surface of a curve $f(x, y) = 0$ and elliptic functions by means of which many properties of the latter may be deduced as corollaries to theorems which have been proved in preceding pages concerning the former, or vice versa. In the following paragraphs, after the proof of the theorem, a number of such properties and their analogues in the theory of rational functions are listed.

THEOREM $65 \cdot 1$. *Every elliptic function $g(u)$ with the periods $2\omega_1$, $2\omega_2$ of an integral*

$(65 \cdot 1)$ $\qquad\qquad u = \int_{(x_0, y_0)}^{(x, y)} \psi(x, y) dx$

of the first kind on the Riemann surface T of an irreducible algebraic curve of genus $p = 1$, is a rational function $\xi(x, y)$ when the value (65·1) for u is substituted in it. Every rational function $\xi(x, y)$ becomes similarly an elliptic function $g(u)$ when the inverse functions $x(u)$, $y(u)$ defined by the equation (65·1) are substituted. For every zero of $g(u)$ in the period parallelogram Γ there is a zero of $\xi(x, y)$ of the same order at the corresponding place on T, and similarly for poles.

To prove the theorem we see first of all that the result of substituting the integral (65·1) in an elliptic function $g(u)$ is a function $\xi(x, y)$ which is independent of the path of integration used for the integral, on account of the periodicity of $g(u)$. Consequently $\xi(x, y)$ is single-valued on the surface T. The expansion for $\xi(x, y)$ near a place P at which the integral (65·1) has the value u_1 on T is found by substituting the series (64·1) in the expansion for $g(u)$ in powers of $u - u_1$. Since the coefficient c in (64·1) is different from zero it follows that the orders of $g(u)$ and $\xi(x, y)$ at corresponding places are the same. Since $g(u)$ has no singularities in the finite u-plane except poles the same is true of $\xi(x, y)$ on the surface T, and $\xi(x, y)$ is therefore rational. It is clear that every rational function $\xi(x, y)$ becomes an elliptic function $g(u)$ when the inverse functions $x(u)$, $y(u)$ are substituted, and by reasoning similar to that described above it follows that the orders of $\xi(x, y)$ and $g(u)$ at corresponding places are the same.

The equation (65·1) defines a one-to-one correspondence between the points of the period parallelogram Γ and the places on the Riemann surface T. According to the last theorem every property of rational functions $\xi(x, y)$ on T should therefore give a corresponding property for elliptic functions on the parallelogram Γ. In the following tabulation a number of such correspondences are listed involving theorems concerning rational functions which have been proved in preceding pages. It is always understood that the functions $\xi(x, y)$, $\eta(x, y)$ of the theorems are rational functions on the Riemann surface T of an algebraic curve $f(x, y) = 0$ of genus $p = 1$, and that the elliptic functions have the periods $2\omega_1$, $2\omega_2$ of an integral of the first kind on T.

A rational function $\xi(x, y)$ with no poles on T is a constant.	An elliptic function $g(u)$ with no poles in its period parallelogram Γ is a constant.
The sum of the orders of the zeros and poles of $\xi(x, y)$ on T is zero.	The sum of the orders of the zeros and poles of an elliptic function $g(u)$ on its period parallelogram Γ is zero.
The sum of the residues of $\xi(x, y)$ on T is zero.	The sum of the residues of an elliptic function in its period parallelogram is zero.

There exists no function $\xi(x, y)$ with a single simple pole on T.

There exists no elliptic function having a single simple pole in its period parallelogram.

The sum of the values of an integral of the first kind at the zeros of a rational function $\xi(x, y)$ differs from the sum of its values at the poles of $\xi(x, y)$ by a period $2m_1\omega_1 + 2m_2\omega_2$.

The sum of the values of u at the zeros of an elliptic function $g(u)$ in the period parallelogram Γ differs from the sum of the values of u at the poles of $g(u)$ in Γ by a period $2m_1\omega_1 + 2m_2\omega_2$.

Every pair of rational functions $\xi(x, y)$, $\eta(x, y)$ on T satisfies an irreducible algebraic equation $\phi(\xi, \eta) = 0$ of genus $p = 1$ or $p = 0$. A necessary and sufficient condition that the curve $\phi = 0$ shall be birationally related to $f = 0$ and have genus $p = 1$ is that there exists a constant α such that the values of η at the zeros of $\xi(x, y) - \alpha$ on T are distinct. The degree of ϕ in η is then the sum of the orders of the zeros of $\xi(x, y)$ on T.

Every pair of elliptic functions $g(u)$, $h(u)$ satisfies identically an irreducible algebraic equation $\phi(g, h) = 0$ of genus $p = 1$ or $p = 0$. A necessary and sufficient condition that the curve $\phi = 0$ shall be birationally related to $f = 0$ and have genus $p = 1$ is that there exists a constant α such that the values of $h(u)$ at the zeros of $g(u) - \alpha$ in Γ are distinct. The degree of ϕ in h is then the sum of the orders of the zeros of $g(u)$ in Γ.

Every rational function $\zeta(x, y)$ on T is expressible rationally in terms of two such functions $\xi(x, y)$, $\eta(x, y)$ for which the corresponding irreducible curve $\phi(\xi, \eta) = 0$ is birationally related to $f = 0$ and has genus $p = 1$.

Every elliptic function $k(u)$ is expressible rationally in terms of two such functions $g(u)$, $h(u)$ for which the corresponding irreducible equation $\phi(g, h) = 0$ is birationally related to $f = 0$ and has genus $p = 1$.

Let us consider for the moment the integral of the first kind

$$(65 \cdot 2) \qquad\qquad u = \int_{(0,1)}^{(x,y)} dx/y$$

for the algebraic function $y(x)$ defined by the equation

$$(65 \cdot 3) \qquad\qquad y^2 - (1 - x^2)(1 - k^2 x^2) = 0 \qquad\qquad (0 < k < 1).$$

The equation $(65 \cdot 2)$ defines inverse functions $x(u)$, $y(u)$, and the fundamental elliptic function $sn\,u$ of Jacobi is by definition the function $x(u)$. Near a place (x, y) on the Riemann surface T of the algebraic function $y(x)$ defined by equation $(65 \cdot 3)$ the integrand of the integral $(65 \cdot 2)$ is a function of x and the upper limit of the integral is x. The equation $(65 \cdot 2)$ becomes an identity in u when $x = sn\,u$ is substituted for this limit. Hence by differentiation with respect to u we find $1 = (1/y)dx/du$ and $y = d\,sn\,u/du$. According to the last theorem in the list above every elliptic function with the periods of the integral $(65 \cdot 2)$ is expressible as a rational function of $sn\,u$ and $d\,sn\,u/du$. In a similar manner the fundamental elliptic function $x = \wp(u)$ of Weierstrass may be defined as the inverse function for the integral (65·2) on the Riemann surface of the algebraic function defined by the equation

$$y^2 - 4x^3 + g_2 x + g_3 = 0,$$

and the corresponding function $y(u)$ is the derivative $y = \wp'(u)$. Every elliptic function with the periods of $\wp(u)$ is rationally expressible in terms of $\wp(u)$ and $\wp'(u)$.

66. **Further remarks concerning elliptic functions.** The theorems concerning elliptic functions in the dual list given in the preceding section may seem at first sight to have only a restricted application, since the periods $2\omega_1$, $2\omega_2$ of the functions must be those of an integral of the first kind on the Riemann surface of an algebraic function of genus $p = 1$. If we are willing to accept the existence of the elliptic function $\wp(u)$ of Weierstrass, however, when two arbitrarily selected periods $2\omega_1$, $2\omega_2$ for it are given, we can show that these periods are those of an integral of the first kind, as described above, and hence that the theorems are true for all elliptic functions. The existence proof for the function $\wp(u)$ is a fundamental one in the books on the theory of elliptic functions.

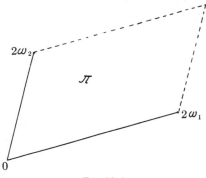

FIG. 66·1

A number of the theorems listed in the last section can be proved directly with very little difficulty for elliptic functions with any independent periods $2\omega_1$, $2\omega_2$ whatsoever. We can see in the first place, with the help of Theorem 6·1, that an elliptic function $g(u)$ with no poles is a constant. For the absolute value of such a function will have an upper bound M in the period parallelogram π of Figure 66·1 which will also be an upper bound for $|g(u)|$ in the whole finite u-plane. A function $g(u)$ with such an upper bound is a constant, as stated in Theorem 6·1.

In every finite region of the u-plane the poles of an elliptic function $g(u)$ are isolated from each other, since otherwise they would have an accumulation point which would be an essential singularity, and an elliptic function has by definition only poles as singularities. If $g(u)$ has poles on the boundary of the period parallelogram π the parallelogram can be translated slightly to a new position in which it contains all the poles of $g(u)$ which lie on π and which is such that no poles of $g(u)$ lie upon its boundary. On account of the periodicity of $g(u)$ the integrals of $g(u)$ in the same direction on two opposite sides of such a period parallelogram are equal, and hence the integral of $g(u)$ around the boundary of the parallelogram is zero. It follows at once that the sum of the residues of an elliptic function in a period parallelogram π is zero, and that there is no elliptic function with a single simple pole in π.

By differentiating the equation

$$g(u + 2m_1\omega_1 + 2m_2\omega_2) = g(u)$$

we see that the derivative $g'(u)$ of an elliptic function is an elliptic function with the same periods. Hence the sum of the residues of the quotient $g'(u)/g(u)$ in the parallelogram π is zero, which means that the sum of the orders of the zeros and poles of $g(u)$ in π is zero.

When two independent periods $2\omega_1$, $2\omega_2$ are selected arbitrarily there exists an elliptic function $\wp(u)$ having these periods, having a pole of order 2 at the origin and no other pole in the period parallelogram π, and having the constant term zero in its expansion at $u=0$. Furthermore this function is an even function so that $\wp(-u) = \wp(u)$. The proof of these results is beyond the scope of this book, but it is an important part of the Weierstrassian theory of elliptic functions and is given in every treatise on the subject. Let us accept these properties of the function $\wp(u)$ and see what further conclusions can be drawn.

By differentiating the relation $\wp(-u) = \wp(u)$ it is seen that $\wp'(-u) = -\wp'(u)$ and hence that $\wp'(u)$ is an odd function. From this and the periodicity of $\wp'(u)$ it follows that

$$\wp'(\omega_1) = -\wp'(-\omega_1) = -\wp'(\omega_1)$$

so that $u=\omega_1$ is a zero of $\wp'(u)$. A similar argument shows that ω_2 and $\omega_1+\omega_2$ are also zeros. All three of these zeros are simple since $\wp'(u)$ has a pole of order 3 at $u=0$ and no other pole in π, and the sum of the orders of its zeros and poles in π is zero. If we denote by e_1, e_2, e_3 the values of $\wp(u)$ at ω_1, $\omega_1+\omega_2$, ω_2, respectively, we may infer readily that e_1, e_2, e_3 must be distinct, since each difference $\wp(u)-e_i$ has no pole in π

other than one of order 2 at $u=0$, and it can have no zero in π other than the one of order 2 which it has at the one of the points ω_1, $\omega_1+\omega_2$, ω_2 which corresponds to e_i. With the help of this result we see that the two elliptic functions

$$\wp'^2(u), \qquad 4[\wp(u) - e_1][\wp(u) - e_2][\wp(u) - e_3]$$

have the same zeros and poles in π and hence that their quotient is a constant. By comparing their expansions at $u=0$, where

$$\wp(u) = 1/u^2 + cu^2 + \cdots, \qquad \wp'(u) = -2/u^3 + 2cu + \cdots,$$

we see that the value of the constant is unity, and that the term in $\wp^2(u)$ in the product on the right must vanish. Hence the functions $x = \wp(u)$, $y = \wp'(u)$ satisfy an algebraic equation of the form

$$(66\cdot1) \qquad\qquad y^2 = 4x^3 - g_2 x - g_3$$

where the roots of the second member are distinct numbers e_1, e_2, e_3 such that $e_1+e_2+e_3=0$. By examining the expansions for the simple algebraic function $y(x)$ determined by this equation we see that the genus of the equation is $p=1$.

If the equation $\wp(u+2\omega) = \wp(u)$ is an identity in u, then $\omega = m_1\omega_1 + m_2\omega_2$, where m_1 and m_2 are integers. This equation in fact implies that for every value of u the sum $u+2\omega$ is congruent modulo a period to either u or $-u$. It is evident that $u+2\omega$ cannot be congruent to $-u$ for all values of u. There must therefore be values u for which $u+2\omega$ is congruent to u, and it follows readily that ω has the form given. A pair of *primitive periods of* $\wp(u)$ is a pair of periods $2\omega_1'$, $2\omega_2'$ which satisfy equations of the form

$$(66\cdot2) \qquad \omega_1' = m_{11}\,\omega_1 + m_{12}\,\omega_2, \qquad \omega_2' = m_{21}\,\omega_1 + m_{22}\,\omega_2$$

in which the coefficients m_{ik} are integers with determinant equal to ±1. Every half-period ω is evidently expressible linearly in terms of ω_1', ω_2' with integral coefficients, as well as in terms of ω_1 and ω_2. With these results in mind we may prove the following theorem.

THEOREM 66·1. *For every pair of independent periods $2\omega_1$, $2\omega_2$ there exists a pair of elliptic functions*

$$(66\cdot3) \qquad\qquad x = \wp(u), \qquad y = \wp'(u)$$

having these periods and satisfying an irreducible algebraic equation $(66\cdot1)$ of genus $p=1$. For each pair (x, y) satisfying the equation $(66\cdot1)$ there exists one and but one solution u of equations $(66\cdot3)$ in the period parallelogram π,

and the totality of solutions of (66·3) *is the set of values* $u + 2m_1\omega_1 + 2m_2\omega_2$
where m_1 *and* m_2 *are integers. These solutions are the values of the integral
of the first kind*

$$(66·4) \qquad\qquad w = \int_{(x_0,y_0)}^{(x,y)} dx/y$$

on the Riemann surface T *of equation* (66·1), *except for an additive constant. The periods* $2\omega_1'$, $2\omega_2'$ *of the integral are a pair of primitive periods
for the function* $\wp(u)$.

The first statement of the theorem has been proved above. For a
given value x the first equation (66·3) has a pair of solutions u and
$-u + 2\omega_1 + 2\omega_2$ in the period parallelogram, at which $\wp'(u)$ has opposite
signs. When x and y satisfy equation (66·1) one and only one of these
solutions makes $\wp'(u) = y$. It is evident then that the solutions u of the
equation (66·3) have the properties described in the second sentence of
the theorem.

Every solution u of the equations (66·3) can be joined to the point
u_0 in π corresponding to (x_0, y_0) by a path C_1 in the u-plane not passing
through any point congruent to a half-period. The equations (66·3)
then define a corresponding path C on the Riemann surface T of equation (66·1) not passing through any branch place $(x, y) = (e_i, 0)$ on T.
On the path C the integral w is a function of u with the derivative
$dw/du = (1/y)dx/du = 1$. Hence at corresponding places on the paths C
and C_1 we have $w = u - u_0$, and it is evident that every solution u of the
equations (66·3) is equal to u_0 plus a value of the integral (66·4) on a
properly chosen path C joining (x_0, y_0) to (x, y).

Every value w of the integral (66·4) defined by a path C joining the
places (x_0, y_0) and (x, y) on the Riemann surface T is equal to a difference $u - u_0$ in which u is a solution of equations (66·3) corresponding
to (x, y). For one can readily see that the equations (66·3) define a path
C_1 in the u-plane corresponding to C and joining u_0 to a solution u of
these equations. The argument of the preceding paragraph then shows
that $w = u - u_0$.

If the variable place (x, y) describes the period cut b_1 on the surface
T from an initial place (x_0, y_0) back to that place again, the corresponding value u describes a path in the u-plane leading from a point u_0 to a
congruent point $u_0 + 2m_{11}\omega_1 + 2m_{12}\omega_2$. If we designate the periods of the
integral (66·4) by $2\omega_1'$, $2\omega_2'$, then on the path b_1 we have $w = 2\omega_1'$,
and hence by the relation $w = u - u_0$ on the paths b_1 and C_1 it follows
that ω_1' is expressible in the form (66·2). A similar argument justifies

the second equation for ω_2'. By starting from paths C_1 in the u-plane leading from a fixed point u_0 to points $u_0+2\omega_1$ and $u_0+2\omega_2$, we may see similarly that equations of the form

$$(66\cdot5) \qquad \omega_1 = n_{11}\,\omega_1' + n_{12}\,\omega_2', \qquad \omega_2 = n_{21}\,\omega_1' + n_{22}\,\omega_2'$$

hold with integral coefficients n_{ik}. Since the succession of the two transformations $(66\cdot2)$ and $(66\cdot5)$ must be the identity it follows readily that the determinant of the coefficients m_{ik} is either $+1$ or -1, and the theorem is proved.

Theorem $66\cdot1$ makes it clear that for every pair of independent periods $2\omega_1$, $2\omega_2$ there is an algebraic curve $f(x,\,y)=0$ of genus $p=1$ whose integral of the first kind has $2\omega_1$ and $2\omega_2$ as primitive periods. Hence we see that the theorems of Section 65 must hold for all elliptic functions.

COROLLARY. *If a pair of elliptic functions $g(u)$, $h(u)$ define parametrically a curve*

$$(66\cdot6) \qquad x = g(u), \qquad y = h(u)$$

such that to each point $(x,\,y)$ on the curve there corresponds one and but one point u on a period parallelogram, then the curve has an irreducible algebraic equation $f(x,\,y)=0$ of genus $p=1$. The values u corresponding by equations $(66\cdot6)$ to the places $(x,\,y)$ on the curve are the values of an integral of the first kind

$$w = \int_{(x_0,\,y_0)}^{(x,\,y)} \psi(x,\,y)dx$$

on the Riemann surface T of $f=0$. The periods of the integral are a pair of primitive periods of the functions $g(u)$ and $h(u)$.

The first statement of this theorem is a consequence of the next to last theorem concerning elliptic functions, in the dual list of Section 65. Let u_0 be the solution of equations $(66\cdot6)$ in the period parallelogram π corresponding to the place $(x_0,\,y_0)$ on the Riemann surface T of the equation $f(x,\,y)=0$. By a proof similar to that of Theorem $66\cdot1$ we may see that to every path C on the Riemann surface T of the curve $f=0$, joining $(x_0,\,y_0)$ to $(x,\,y)$ and consisting only of finite ordinary places $(x,\,y)$ on T, there corresponds by means of equations $(66\cdot6)$ a unique path C_1 on the u-plane joining u_0 to a solution u of equations $(66\cdot6)$ and not passing through any pole of $g(u)$ or $h(u)$ or any zero of $g'(u)$. Conversely every path C_1 with these properties defines a corresponding path C. On such a path C the values of the derivative

$$dw/du = \psi(x, y)dx/du = \psi(x, y)g'(u)$$

are the values of a rational function of x and y since the derivative $g'(u)$ is rationally expressible in terms of $g(u)$ and $h(u)$, by the last theorem of the list for elliptic functions in Section 65. The rational function representing dw/du has no poles on the Riemann surface T, since otherwise w itself would have singularities in the u-plane when the functions (66·6) are substituted and would not remain finite near corresponding places (x, y) on T, which is impossible for an integral of the first kind. Hence dw/du is a rational function with no poles on T and therefore a constant, and we see that it will be unity if we modify w by a suitable constant factor. Let us suppose that this has been done. Then for the paths C and C_1 we have $w = u - u_0$ as in the proof of Theorem 60·1. The remainder of the proof of the corollary is the same as that of the original theorem.

REFERENCES FOR CHAPTER IX

References for the inversion problem when $p = 1$ are: 2, 1st ed., Vorlesung IX; 18, Chapter X; 27, Chapter XXII. For the theory of elliptic functions one may consult the standard texts. For more general inversion problems see 4; 11, Memoire VI; 13, Chapter X; 18, Chapter X; 20, Part II; 21, Chapter IX; 27, Abschnitt III; 47, Chapter VIII.

EXAMPLES

67. **Introduction.** It is not always easy to apply the theorems developed in the preceding pages to an arbitrarily given special case of an algebraic function. Examples can be selected, however, for which various parts of the theory can be carried through with reasonable calculation. In the following pages a number of such cases are worked out in considerable detail, and other examples are listed which can be similarly discussed. Sections 68–70 are devoted to examples for which the expansions at singular points and at $x = \infty$, or the Riemann surfaces, can be determined without serious difficulty. In Section 70, in particular, equations of the elliptic and hyperelliptic types are treated. Additional methods are developed in Sections 71–76 for algebraic curves $f(x, y) = 0$ which are of the third degree in y, or of the fourth degree in x and y. For the former case the results are attained by rational methods depending upon the computation of greatest common divisors. In the final section of the chapter examples are given to which this theory can be applied.

68. **Examples for expansions.** For the purpose of illustrating the determination of the expansions of an algebraic function let us consider the special equation

$$(68 \cdot 1) \qquad f(x, y) = y^3 + x^3 y + x = 0$$

which has been discussed by Baur [19, p. 56]. The discriminant of this equation, according to the results of Section 8, is

$$D(x) = 3x^2(4x^7 + 27),$$

and the values of x over which there may be branch places are therefore $x = 0$, $x = \infty$, and the seven roots $x = \xi$ of the equation $4\xi^7 + 27 = 0$. We can readily tabulate the corresponding solutions y of equation (68·1) as follows:

x	$y,$	$y,$	y
0	0,	0,	0
∞	0,	∞,	∞
ξ	$-3/2\xi^2,$	$-3/2\xi^2,$	$3/\xi^2.$

The first two values in the last row are equal to the one of the two roots $(-\xi^3/3)^{1/2} = \pm 3/2\xi^2$ of the derivative $f_y(\xi, y) = 3y^2 + \xi^3$ which satisfies $f(\xi, y) = 0$ also. The branches corresponding to these values of x will be determined in the following paragraphs, but the results may be collected in advance as indicated in the following list:

At $x = 0$; $x = t^3$, $y = \omega t + (\omega^2/3)t^8 + \cdots$ $(\omega^3 = -1)$,

At $x = \infty$; $x = 1/t$, $y = -t^2 + t^9 + \cdots$,

             $x = 1/t^2$, $y = t^{-3}(i + t^7/2 + \cdots)$,

At $x = \xi$; $x = \xi + t^2$, $y = -3/2\xi^2 + (i\xi\, 7^{1/2}/3)t + \cdots$,

             $x = \xi + t$, $y = 3/\xi^2 + (10/3\xi^3)t + \cdots$.

At the place $(x, y) = (0, 0)$ Newton's polygon has the simple form shown in Figure 68·1. The corresponding substitution is $x = t^3$, $y = tu$ which with the help of (68·1) gives the equation

$$u^3 + t^7 u + 1 = 0$$

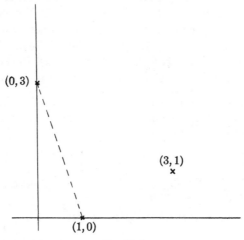

FIG. 68·1

in the variables t, u. If we substitute the series

$$u = c_0 + c_1 t + c_2 t^2 + \cdots$$

in this equation and determine its coefficients by comparison we find

$$u = \omega + (\omega^2/3)t^7 + \cdots,$$

where ω is a primitive cube root of -1. This gives at once the branch indicated in the above list.

To determine the expansions at $x = \infty$ we first substitute $x = 1/x'$ in equation (68·1) obtaining

$$(68·2) \qquad\qquad x'^3 y^3 + y + x'^2 = 0.$$

The first expansion of the list for $x = \infty$ is found by substituting

$$y = c_0 + c_1 x' + \cdots$$

in this equation and determining the coefficients by comparison. To determine the other expansions we use the equation

$$x'^3 + y'^2 + x'^2 y'^3 = 0$$

found from (68·2) by substituting $y = 1/y'$. The Newton polygon for $(x', y') = (0, 0)$ gives the substitution $x' = t^2$, $y' = t^3 u$ and the equation

$$1 + u^2 + t^7 u^3 = 0,$$

from which we find

$$u = -i + t^7/2 + \cdots ,$$
$$y = 1/t^3 u = (1/t^3)(i + t^7/2 + \cdots).$$

At the place $(x, y) = (\xi, -3/2\xi^2)$ Taylor's formula gives

$$f(x, y) = -7(x - \xi)/2 + 3\xi\eta(x - \xi)^2 + 3\xi^2(x - \xi)(y - \eta)$$
$$+ 3\eta(y - \eta)^2 + \cdots .$$

The corresponding Newton Polygon is easily constructed and gives the substitution $x = \xi + t^2$, $y = \eta + tu$. The equation for t, u is

$$-7/2 + 3\xi\eta t^2 + 3\xi^2 tu + 3\eta u^2 + \cdots = 0$$

from which we find easily the first expansion for $x = \xi$ in the list above. A similar process gives the last expansion of the list.

One can now determine readily the genus of the algebraic function defined by equation (68·1) from the formula (21·8) or (31·1),

$$p = (1/2)\sum(r - 1) - n + 1.$$

For the particular curve (68·1) the genus has the value $p = 3$, since there is one cycle of $r = 3$ sheets at $x = 0$, one of two sheets at $x = \infty$, and one of two sheets at each of the seven roots ξ of the equation $4\xi^7 + 27 = 0$.

The following examples have been collected from various sources which are indicated in the references given in the brackets adjoining each of them. The numbers refer to the list of references at the end of the book.

EXAMPLES FOR EXPANSIONS

1. $y^3 - 3y + 2x$ [18, 1st ed. p. 193, 2nd ed. p. 180]

2. $y^3 + 3y - x$ [35, 1st ed. p. 313, 5th ed. p. 403]

3. $y^3 - 3y^2 - x$ [35, 2nd ed. p. 377, 5th ed. p. 396]

4. $y^4 - 4y - x$ [35, 1st ed. p. 331, 5th ed. p. 401]

5. $y^4 + 2(1 - 2x)y^2 + 1$

6. $y^3 - 3y^2 + x^6$ [18, 1st ed. p. 193, 2nd ed. p. 181; 34, p. 422]

7. $y^3 - 3y + 2x^2(2 - x^2)$ [34, p. 422]

8. $y^3 - 3y + 2x^3(2 - x^3)$ [34, p. 422]

9. $3x(x - 1)y^4 - 4(x - 1)(x - 2)y^3 + (4/27)(x - 2)^4$

                                      [34, p. 418]

10. $y^5 + (x^2 - 1)y^4 - (4^4/5^5)x^2(x^2 - 1)$

                                      [34, p. 422]

11. $y^3 - 3axy + x^3$ [34, p. 422]

12. $y^3 - xy - x^2$ [42, pp. 31, 41]

13. $y^3 - 3x^2y + 2x$ [42, p. 141]

14. $y^3 - 3xy + 2x^2$ [42, p. 134]

15. $y^3 - 3y + x^6$

69. Examples for Riemann surfaces.

Let us consider the equation

$$(69 \cdot 1) \qquad\qquad y^4 - 4y - x = 0.$$

It is evidently of genus $p = 0$ since the equation is linear in x and therefore defines a unicursal curve. The discriminant is found to be

$$D(x) = -4^6(x^3 + 27).$$

The roots of $D(x)$ have the values $-3\omega^k$ ($k = 1, 2, 3$), where ω is the primitive cube root of unity in the second quadrant of the x-plane. One finds readily that the roots y of equation (69·1) corresponding to $x = -3\omega^k$ have the values ω^k, ω^k, $\omega^k(-1 \pm i2^{1/2})$.

The Riemann surface for the function $y(x)$ defined by equation (69·1) has four sheets which may be cut along the radii through the origin and the points $-3\omega^k$, as shown in Figure 69·1. If we designate the sheets by the values of the roots of equation (69·1) at the point

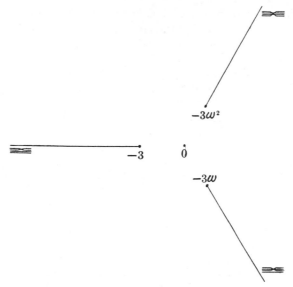

$$-3\omega^2$$

$$-3 \qquad \overset{.}{0}$$

$$-3\omega$$

FIG. 69·1

$x = 0$, we find the following table for the roots belonging to the various sheets at the singular points $x = -3\omega^k$:

x	y_1	y_2	y_3	y_4
0	0	$2^{2/3}$	$2^{2/3}\omega$	$2^{2/3}\omega^2$
-3	1	1	$-1 + i2^{1/2}$	$-1 - i2^{1/2}$
-3ω	ω	$\omega(-1 - i2^{1/2})$	ω	$\omega(-1 + i2^{1/2})$
$-3\omega^2$	ω^2	$\omega^2(-1 + i2^{1/2})$	$\omega^2(-1 - i2^{1/2})$	ω^2

The values into which the roots y_i at $x=0$ vary continuously as x traverses a radius from the origin can be found by substituting $x = -3\xi\omega^k$, $y = \eta\omega^k$ in equation (69·1), which then becomes

$$\eta^4 - 4\eta + 3\xi = 0.$$

As ξ increases from 0 to 1 the two real roots η of this equation vary from the values 0, $2^{2/3}$ to the value 1, as shown in Figure 69·2, and the two imaginary roots remain imaginary and keep the same signs for their imaginary parts. Hence as x varies from $x = 0$ to $x = -3\omega^k$ along a radius the roots $y = 0$, $2^{2/3}\omega^k$ vary continuously into ω^k. For each other root the values of $\eta = y/\omega^k$ at $x = 0$ and $x = -3\omega^k$, and in the same sheet, must have imaginary parts with the same sign. Thus we see that the numbering of the roots in the table is the correct one.

The character of the expansions at the branch places can readily be determined by the methods of the last section. Each of the double roots y in the table corresponds to the vertex of a cycle of two sheets, and at

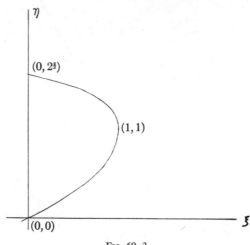

Fig. 69·2

$x = \infty$ there is a single cycle of four sheets. Thus the sheets of the Riemann surface should be joined along the edges of the cuts as indicated in Figure 69·1.

One of the difficulties in constructing a Riemann surface is the identification of the values of y belonging to the various sheets near the branch values of x, when values of y have been assigned to the sheets at a particular non-singular value of x. Theoretically one should be able to find corresponding values by analytic continuation, but this process is often very difficult. The following examples can be discussed by the method used above or suitable modifications of it. When the genus p is greater than zero it is interesting to try to find a system of cuts which will make the surface simply connected, as described in Section 32.

EXAMPLES FOR RIEMANN SURFACES

1. Examples 1–8, 11–15 of the list at the end of Section 68.

2. $y^6 - (x - a)^2(x - b)^3$ [35, 1st ed. p. 319, 5th ed. p. 388]

3. $y - [(x - a)/(x - c)^2]^{1/3} - (x - b)^{1/2}$

          [35, 1st ed. p. 318, 5th ed. p. 388]

4. $y - x^{1/3} - (x - 1)^{1/2}$ [42, p. 37]

5. $y^3 - x^6 + 1$ [42, p. 132]

6. $(x - c)y^3 - (x - b)$ [35, 1st ed. p. 318, 5th ed. p. 388]

7. $y^4 - A(x - \alpha)(x - \beta)^2(x - \gamma)$ [18, 1st ed. p. 236, 2nd ed. p. 229]

8. $y^4 - A(x - \alpha)(x - \beta)^2(x - \gamma)^3$ [18, 1st ed. p. 237, 2nd ed. p. 229]

9. $y^3 - A(x - \alpha)(x - \beta)(x - \gamma)(x - \delta)$

                                       [18, 1st ed. p. 237, 2nd ed. p. 231]

10. $y^3 - \dfrac{(x - a_1)^{k_1} \cdots (x - a_m)^{k_m}}{(x - b_1)^{l_1} \cdots (x - b_n)^{l_n}}$ [35, 1st ed. p. 318, 5th ed. p. 388]

11. $y^n - R(x)$, $R(x)$ rational   [18, 1st ed. p. 238 ff., 2nd ed. p. 231 ff.]

70. **Elliptic and hyperelliptic curves.** One of the very important classes of algebraic functions is the class defined by equations of the form

$$(70 \cdot 1) \qquad\qquad y^2 = A(x - \alpha_1) \cdots (x - \alpha_m)$$

in which $\alpha_1, \cdots, \alpha_m$ are distinct complex numbers. When $m = 3$ or 4 these are elliptic curves of genus $p = 1$. For $m > 4$ they are hyperelliptic and the values of the genus p are greater than 1.

Let us consider the case when m is even and can therefore be represented in the form $m = 2k + 2$. One can readily construct the discriminant

$$D(x) = 4A(x - \alpha_1) \cdots (x - \alpha_m)$$

of equation $(70 \cdot 1)$ and verify the fact that at each of the values $x = \alpha_i$ there is a cycle of two sheets. At $x = \infty$ there is no branch place when m is even. Hence we find

$$p = m/2 - 2 + 1 = k \qquad\qquad (m = 2k + 2).$$

The two-sheeted Riemann surface can readily be constructed by cutting each of the sheets along a broken line passing through all of the points $x = \alpha_i$ and out to $x = \infty$, as shown in Figure $70 \cdot 1$. If we assign the

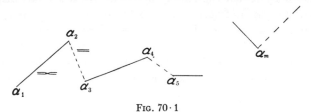

FIG. 70·1

values of y arbitrarily on the two sheets at a particular non-singular point x_0, then by writing

$$x - \alpha_k = r_k e^{i\phi_k}$$

and following the variations of the arguments ϕ_k we find from the expression

$$y = (A r_1 \cdots r_m)^{1/2} e^{i(\phi_1 + \cdots + \phi_m)/2}$$

that a value y_0 at $x = x_0$ goes continuously into the same value along paths leading from $x = x_0$ to opposite sides of one of the dotted lines in the figure, and to values with opposite signs on paths leading to opposite sides of the non-dotted lines. Thus we see that the sheets of the Riemann surface should be joined along the heavy and dotted lines, as indicated by the diagrams adjoining the first two of them in the figure.

For the hyperelliptic case here under consideration a canonical system of cuts reducing the Riemann surface to a simply connected one is shown in Figure 70·2. One verifies readily that none of the cuts severs the surface, and hence that after $2p$ of them have been drawn the remaining surface T' is simply connected.[1] The figure is for the case $m = 8$ when the genus is $p = 3$.

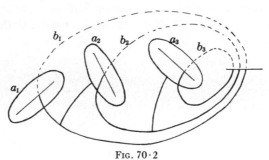

Fig. 70·2

It is often difficult in special cases to construct elementary integrals of the three kinds described in Sections 20 and 36, but for hyperelliptic curves the constructions can readily be made. We can see by inspection of the determinant Δ of Section 20, for the pair of functions 1, y, that these functions are a basis for the divisor $Q = 1$. Hence by Theorem 22·2 the complementary basis is a basis for the divisor $R = 1/X$, where X is the divisor of the branch places. But the basis ζ_1, ζ_2 complementary to a basis η_1, η_2 is related to these functions by equations of the form

$$\eta_1 = r_{11} \zeta_1 + r_{12} \zeta_2, \qquad \eta_2 = r_{21} \zeta_1 + r_{22} \zeta_2$$

in which the coefficients have the values $r_{ik} = T(\eta_i \eta_k)$, since by definition of a complementary basis the trace $T(\eta_i \zeta_k)$ is zero for $i \neq k$ and unity for $i = k$. From this relationship, set up for the basis $(\eta_1, \eta_2) = (1, y)$, we find readily that the complementary basis, except for a constant factor, is $(\zeta_1, \zeta_2) = (1, 1/y)$. If we wish to find the integrands of functions of the first kind we must examine the expansions for $1/y$ at $x = \infty$. We find

$$1/y_1 = A^{-1/2} x^{-k-1} \{ 1 + \cdots \},$$
$$1/y_2 = - A^{-1/2} x^{-k-1} \{ 1 + \cdots \}.$$

Hence the column orders of 1, $1/y$ at $x = \infty$ are $r_1 = 0$, $r_2 = k+1$. The integrands of integrals of the first kind are multiples of the divisor D^2/X and therefore must have orders ≥ 2 at $x = \infty$. Hence they are products of $1/y$ by polynomials in x of degree at most $k-1$, as indicated in the proof of Theorem 22·3. We have therefore the following result:

THEOREM 70·1. *For an algebraic function of hyperelliptic type defined by an equation* (70·1) *with* $m = 2k+2$ *the genus is* $p = k$ *and the functions*

$$1/y, \qquad x/y, \qquad \cdots, \qquad x^{p-1}/y$$

are the integrands of p linearly independent integrals of the first kind.

The integrands of elementary integrals of the third kind are multiples of divisors of the form $D^2/P_1 P_2 X$. Such an elementary integral can easily be constructed for two non-singular non-conjugate finite places $P_1 = (x_1, y_1)$ and $P_2 = (x_2, y_2)$ by modifying the basis 1, $1/y$ of the divisor $1/X$, as indicated in the proof of Theorem 20·2, so that it becomes a basis for $1/P_1 P_2 X$. The only two places where modification is necessary are P_1 and P_2. At the point $x = x_1$ the determinant Δ of the basis 1, $1/y$ with respect to the divisor $1/P_1 P_2 X$ is

$$\begin{vmatrix} 0 & 0 \\ 1 & -1/y_1 \end{vmatrix},$$

where the first row belongs to the place P_1 and the second row to the place conjugate to P_1 over $x = x_1$. If we set $c_1 = 1/2$, $c_2 = y_1/2$ the two functions

$$(70·2) \qquad 1/y, \qquad (c_1 + c_2/y)/(x - x_1) = (y + y_1)/2(x - x_1)y$$

will have their determinant Δ with respect to the divisor $1/P_1 P_2 X$ different from zero at $x = x_1$, as one readily verifies. Similarly at the point $x = x_2$ the functions (70·2) have the determinant

$$\Delta = \begin{vmatrix} 0 & 0 \\ -1/y_2 & (y_2 - y_1)/2(x_2 - x_1)y_2 \end{vmatrix}.$$

If we set

$$c_1 = (y_1 - y_2)/2, \qquad c_2 = x_1 - x_2$$

we find a pair of functions

$$(70 \cdot 3) \quad 1/y, \quad \frac{1}{x - x_2}\left(\frac{c_1}{y} + c_2 \frac{y + y_1}{2(x - x_1)y}\right) = \frac{1}{2y}\left(\frac{y + y_1}{x - x_1} - \frac{y + y_2}{x - x_2}\right)$$

whose determinant Δ with respect to the divisor $1/P_1P_2X$ is different from zero at $x = x_2$ also, and which is therefore a basis for the divisor $1/P_1P_2X$. The basis $(70 \cdot 3)$ is normal at $x = \infty$ with column orders $r_1 = p+1$, $r_2 = 2$, as can be verified by substituting the expansions for y at $x = \infty$. The multiples of the divisor D^2/P_1P_2X are therefore sums of products of the two functions of this basis by polynomials of degrees at most $r_1 - 2 = p - 1$ and $r_2 - 2 = 0$, respectively, and we have the following theorem:

THEOREM 70 · 2. *For an algebraic function of hyperelliptic type defined by an equation* $(70 \cdot 1)$ *with* $m = 2k+2$, *and for two non-singular places* $P_1 = (x_1, y_1)$, $P_2 = (x_2, y_2)$, *the integral*

$$(70 \cdot 4) \quad I = \int (1/2y)[(y + y_1)/(x - x_1) - (y + y_2)/(x - x_2)]dx$$

is an elementary integral of the third kind with logarithmic singularities at P_1 *and* P_2. *Its expansions at these places have the forms*

$$(70 \cdot 5) \quad \begin{aligned} I &= \log (x - x_1) + c_0 + c_1(x - x_1) + \cdots, \\ I &= -\log (x - x_2) + d_0 + d_1(x - x_2) + \cdots, \end{aligned}$$

respectively.

The character of the expansions, and the fact that the theorem holds even when P_1 and P_2 are conjugate places, can be readily verified.

From the last theorem one may readily deduce the following one:

THEOREM 70 · 3. *For an algebraic function defined by an equation* $(70 \cdot 1)$ *with* $m = 2k+2$, *and for a non-singular finite place* $P_1 = (x_1, y_1)$, *the integral*

$$\zeta_\nu(x, y; P_1) = -\int (\partial^{\nu+1}/\partial x_1^{\nu+1})[(y + y_1)/2y(x - x_1)]dx$$

is an elementary integral of the second kind with an expansion at its single pole P_1 *of the form*

$$\zeta_\nu(x, y! P_1) = \nu!/(x - x_1)^{\nu+1} + c_0 + c_1(x - x_1) + \cdots.$$

The form of the integral of the theorem for $\nu = 0$ is suggested by the fact that when the first of the expansions (70·5) is differentiated with respect to x_1 a new expansion is found with the form given in Theorem 70·3, where we understand that the notation 0! is to be interpreted as 1. The properties of the integral of the theorem can also be proved directly for the case $\nu = 0$ by examining its expansions. By successive differentiations with respect to x_1 the theorem is established for all values ν.

THEOREM 70·4. *If a set of non-singular finite places* $P_i(x_i, y_i)$ $(i = 1, \cdots, p)$ *have distinct values* x_i *the* $2p$ *integrals*

$$\int (x^{i-1}/y)dx, \qquad \zeta_0(x, y; P_i) \qquad (i = 1, \cdots, p)$$

form a fundamental system of integrals of the first and second kinds.

This follows from Theorem 38·1 since the determinant $\left| x_j^{i-1}/y_j \right|$ of the integrands of the integrals of the first kind at the places P_j is different from zero.

For the elliptic case when

$$(70·6) \qquad\qquad y^2 = (1 - x^2)(1 - k^2x^2) = R(x)$$

the two fundamental integrals of the first and second kinds are usually taken in the forms

$$(70·7) \qquad\qquad \int dx/y, \qquad \int [(1 - k^2x^2)/y]dx.$$

We can prove that they form a fundamental system according to the definition of Section 36. If they were not a fundamental system there would be a pair of constants c, d not both zero, and a rational function $\eta(x, y)$, such that

$$(70·8) \qquad c\int dx/y + d\int [(1 - k^2x^2)/y]dx = \eta(x, y),$$

according to Theorem 36·2. The limits of the integrals are understood to be (x_0, y_0) and a variable place (x, y). The integrals in equation (70·8) have no poles on the finite part of the Riemann surface, and hence $\eta(x, y)$ would have none and would be expressible in the form

$$\eta(x, y) = A(x) + B(x)y$$

with polynomial coefficients A, B, since the functions 1, y are a basis for the divisor $Q = 1$. By differentiating equation (70·8) we find

$$[c + d(1 - k^2x^2)]/y = A' + B'y + BR'/2y$$
$$= A' + (B'R + BR'/2)/y,$$

from which it follows that $A' = 0$, and by comparing the degrees of the two sides of the equation that $B' = 0$, $B = 0$. Consequently $c = d = 0$, contrary to the assumption made above. Hence we have the following theorem:

THEOREM 70·5. *For the algebraic function defined by the elliptic equation* (70·6) *the integrals* (70·7) *are a fundamental system of integrals of the first and second kinds. According to Theorem 36·5 every elliptic integral on the Riemann surface of the equation* (70·6) *is expressible as a sum of integrals* (70·4) *of the third kind with constant coefficients, plus a sum of the two integrals* (70·7) *with constant coefficients, plus a rational function* $\eta(x, y)$.

The following examples are not all of hyperelliptic type but their expansions and Riemann surfaces can be found by the methods used in this section. It would be interesting to see if elementary integrals can be constructed for them in the manner described above for the hyperelliptic case.

EXAMPLES OF ELLIPTIC OR HYPERELLIPTIC TYPE

1. Discuss the algebraic function defined by the equation (70·1) and its integrals when $m = 2k + 1$.

2. Construct the elementary integrals of the 2nd and 3rd kinds for singularities at $x = \infty$ or branch places when $m = 2k + 2$ or $m = 2k + 1$.

3. $y^2 = [R(x)]^2(x - x_1) \cdots (x - x_m)$.

71. Normal forms for equations of the third degree in y. An irreducible equation

$$a_0(x)u^3 + a_1(x)u^2 + a_2(x)u + a_3(x) = 0$$

of the third degree in u, with polynomial coefficients, can always be reduced by the transformation $v = a_0u + a_1/3$ to an irreducible equation of the form

$$v^3 + b_2(x)v + b_3(x) = 0$$

in which b_2 and b_3 are also polynomials in x. If $d(x)$ is the polynomial of highest degree such that d^2 and d^3 are factors in b_2 and b_3, respectively, then the transformation $v = d(x)y$ takes the last equation into an irreducible equation

(71·1) $$f(x, y) = y^3 + f_2(x)y + f_3(x) = 0$$

in which f_2 and f_3 are polynomials having no common factor which occurs twice in f_2 and three times in f_3. In this and the succeeding sections of this chapter we shall consider cubic equations (71·1) whose coefficients have the property just described.

An algebraic function which has no poles for finite values of x will be called an *integral algebraic function*. The characteristic property of such a function $y(x)$ is that it satisfies an algebraic equation with polynomial coefficients and with the coefficient of the highest power of y a constant different from zero. The algebraic function $y(x)$ defined by equation (71·1) is evidently integral, and it has the further property that no quotient of the form $z = y/(x-c)$ is integral, on account of the restriction made above on the coefficients f_2 and f_3.

Every rational function $\eta(x, y)$ on the Riemann surface of the equation (71·1) is expressible in the form

(71·2) $$\eta = r_1 + r_2 y + r_3 y^2$$

with coefficients r_1, r_2, r_3 rational in x, as we have seen in Section 19. Such a function η satisfies an equation of the third degree with coefficients polynomials in x which can be determined as follows. With the help of equation (71·1) we see that

$$\eta y = -f_3 r_3 + (r_1 - f_2 r_3)y + r_2 y^2,$$
$$\eta y^2 = -f_3 r_2 - (f_2 r_2 + f_3 r_3)y + (r_1 - f_2 r_3)y^2.$$

From these equations and (71·2) it follows that

$$\begin{vmatrix} r_1 - \eta & r_2 & r_3 \\ -f_3 r_3 & r_1 - f_2 r_3 - \eta & r_2 \\ -f_3 r_2 & -f_2 r_2 - f_3 r_3 & r_1 - f_2 r_3 - \eta \end{vmatrix} = 0.$$

When written in the form

(71·3) $$\eta^3 - B_1 \eta^2 + B_2 \eta - B_3 = 0$$

this equation has the coefficients

(71·4)
$$B_1 = 3r_1 - 2f_2 r_3,$$
$$B_2 = 3r_1^2 - 4f_2 r_1 r_3 + f_2 r_2^2 + 3f_3 r_2 r_3 + f_2^2 r_3^2,$$
$$B_3 = r_1^3 - 2f_2 r_1^2 r_3 + f_2 r_1 r_2^2 + 3f_3 r_1 r_2 r_3 + f_2^2 r_1 r_3^2$$
$$- f_3 r_2^3 - f_2 f_3 r_2 r_3^2 + f_3^2 r_3^3.$$

If we denote by $\Delta(\eta_1, \eta_2, \eta_3)$ the square of the determinant of conjugates of three functions η_1, η_2, η_3, the discriminant of equation (71·1) except for an unessential constant factor is

(71·5) $4f_2^3 + 27f_3^2 = - \prod_{i<k}(y_i - y_k)^2 = - \Delta(1, y, y^2),$

as we see with the help of equation (8·5). It will be convenient in later
sections to have the following formulas for B_2 and B_3 in terms of B_1, Δ,
and the quantity $2f_2r_2 + 3f_3r_3$. They can be verified by elementary com-
putations.

$$B_2 = B_1^2/3 + (2f_2r_2 + 3f_3r_3)^2/4f_2 + \Delta r_3^2/12f_2,$$

(71·6)
$$B_3 = B_1^3/27 + B_1[3(2f_2r_2 + 3f_3r_3)^2 + \Delta r_3^2]/36f_2$$
$$- f_3(2f_2r_2 + 3f_3r_3)^3/8f_2^3$$
$$- \Delta(2f_2r_2 + 3f_3r_3)r_2r_3/12f_2^2 + \Delta^2 r_3^3/216f_2^3 .$$

72. **A basis for the divisor $Q = 1$.** The multiples of the divisor $Q = 1$
on the Riemann surface of the equation (71·1) are called *integral rational functions* $\eta(x, y)$ since they have no poles at finite values x. A
basis for the divisor $Q = 1$, according to the definition in Section 20, is a
basis of rational functions η_1, η_2, η_3 such that the totality of integral
rational functions is identical with the totality of functions expressible
in the form

(72·1) $\eta = g_1(x)\eta_1 + g_2(x)\eta_2 + g_3(x)\eta_3$

with polynomial coefficients. We can readily prove the following theorem:

THEOREM 72·1. *A basis* η_1, η_2, η_3 *of rational functions is a basis for the
divisor* $Q = 1$ *if each function* η_i *is integral, and if there exists no function
of the form*

$$(c_1\eta_1 + c_2\eta_2 + c_3\eta_3)/(x - x_0)$$

which is integral except the one for which the constants c_i *are all zero.*

For a set of functions η_1, η_2, η_3 satisfying the conditions of the theorem every function of the form (72·1) is evidently integral. Furthermore every integral function η is expressible in the form

$$\frac{g_1(x)\eta_1 + g_2(x)\eta_2 + g_3(x)\eta_3}{d(x)}$$

where g_1, g_2, g_3 and d are polynomials having no common factor. To
prove that η_1, η_2, η_3 is a basis for the divisor $Q = 1$ we must show that
$d(x)$ is a constant. This is easy to do since the argument following Theorem 20·1 shows that if $d(x)$ had a factor $x - x_0$ the quotient

$$\frac{g_1(x_0)\eta_1 + g_2(x_0)\eta_2 + g_3(x_0)\eta_3}{x - x_0}$$

would also be an integral function, and this is impossible under the conditions of the theorem.

If the coefficients f_2, f_3 in equation $(71 \cdot 1)$ have a common factor it must be on the form AB^2, where A and B are polynomials in x prime to each other with distinct linear factors, since f_2 and f_3 have no common factor which occurs to the second power in f_2 and the third power in f_3. Using the notation of Baur, who has studied cubic equations comprehensively [14, 19], we may write

$$f_2 = AB^2h_2, \qquad f_3 = AB^2h_3,$$

where h_3 is prime to h_2 and also to B, since f_3 contains no factor to the third power whose square occurs in f_2. Furthermore if A_1 is the greatest common divisor of A and h_3, so that $A = A_1A_2$, $h_3 = A_1h_4$, we have

$$(72 \cdot 2) \qquad f_2 = A_1A_2B^2h_2, \qquad f_3 = A_1^2A_2B^2h_4,$$

where now h_2 *is prime to* A_1, h_4 *is prime to* A_2Bh_2, *and* A_1, A_2, B *are polynomials prime to each other and having distinct linear factors*. Expressed in terms of these polynomials the discriminant $(71 \cdot 5)$ has the value

$$(72 \cdot 3) \qquad \Delta(1, \ y, \ y^2) = - A_1^3 A_2^2 B^4 \Delta_2$$

where

$$(72 \cdot 4) \qquad \Delta_2 = 4A_2B^2h_2^3 + 27A_1h_4^2,$$

and Δ_2 *is readily seen to be prime to* A_1, A_2, B, h_2, h_4. Thus the factors in the expression $(72 \cdot 3)$ for Δ are all prime to each other. It will be useful in succeeding sections to have Δ_2 written in the form $\Delta_2 = C^2\Delta_3$ where Δ_3 contains only linear factors. Then

$$\Delta(1, \ y, \ y^2) = - A_1^3 A_2^2 B^4 C^2 \Delta_3$$

where all the factors are prime to each other except possibly Δ_3 and C which might have linear factors in common.

To construct a basis for the divisor $Q = 1$ we may start from the basis 1, y, y^2. All three of these functions are integral and the quotient of 1 or y by a factor $x - x_0$ is never integral. The equation $(71 \cdot 3)$ satisfied by y^2 is readily found to be

$$(y^2)^3 + 2f_2(y^2)^2 + f_2^2 y^2 - f_3^2 = 0.$$

With the help of the expressions $(72 \cdot 2)$ it is seen that the function $z = y^2/A_1B$ satisfies the equation

$$z^3 + 2A_2Bh_2z^2 + A_2^2B^2h_2^2z - A_1A_2Bh_4^2 = 0,$$

and no quotient $u = z/(x - x_0)$ is integral, as one finds by setting up the equation for u and examining its coefficients in view of the properties of the polynomials A, B, h. The basis

$$\omega_1 = 1, \qquad \omega_2 = y, \qquad \omega_3 = y^2/A_1B$$

has therefore the property that each of its functions is integral and no quotient of the form $\omega_i/(x - x_0)$ is integral. Furthermore

$$(72 \cdot 5) \quad \Delta(1, y, y^2/A_1B) = (1/A_1^2B^2)\Delta(1, y, y^2) = -A_1A_2^2B^2C^2\Delta_3.$$

The functions ω_i may not have the last property described in Theorem $72 \cdot 1$, but it can be shown that a function of the form

$$(72 \cdot 6) \qquad \omega = \frac{c_1 + c_2y + c_3y^2/A_1B}{x - x_0}$$

can be integral only if $x - x_0$ is a factor of the polynomial C. If a function ω with coefficient $c_1 \neq 0$, for example, is integral, then ω, y, y^2/A_1B are also integral functions and

$$\Delta(\omega, y, y^2/A_1B) = \frac{c_1^2}{(x - x_0)^2} \Delta(1, y, y^2/A_1B).$$

The functions Δ in this equation are polynomials in x since they are rational and have no poles except at $x = \infty$. From this it follows that if a quotient ω of the form above given is integral its denominator must occur twice in $\Delta(1, y, y^2/A_1B)$. The expression $(72 \cdot 5)$ shows therefore that the only denominators $x - x_0$ possible for integral functions ω are factors in A_2, B, or C.

In order to investigate further the character of these denominators let us consider a function

$$\eta = v_1 + v_2y + v_3y^2/A_1B.$$

The coefficients of the equation $(71 \cdot 3)$ for η take the form

$$(72 \cdot 7) \quad \begin{aligned} B_1 &= 3v_1 - 2A_2Bh_2v_3, \\ B_2 &= 3v_1^2 - 4A_2Bh_2v_1v_3 + A_1A_2B^2h_2v_2^2 + 3A_1A_2Bh_4v_2v_3 \\ &\quad + A_2^2B^2h_2^2v_3^2, \\ B_3 &= v_1^3 - 2A_2Bh_2v_1^2v_3 + A_1A_2B^2h_2v_1v_2^2 + 3A_1A_2Bh_4v_1v_2v_3 \\ &\quad + A_2^2B^2h_2^2v_1v_3^2 - A_1^2A_2B^2h_4v_2^3 - A_1A_2^2B^2h_2h_4v_2v_3^2 \\ &\quad + A_1A_2^2Bh_4^2v_3^3 \end{aligned}$$

when the expressions

$$r_1 = v_1, \qquad r_2 = v_2, \qquad r_3 = v_3/A_1B$$

for the coefficients in equations (71·2), and the values (72·2), are substituted in the formulas (71·4).

The formulas (72·7) hold for all coefficients v_i which are rational in x, but we are for the moment interested in the case when they are constants c_i. Let $x-a_2$ be a factor of the polynomial A_2. Then if $\eta/(x-a_2)$ were an integral function, the coefficient B_i would necessarily be divisible by $(x-a_2)^i$. If B_1 were divisible by $x-a_2$ we should have $v_1=c_1=0$. Then B_2 divisible by $(x-a_2)^2$ would imply $v_2=c_2=0$, and B_3 divisible by $(x-a_2)^3$ would imply $v_3=c_3=0$. A similar argument is effective for a factor $(x-b)$ of B. Hence the only non-vanishing quotients $\eta/(x-x_0)$ with constant coefficients v_i which are integral have factors $x-x_0$ belonging to the factor C in equation (72·5).

It is now possible to show that the quotient η/C is integral provided that the coefficients v_1, v_2, v_3 are properly chosen polynomials in x. Since Δ has the factor C^2 and f_2 is prime to Δ_2 and therefore to C, it follows from the first formula (72·7) and the formulas (71·6) that B_i will be divisible by C^i, and η/C will therefore be an integral function, when $v_3=1$ and

$$v_1 = 2A_2Bh_2/3 = 2f_2/3A_1B, \quad 2f_2v_2 + 3f_3/A_1B \equiv 0 \text{ (modulo } C).$$

When we substitute the values of f_2 and f_3 the latter congruence is equivalent to

$$2Bh_2v_2 + 3h_4 \equiv 0 \text{ (modulo } C).$$

If $v_2=l(x)$ is the polynomial of lowest degree which satisfies this condition we see that the coefficients $v_1=2f_2/3A_1B$, $v_2=l$, $v_3=1$ define a quotient $\lambda = \eta/C$ which is an integral function. The value of λ is

$$(72·8) \qquad \lambda = (1/C)(2f_2/3A_1B + ly + y^2/A_1B).$$

We can now prove the following theorem:

THEOREM 72·2. *The three functions* 1, y, λ *are a basis for the divisor* $Q=1$ *and the equation* (71·1) *when* λ *is defined by the equation* (72·8) *and the coefficient* $l(x)$ *is the polynomial of lowest degree which satisfies the congruence*

$$2Bh_2l + 3h_4 \equiv 0 \text{ (modulo } C).$$

We have seen that 1, y, λ are all integral functions. The theorem can therefore be proved with the help of Theorem 72·1 by showing that no quotient

$$\eta = (k_1 + k_2 y + k_3\lambda)/(x - x_0)$$

with constant coefficients is an integral function except the one for which the coefficients k_i are all zero. If η is an integral function the denominator $x - x_0$ is necessarily a squared factor in the polynomial $\Delta(1, y, \lambda)$. With the help of equation (72·5) this function Δ is seen to have the value

(72·9) $\Delta(1, y, \lambda) = (1/C^2)\Delta(1, y, y^2/A_1B) = -A_1 A_2^2 B^2 \Delta_3.$

Hence $x - x_0$ is a factor in A_2 or B. But in that case

$$\frac{C\eta}{x - x_0} - k_3 \frac{2f_2}{3(x - x_0)A_1 B} = \frac{k_1 C + (k_2 C + k_3 l)y + k_3 y^2/A_1 B}{x - x_0}$$

is also integral, as we see from the formulas (72·2). The coefficients $k_1 C$, $k_2 C + k_3 l$, k_3 are all divisible by $x - x_0$, since otherwise, by the argument following Theorem 72·1, there would be an integral function of the form (72·6) with denominator a factor of A_2 or B and coefficients c_i not all zero, which is impossible. Since C does not contain the factor $x - x_0$ the coefficients $k_1 C$, $k_2 C + k_3 l$, k_3 can be divisible by $x - x_0$ only when $k_1 = k_2 = k_3 = 0$. Thus the functions 1, y, λ have the properties described in Theorem 72·1 and are a basis for the divisor $Q = 1$.

73. The complementary basis. In calculating complementary bases two principles are useful. According to the definition in Section 22 a basis ζ_1, ζ_2, ζ_3 is complementary to a basis η_1, η_2, η_3 if the relations $T(\eta_i\zeta_k) = \delta_{ik}$ hold, where $\delta_{ik} = 1$ if $i = k$, and $\delta_{ik} = 0$ if $i \neq k$. If we express the functions η_i in terms of the functions ζ_i in the form

(73·1) $\eta_i = a_{i1}\zeta_1 + a_{i2}\zeta_2 + a_{i3}\zeta_3$ $(i = 1, 2, 3)$

the coefficients have the values $a_{ik} = T(\eta_i\eta_k)$, as is readily verified. If H_1, H_2, H_3 is a basis related to η_1, η_2, η_3 by the equations

$$H_i = b_{i1}\eta_1 + b_{i2}\eta_2 + b_{i3}\eta_3 \qquad (i = 1, 2, 3),$$

and if (B_{ik}) is the matrix reciprocal to (b_{ik}), then the basis Z_1, Z_2, Z_3 defined by the equations

(73·2) $Z_k = B_{1k}\zeta_1 + B_{2k}\zeta_2 + B_{3k}\zeta_3$ $(k = 1, 2, 3)$

is the complementary basis to H_1, H_2, H_3. For using the summation notation of tensor analysis, we see that

$$T(H_i Z_k) = b_{il}B_{mk}T(\eta_l\zeta_m) = b_{il}B_{lk} = \delta_{ik}.$$

With these two principles in mind we may compute successively the basis ζ_1, ζ_2, ζ_3 complementary to $(\eta_1, \eta_2, \eta_3) = (1, y, y^2)$, and the basis Z_1, Z_2, Z_3 complementary to $(H_1, H_2, H_3) = (1, y, \lambda)$. With the help of the relations

$$(73 \cdot 3) \qquad \begin{aligned} T(1) &= 3, \qquad T(y) = 0, \\ T(y^2) &= (\Sigma y_i)^2 - 2\Sigma y_i y_k = -2f_2, \\ T(y^3) &= T(-f_2 y - f_3) = -3f_3, \\ T(y^4) &= T(-f_2 y^2 - f_3 y) = 2f_2^2, \end{aligned}$$

we find the matrix of coefficients of the equations $(73 \cdot 1)$ to be

$$(a_{ik}) = \begin{pmatrix} 3 & 0 & -2f_2 \\ 0 & -2f_2 & -3f_3 \\ -2f_2 & -3f_3 & 2f_2^2 \end{pmatrix}.$$

When the equations $(73 \cdot 1)$ are solved for ζ_1, ζ_2, ζ_3 and the results multiplied by $f_y = 3y^2 + f_2$ it is found that the basis complementary to $1, y, y^2$ is expressible in the form

$$\zeta_1 = (y^2 + f_2)/f_y, \qquad \zeta_2 = y/f_y, \qquad \zeta_3 = 1/f_y.$$

The matrix (b_{ik}) by means of which the basis $1, y, \lambda$ is expressed in terms of $1, y, y^2$, and its reciprocal (B_{ik}), are

$$\begin{pmatrix} 1 & 0 & 0 \\ 0 & 1 & 0 \\ 2f_2/3A_1BC & 1/C & 1/A_1BC \end{pmatrix} \begin{pmatrix} 1 & 0 & 0 \\ 0 & 1 & 0 \\ -2f_2/3 & -A_1Bl & A_1BC \end{pmatrix}.$$

By simple calculations we justify the following theorem:

THEOREM $73 \cdot 1$. *The basis complementary to the basis* (H_1, H_2, H_3) $= (1, y, \lambda)$ *of the divisor* $Q = 1$ *is*

$$(73 \cdot 4) \qquad Z_1 = 1/3, \qquad Z_2 = (y - A_1Bl)/f_y, \qquad Z_3 = A_1BC/f_y.$$

The functions Z_1, Z_2, Z_3 *are a basis for the divisor* $R = 1/X_1$ *where* X_1 *is the divisor of the branch places corresponding to finite values of* x.

The last statement of the theorem is a consequence of Theorem $22 \cdot 2$ which was proved under the assumption that there was no branch place at $x = \infty$. If there are branch places at $x = \infty$ the theorem is still true if we replace X by X_1, and the proof is unchanged.

If there is no branch place for the function $y(x)$ at $x = \infty$ then $X = X_1$, and the basis Z_1, Z_2, Z_3 is a basis for the divisor $1/X$. It can be transformed into a basis normal at $x = \infty$ by the process described in the proof of Theorem 21·2. In order to apply the result so attained it is important to know that the equation (71·1) can always be replaced by an equation with similar properties and having no branch place at $x = \infty$, as indicated in the following theorem.

THEOREM 73·2. *If $x = c$ is a point at which the discriminant of the equation (71·1) and the coefficients f_2, f_3 are different from zero, and if r is the smallest integer for which y/x^r remains finite at $x = \infty$, then the functions*

$$(73·5) \qquad \xi = 1/(x - c), \qquad \eta = y/(x - c)^r$$

satisfy an equation

$$(73·6) \qquad \eta^3 + \phi_2(\xi)\eta + \phi_3(\xi) = 0$$

with the properties prescribed for equation (71·1). Furthermore ϕ_2 is of degree $2r$, ϕ_3 is of degree $3r$, r is the smallest integer for which η/ξ^r remains finite at $\xi = \infty$, there is no branch place at $\xi = \infty$, and the expansions for η at $\xi = \infty$ have the form

$$\eta = \xi^r(\gamma_i + \delta_i/\xi + \cdots) \qquad\qquad (i = 1, 2, 3),$$

where the constants γ_i are the three distinct roots of equation (71·1) for $x = c$.

By setting $x = 1/x'$, $y = z/x'^r$ in equation (71·1) we see that the integer r is the smallest integer for which z remains finite at $x' = 0$, and that this integer is the smallest for which $2r - m_2$ and $3r - m_3$ are both positive, where m_2 and m_3 are the degrees of $f_2(x)$ and $f_3(x)$, respectively. The solutions of equations (73·5) for x and y are

$$(73·7) \qquad x = c + 1/\xi, \qquad y = \eta/\xi^r.$$

By substituting these solutions in equation (71·1) we find the equation (73·6) with

$$\phi_2(\xi) = \xi^{2r}f_2(c + 1/\xi), \qquad \phi_3(\xi) = \xi^{3r}f_3(c + 1/\xi),$$

and the properties stated in the theorem can be readily verified.

THEOREM 73·3. *If the equation (71·1) has no branch place at $x = \infty$ and has the properties at $x = \infty$ described for equation (73·6) in the last theorem, and if the column orders $r_1 = 0$, $-r_2$, $-r_3$ of the basis 1, y, λ at $x = \infty$ satisfy the relation $r_2 \leqq r_3$, then this basis is normal at $x = \infty$. According to Theorem 22·1 the complementary basis Z_1, Z_2, Z_3 is also normal and has the column orders $r_1 = 0$, r_2, r_3 at $x = \infty$.*

We know that the column orders of y and λ at $x = \infty$ are negative, since these functions are not constants and have no poles at finite values of x. The column order at $x = \infty$ of the second term in

$$\lambda = 2f_2/3A_1BC + ly/C + y^2/A_1BC$$

is greater than $-r_2$ since l is of lower degree than C. The terms of degree $-r_3$ in the expansions for λ at $x = \infty$ therefore come from the first and third terms. The expansions for y at $x = \infty$ have by hypothesis the form

$$y = x^{r_2}(c_i + d_i/x + \cdots) \qquad\qquad (i = 1, 2, 3)$$

with distinct constants c_i. If we denote by α_1, β, γ the degrees of A_1, B, C, respectively, then since f_2 has by hypothesis the degree $2r = 2r_2$ we see that the expansions for λ at $x = \infty$ have the form

$$\lambda = x^{r_3}(a + bc_i^2 + e_i/x + \cdots),$$

where $r_3 = 2r_2 - \alpha_1 - \beta - \gamma$ and the constant b is different from zero. Hence the determinant of leading coefficients of 1, y, λ at $x = \infty$ is

$$\begin{vmatrix} 1 & c_1 & a + bc_1^2 \\ 1 & c_2 & a + bc_2^2 \\ 1 & c_3 & a + bc_3^2 \end{vmatrix} \neq 0,$$

and we see that the basis 1, y, λ is normal at $x = \infty$.

THEOREM 73·4. *The transformation*

$$(73\cdot8) \qquad\qquad \xi = x, \qquad \eta = \lambda(x, y)$$

is birational and takes the equation $(71\cdot1)$ *into an equation*

$$\eta^3 + \phi_2(\xi)\eta + \phi_3(\xi) = 0$$

with similar properties. By a succession of transformations of the forms $(73\cdot5)$ *and* $(73\cdot8)$ *equation* $(71\cdot1)$ *can be replaced by an equation of the same form with the properties described in Theorem* 73·3. *For the equation so attained the basis* 1, y, λ *and its complementary basis* Z_1, Z_2, Z_3 *are therefore normal at* $x = \infty$.

To prove the first statement of the theorem we may first note that the equation $(71\cdot3)$ satisfied by the function $\eta = \lambda(x, y)$ is irreducible. Otherwise, according to Theorem 49·1 and its Corollary 1, the first member of equation $(71\cdot3)$ would be the third power of a factor linear in η, and from the formula $(72\cdot8)$ we see that y would satisfy an equation of the second degree, which is impossible since equation $(71\cdot1)$ is by hypothesis irreducible. From the corollary cited above it follows then that the transformation $(73\cdot8)$ is birational. There is no term in η^2 in the equation $(71\cdot3)$ for $\eta = \lambda(x, y)$ since with the help of the formulas $(73\cdot3)$ it follows that $B_1 = T(\lambda) = 0$. The coefficients B_2 and B_3 must be polynomials with no common factor occurring twice in B_2 and three times in B_3, since λ is an integral function and no quotient $\lambda/(x-x_0)$ has this property. Hence the equation $(71 \cdot 3)$ for $\eta = \lambda\,(x, y)$ has the properties prescribed for the equation $(71 \cdot 1)$.

If we first make a suitable transformation

$$x_1 = 1/(x - c), \qquad y_1 = y/(x - c)^r$$

equation $(71 \cdot 1)$ goes into an equation of the same form with no branch place at $x = \infty$, as indicated in Theorem $73 \cdot 2$. If we denote the column orders at $x_1 = \infty$ of the basis 1, y_1, λ_1 for the new equation by $r_{11} = 0$, $-r_{12}$, $-r_{13}$ the transformations

$$\xi = x_1, \qquad\qquad \eta = \lambda_1(x_1, y_1),$$
$$x_2 = 1/(\xi - c), \qquad y_2 = \eta/(x - \xi)^{r_{12}}$$

are again birational and provide a new equation with a basis 1, y_2, λ_2. Continuing the process we find a sequence of equations with bases 1, y_k, λ_k having column orders at $x_k = \infty$ which may be denoted by $r_{k1} = 0$, $-r_{k2}$, $-r_{k3}$, and such that $r_{k2} = r_{k-1,3}$. The function $\Delta(1, y_k, \lambda_k)$ is a polynomial in x_k equal to the norm of the divisor of branch places, by Theorem $21 \cdot 4$. It is of the same degree in x_k for every k, since the transformations which have been applied are bilinear in the variables x, ξ and do not change the orders of the branch places. The order of $\Delta(1, y_k, \lambda_k)$ at $x_k = \infty$ is, however, at least $-2(r_{k2} + r_{k3})$, and since $r_{k2} = r_{k-1,3}$ the difference between this expression and the similar one for $k - 1$ is at least 4 if the relations $r_{k-1,2} > r_{k-1,3}$, $r_{k2} > r_{k3}$ are satisfied. Hence we see that for some finite value of k we must have $r_{k2} \leqq r_{k3}$, and the corresponding basis 1, y_k, λ_k will be normal at $x = \infty$, by Theorem $73 \cdot 3$.

74. **A theorem of Baur.** The theorems in the preceding sections were developed with the aid of transformations which led to equations of the form $(71 \cdot 1)$ having no branch places at $x = \infty$. Baur has proved an interesting theorem which is applicable in other cases also.

A simple procedure in order to investigate the behavior of the algebraic function $y(x)$ at $x = \infty$ is to make the substitution $x = 1/x'$, $y = y'/x'^r$ in equation $(71 \cdot 1)$, where r is the smallest integer such that y/x^r remains finite at $x = \infty$. The resulting equation has the form

$$(74 \cdot 1) \qquad\qquad y'^3 + g_2(x')y' + g_3(x') = 0,$$

in which

$$g_2(x') = x'^{2r}f_2(1/x'), \qquad g_3(x') = x'^{3r}f_3(1/x').$$

It is evident that r is the smallest integer such that $2r - m_2$ and $3r - m_3$ are positive, m_2 and m_3 being the degrees of the polynomials $\dot{f}_2$ and f_3, respectively. The notations A_1', A_2', B', C', Δ_3' will be used to designate the polynomials for the equation (74·1) analogous to the similar un-primed polynomials for equation (71·1). On account of the possibility of factors which are powers of x' alone in the coefficients g_2 and g_3 we see readily that $A_1' = A_1 x'^{\alpha'}$, where α' is a positive integer which is at least equal to the degree α of A_1 and may be greater. Similar relations and notations hold for the other polynomials listed above. Baur's theorem is then as follows:

THEOREM 74·1. *Let* $r_1 = 0$, r_2, r_3 *be the smallest integers for which the quotients* H_i/x^{r_i} *belonging to the basis* $(H_1, H_2, H_3) = (1, y, \lambda)$ *for equation* (71·1) *remain finite at* $x = \infty$, *and let* Z_1, Z_2, Z_3 *be the basis complementary to* H_1, H_2, H_3. *If* $r_2 \leqq r_3$, *and if the factor* C' *of the discriminant of the equation* (74·1) *arising from* (71·1) *is not divisible by* x', *then the functions*

$$(74\cdot2) \qquad\qquad x^{\rho_i} Z_i \qquad (\rho_i \geqq 0; \rho_i = 0, 1, \cdots, r_i - 2; i = 2, 3)$$

are a set of p *linearly independent integrands of integrals of the first kind for the equation* (71·1.)

To prove this we use the property, from Section 24, that every integrand $\eta(x, y)$ of an integral of the first kind is a multiple of the divisor D^2/X, and hence also of the divisor $1/X_1$ for which Z_1, Z_2, Z_3 are a basis. Such a function $\eta(x, y)$ is expressible in the form

$$\eta = g_1(x)Z_1 + g_2(x)Z_2 + g_3(x)Z_3$$

with polynomial coefficients whose values are $g_i = T(\eta H_i)$, on account of the relations $T(H_k Z_i) = \delta_{ik}$. The divisors of η and x have the forms $Q_\eta = ID^2/X$, $Q_x = N/D$, where I is a divisor with no negative exponents. Hence $Q_{\eta x} = IDN/X$, and it is evident that the product ηx vanishes at each place P over $x = \infty$ since D contains a higher power of P than X. Consequently $g_i/x^{r_i-1} = T(\eta x \cdot H_i/x^{r_i})$ vanishes at $x = \infty$, since H_i/x^{r_i} is finite, and it follows that the degree of g_i is at most equal to $r_i - 2$. This shows that every integrand function η of an integral of the first kind is expressible as a linear combination of the functions (74·2). It remains to be proved that every such linear combination is a multiple of the divisor D^2/X.

To prove this it may first be shown that the functions $(1, y/x^{r_2}, \lambda/x^{r_3})$, when expressed in terms of the variables x' and y', are a basis for the divisor $Q = 1$ and the equation (74·1). Equation (74·1) has a basis $(1, y', \lambda')$ for the divisor $Q = 1$ of the kind described in Theorem 72·2.

Since the quotient λ/x^{r_3} is finite for all values of x' except possibly $x' = \infty$ it must be expressible in terms of this basis in the form

$$(74 \cdot 3) \qquad \lambda/x^{r_3} = k_1(x') + k_2(x')y' + k_3(x')\lambda',$$

the coefficients k_i being polynomials. These coefficients can have no power of x' in common as a factor, since r_3 is the smallest integer for which λ/x^{r_3} remains finite at $x = \infty$. Since the traces of λ, y', λ' are all zero it follows that $k_1 = 0$. We may express the value of λ from $(72 \cdot 8)$ in terms of y' by means of the formula $y = y'/x'^{r_3}$. By comparing coefficients of powers of y' in equation $(74 \cdot 3)$ we then see, with the help of the relation $C' = Cx'^{\gamma'}$, that

$$k_3 = x'^a, \qquad k_2 = (lx'^{\gamma'+r_3-r_2} - l'x'^a)/C',$$

where a is a positive integer or zero since k_3 is a polynomial. The first term in the parenthesis has a factor x' since $r_2 \leqq r_3$ and γ' is greater than the degree γ of C and consequently than the degree of l in $x = 1/x'$. Furthermore C' contains no factor x' by hypothesis. Since k_2 and k_3 can have no power of x' as a common factor, the last equation shows that $a = 0$. Hence the bases $(1, y/x^{r_2}, \lambda/x^{r_3})$ and $(1, y', \lambda')$ are related by the equations

$$y/x^{r_2} = y', \qquad \lambda/x^{r_3} = k_2y' + \lambda'.$$

The former must therefore be a basis for the divisor $Q = 1$ and the equation $(74 \cdot 1)$, since the latter has this property.

With this result in mind we can prove that every linear combination $\eta(x, y)$ of the functions $(74 \cdot 2)$, with constant coefficients, is an integrand of an integral of the first kind for equation $(71 \cdot 1)$. Such a function η has the form

$$(74 \cdot 4) \qquad\qquad \eta = g_2(x)Z_2 + g_3(x)Z_3$$

where g_2 and g_3 are of degrees at most $r_2 - 2$ and $r_3 - 2$, respectively. The basis complementary to $(H_1', H_2', H_3') = (1, y/x^{r_2}, \lambda/x^{r_3})$ is $(Z_1', Z_2', Z_3') = Z_1, Z_2x^{r_2}, Z_3x^{r_3})$, according to the first paragraph of Section 73. Hence from equation $(74 \cdot 4)$ the product ηx^2 is expressible in the form

$$\eta x^2 = G_2(x') Z_2' + G_3(x') Z_3'$$

where the coefficients $G_i = x'^{r_i-2}g_i$ are also polynomials. Let us set $X = X_0X_2X_\infty$ where X_0 and X_∞ are the divisors of the branch places at $x = 0$ and $x = \infty$, respectively. Equation $(74 \cdot 4)$ shows that η is a multiple of the divisor $1/X_1 = 1/X_0X_2$ for which the functions Z_1, Z_2, Z_3 are a basis, according to Theorem 73·1. Similarly the last equation shows that ηx^2 is a multiple of the divisor $1/X_2X_\infty$. Hence

$$Q_\eta = I_1/X_0X_2, \qquad Q_{\eta x^2} = I_2/X_2X_\infty,$$

where I_1 and I_2 are divisors with no negative exponents. But from these equations and the equation $Q_x = N/D$ it follows that

$$I_1 = X_0I_2D^2/X_\infty N^2 = I_3D^2/X_\infty$$

since I_1 is integral and D is prime to N. Hence $Q_\eta = I_3D^2/X$ and η is a multiple of the divisor D^2/X. Thus we see that every linear combination (74·4) of the functions (74·2) with constant coefficients is an integrand of an integral of the first kind, and the proof of the theorem is complete.

75. Applications to equations of the third degree in y. The results of the preceding sections are useful in the study of special equations of the third degree in y, as indicated in the following theorems.

THEOREM 75·1. *At every root $x = \xi$ of the factor $A_1\Delta_3$ of the function $\Delta(1, y, \lambda) = -A_1A_2{}^2B^2\Delta_3$ there is a cycle of two sheets for the equation (71·1), and at every root of A_2B there is a cycle of three sheets. There are no other branch places at finite values of x. If the number of cycles with two sheets at $x = \infty$ is represented by κ_2, and the number with three sheets by κ_3, then the genus of the equation (71·1) is given by the formula*

$$(75·1) \qquad 2p = \alpha_1 + 2\alpha_2 + 2\beta + \delta_3 + \kappa_2 + 2\kappa_3 - 4,$$

where α_1, α_2, β, δ_3 are the degrees of the polynomials A_1, A_2, B, Δ_3, respectively.

To prove this we first notice that Theorem 21·4 holds even if there are branch places at $x = \infty$, provided that we replace X by X_1. The proof is identical with that given in Section 21. Hence for the basis 1, y, λ of the divisor $Q = 1$ we have

$$\Delta(1, y, \lambda) = cN(X_1).$$

The branch places at finite values of x can occur therefore only at the roots of the expression $\Delta(1, y, \lambda)$. The statements in the theorem concerning branch places at finite values of x follow at once since $N(X_1)$ contains a linear factor $x - x_0$ only when there is a cycle with two sheets at $x = x_0$, and a factor $(x - x_0)^2$ only when there is a cycle with three sheets. Thus for every cubic equation of the form (71·1) the cycles at finite values of x can be readily determined.

The character of the places at $x = \infty$ can be found from their expansions, or by applying the theorem just proved to the equation (74·1).

If x' is a factor in $A_1' \Delta_3'$ there is a cycle with two sheets at $x = \infty$, or if x' is a factor in $A_2' B'$ there is a cycle of three sheets. The genus is determined, according to formula $(21 \cdot 8)$, by the equation

$$p = (\alpha_1 + 2\alpha_2 + 2\beta + \delta_3 + \kappa_2 + 2\kappa_3)/2 - 3 + 1,$$

where κ_2 and κ_3 are the powers of x' in $A_1' \Delta_3'$ and $A_2' B'$, respectively. The only possible pairs of values (κ_2, κ_3) are $(0, 0)$, $(1, 0)$, $(0, 1)$ since A_1', A_2', B', Δ_3' have no repeated factors and are prime to each other.

In order to find p linearly independent integrand functions of integrals of the first kind for a numerical case of equation $(71 \cdot 1)$ we may adopt the one of the procedures described in the theorems of the preceding sections which seems most convenient for the special case in question. A first method is to transform the equation $(71 \cdot 1)$ into one with no branch place at $x = \infty$, as described in Theorem $73 \cdot 2$. The basis Z_1, Z_2, Z_3 of Theorem $73 \cdot 1$ for the divisor $Q = 1/X$ will perhaps not be normal at $x = \infty$, but it can be transformed into an equivalent normal basis by the method used in proving Theorem $21 \cdot 2$. It will not cause confusion if we denote this new basis by Z_1, Z_2, Z_3 and its column orders by r_1, r_2, r_3. Then the functions

$$(75 \cdot 2) \qquad x^{\rho_i} Z_i \quad (\rho_i \geqq 0; \rho_i = 0, 1, \cdots, r_i - 2; i = 1, 2, 3)$$

are a set of p linearly independent integrands of integrals of the first kind, as indicated in the proof of Theorem $21 \cdot 3$ and its corollary.

A second method of finding a basis normal at $x = \infty$ for the divisor $1/X$ is to apply successively transformations of the forms $(73 \cdot 5)$ and $(73 \cdot 8)$ until an equation is reached with a basis $1, y, \lambda$ which is normal at $x = \infty$, as indicated in Theorem $73 \cdot 4$. The complementary basis Z_1, Z_2, Z_3 for the divisor $1/X$ is then also normal, and the p linearly independent integrands of integrals of the first kind are again the functions $(75 \cdot 2)$. The column order of Z_1 in this case is zero, so that the only products occurring among the functions $(75 \cdot 2)$ are those involving Z_2 and Z_3.

If the equation $(71 \cdot 1)$ has a branch place at $x = \infty$ it may be that the polynomial C' for equation $(74 \cdot 1)$ does not contain x' as a factor, and that the smallest integers r_2, r_3 for which the quotients $y/x^{r_2}, \lambda/x^{r_3}$ are finite at $x = \infty$ satisfy the relation $r_2 \leqq r_3$. Then Theorem $74 \cdot 1$ is applicable, and the functions $(74 \cdot 2)$ are p linearly independent integrals of the first kind.

To construct an integrand of an elementary integral of the third kind with logarithmic singularities at two non-singular places $P_1 = (x_1, y_1)$

and $P_2 = (x_2, y_2)$ we may presuppose that equation $(71 \cdot 1)$ has no branch place at $x = \infty$ and has properties at $x = \infty$ similar to those of equation $(73 \cdot 6)$ in Theorem $73 \cdot 2$. Let H_1, H_2, H_3 be a basis for the divisor $Q = 1$ normal at $x = \infty$, constructed in any way. In the proof of Corollary 2 of Theorem $21 \cdot 4$ it was shown that one of the column orders at $x = \infty$ of such a basis is zero, and that the others are negative, so that we may represent them by $r_1 = 0$, $-r_2$, $-r_3$. The function H_1 is then a constant since it has no poles. The complementary basis Z_1, Z_2, Z_3 belongs to the divisor $R = 1/X$ and is normal at $x = \infty$ with the column orders $r_1 = 0$, r_2, r_3, by Theorems $22 \cdot 2$ and $22 \cdot 1$. An integrand function $\eta(x, y; P_1, P_2)$ of an elementary integral of the third kind with logarithmic singularities at P_1 and P_2 is a multiple of the divisor $D^2/P_1 P_2 X$. We might construct a basis for this divisor by starting from the basis Z_1, Z_2, Z_3 for $1/X$ and applying the method used in proving Theorem $20 \cdot 2$. But when this has once been done the result may be attained more directly in the following manner. The matrix of conjugates of the functions H_i is both a right and left reciprocal of the matrix of conjugates of the functions Z_i with rows and columns interchanged. Consequently the functions

$$H_i(x_1, y_1)Z_i(x, y)/(x - x_1),$$

where the notation of tensor analysis for a sum is used, has a simple pole with residue 1 at $P_1 = (x_1, y_1)$ and is finite at the other two places over $x = x_1$. It is a multiple of the divisor $1/P_1 X$. Similarly

$$H_i(x_2, y_2)Z_i(x, y)/(x - x_2)$$

is a multiple of $1/P_2 X$, and we can see without difficulty that the difference

$$(75 \cdot 3) \quad \eta(x, y; P_1, P_2) = \frac{H_i(x_1, y_1)Z_i(x, y)}{x - x_1} - \frac{H_i(x_2, y_2)Z_i(x, y)}{x - x_2}$$

is a multiple of $D^2/P_1 P_2 X$. The function so defined has in fact a zero of order two at each place at $x = \infty$, since the column orders of Z_2 and Z_3 at $x = \infty$ are both positive, and since at each place over $x = \infty$ the first factor in the product

$$\left(\frac{H_1(x_1, y_1)}{x - x_1} - \frac{H_1(x_2, y_2)}{x - x_2} \right) Z_1(x, y)$$

has an expansion beginning with $(1/x)^2$ because $H_1(x, y)$ is a constant.

THEOREM $75 \cdot 2$. *For an equation* $(71 \cdot 1)$ *with no branch place at* $x = \infty$, *as described for equation* $(73 \cdot 6)$ *in Theorem* $73 \cdot 2$, *the function defined by equation* (75·3) *is an integrand* $\eta(x, y; P_1, P_2)$ *of an elementary integral* $\pi(x, y; P_1, P_2)$ *of the third kind with logarithmic singularities and residues* $+1$, -1 *at two non-singular places* P_1 *and* P_2. *The function*

$$(75\cdot4) \qquad \eta_\nu(x, y; P_1) = - d^{\nu+1}\eta(x, y; P_1, P_2)/dx_1{}^{\nu+1}$$

is an integrand of an elementary integral $\zeta_\nu(x, y; P_1)$ *of the second kind with no singularity except a pole at* P_1. *The expansion of* ζ_ν *at* P_1 *has the form*

$$\zeta_\nu(x, y; P_1) = \nu!/(x - x_1)^{\nu+1} + c_0 + c_1(x - x_1) + \cdots .$$

The last part of the theorem concerning elementary integrals of the second kind can be readily proved by differentiating the expansion of $\eta(x, y; P_1, P_2)$ or $\pi(x, y; P_1, P_2)$ with respect to x_1.

It should be noted in concluding this section that the methods described in Sections 71–75 are rational in character. The common factors $d(x)$ of the coefficients f_2 and f_3, and the squared factor in $d(x)$, can be found by the greatest common divisor process. The squared factor is the greatest common divisor of $d(x)$ and its derivative. A similar remark applies to the squared factor C in the factor Δ_2 of the discriminant, in the equation following (72·4).

76. Equations of the fourth degree in x and y. An irreducible equation of the fourth degree in x and y may be reduced to one of the third degree or less in y by a simple transformation. Let the equation be written in the form

$$f(x, y) = (x, y)_0 + \cdots + (x, y)_4 = 0,$$

where the parenthesis $(x, y)_k$ is homogeneous and of degree k in the variables x and y, and let a, b, c, d be constants such that $(b, d)_4 = 0$, $ad - bc \neq 0$. Then the transformation

$$(76\cdot1) \qquad x = a\xi + b\eta, \qquad y = c\xi + d\eta$$

takes the equation $f(x, y) = 0$ into an equation of the fourth degree in ξ and η, but of the third degree at most in η. This is evident when we substitute the values (76·1) in $f(x, y)$ and set $\xi = 0$. If the resulting equation in ξ and η is of the first degree in η it defines a unicursal curve of genus $p = 0$. If it is of the second degree in η it may be reduced to an elliptic or hyperelliptic curve by the method used in proving Theorems 50·2 and 50·3. If it is of the third degree in η the methods of Sections 71–5 are applicable. Thus every curve of the fourth degree in x and y can be discussed by methods described in the preceding sections.

A simple geometrical argument also shows that every irreducible algebraic curve of the fourth degree in x and y can be transformed bilinearly into one of the fourth degree in ξ and η but of the third degree only in η, and with the coefficient of η^3 a constant different from zero. For if we take the lines

$$l_i = a_i x + b_i y + c_i = 0 \qquad (i = 1, 2, 3)$$

as indicated in Figure 76·1, the transformation $\xi = l_1/l_3$, $\eta = l_2/l_3$ will take the curve $f(x, y) = 0$ into a curve

$$\phi(\xi, \eta) = (\xi, \eta)_0 + \cdots + (\xi, \eta)_4$$

which has two intersections with the line at infinity at the intersection of the line at infinity with the ξ-axis. This means that in the polynomial

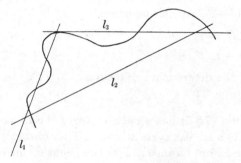

FIG. 76·1

$(\xi, \eta)_4$ the terms in η^4 and η^3 are missing. Furthermore in the polynomial $\phi(0, \eta)$ the term of the third degree is present, since the line $\xi = 0$ has three finite intersections with the curve.

77. Examples. The theory developed in the preceding sections is illustrated by the example

$$(77 \cdot 1) \qquad y^3 - 3xy + x^6(9x - 11) = 0$$

which was discussed by Baur [19, p. 57]. For this equation we readily calculate, from the formulas in Section 72,

$$f_2 = -3x, \qquad f_3 = x^6(9x - 11),$$
$$A_1 = x, \qquad A_2 = 1, \qquad B = 1, \qquad h_2 = -3, \qquad h_4 = x^4(9x - 11),$$
$$\Delta_2 = 27[x^9(9x - 11)^2 - 4] = (x - 1)^2(81x^9 + \cdots),$$
$$C = x - 1, \qquad \Delta_3 = 81x^9 + \cdots .$$

The squared factor C in Δ_2 is found by finding the common factor of Δ_2 and $d\Delta_2/dx$. According to Theorem 72·2, a basis for the divisor $Q=1$ is

(77·2) $H_1 = 1$, $H_2 = y$, $H_3 = \lambda = (-2x - xy + y^2)/x(x-1)$,

and by formula (72·9) the square of the determinant of the basis is

$$\Delta(1, y, \lambda) = -A_1 A_2{}^2 B^2 \Delta_3 = -x(81x^9 + \cdots).$$

Applying Theorem 75·1 we see that the algebraic function defined by equation (77·1) has a cycle of two sheets at the origin $x=0$, and a cycle of two sheets at each of the nine roots of the polynomial Δ_3.

By substituting $x=1/x'$, $y=y'/x'^3$ in equation (77·1) we find the equation

(77·3) $y'^3 - 3x'^5 y' + x'^2(9 - 11x') = 0$

analogous to (74·1). For this equation

$A_1' = 1$, $A_2' = 1$, $B' = x'$, $h_2' = -3x'^3$, $h_4' = 9 - 11x'$

$\Delta_2' = 27[(9 - 11x')^2 - 4x'^{11}]$, $C' = x' - 1$.

The square of the determinant of the basis $(1, y', \lambda')$ is

$$\Delta(1, y', \lambda') = -x'^2 \Delta_3'$$

so that equation (77·3) has a cycle of three sheets at $x'=0$, and the equation (77·1) a similar cycle at $x=\infty$. The constants κ_2, κ_3 have the values 0, 1, and from formula (75·1) the genus of the equation (77·1) is $p=4$.

The conclusions of Theorem 74·1 are applicable to this example, since C' has no factor x' and since the values of the integers r_2, r_3 for the functions y, λ are both 3, as we shall now see. The value of r_2 is the exponent of x' in the transformation $y=y'/x'^3$ giving equation (77·3). To find the value of r_3 we may apply the Newton polygon method to equation (77·3) at the point $(x', y') = (0, 0)$ and so secure the expansion for y', and the corresponding branch

(77·4) $x = t^{-3}$, $y = t^{-7}(\omega 3^{2/3} + \cdots)$ $(\omega^3 = -1)$

for y at $x=\infty$. When substituted in the expression for λ from (77·2) we see that λ has a pole of order -8 at $x=\infty$, and hence that $r_3=3$. By Theorem 73·1 the basis complementary to 1, y, λ is

$Z_1 = 1/3$, $Z_2 = (y + x)/3(y^2 - x)$, $Z_3 = x(x - 1)/3(y^2 - x)$.

Hence by Theorem 74·1 the functions

$$Z_2, \qquad xZ_2, \qquad Z_3, \qquad xZ_3$$

are four linearly independent integrand functions for integrals of the first kind.

The integrand function defined by equation (75·3) has the form

$$\eta(x, y; P_1, P_2) = \frac{1}{3}\left(\frac{1}{x - x_1} - \frac{1}{x - x_2}\right)$$
$$+ \frac{1}{3}\left(\frac{y_1}{x - x_1} - \frac{y_2}{x - x_2}\right)\frac{y + x}{y^2 - x}$$
$$+ \frac{1}{3}\left(\frac{\lambda_1}{x - x_1} - \frac{\lambda_2}{x - x_2}\right)\frac{x(x - 1)}{y^2 - x}$$

for the equation (77·1), where y_1, y_2, λ_1, λ_2 are the values of y and λ belonging to the places P_1 and P_2. The argument of the last section shows that this function is a multiple of the divisor $1/P_1P_2X_1$ and has simple poles with residues $+1$, -1 at the places P_1 and P_2, but it does not assure us that $\eta(x, y; P_1, P_2)$ is an integrand of an elementary integral of the third kind because the curve (77·1) has a branch place at $x = \infty$. We may easily see, however, that the product $\eta dx/dt$ is finite at $x = \infty$, and hence that η is an integrand function as desired. For from the expansions (77·4) it follows readily that η has a zero of order 6, and dx/dt a pole of order -4, at $x = \infty$.

From the formula (75·4) the integrand functions of elementary integrals of the second kind could be calculated without difficulty if needed.

EXAMPLES FOR THE METHOD OF BAUR

1. Discuss the example of the text above by first transforming so that there is no branch place at $x = \infty$.

2. $y^3 + x^3y + x = 0$ [19, p. 56]

3. Discuss the last example by first transforming so that there is no branch place at $x = \infty$.

4. Apply the methods of Baur to examples 6–8, 11–15 of Section 68.

REFERENCES FOR CHAPTER X

References for equations of elliptic and hyperelliptic type are the following: 5; 18, Chapters II, III; 35, Chapter VIII. For the special theory of Sections 71–76 above, concerning curves of the third degree in y, see 14; 19; 28, Vorlesung XIII.

LIST OF REFERENCES

The list below is a list of books which are of interest on account of the influence which they have had in the development of the theory of algebraic functions, or on account of their usefulness as presentations of parts of the theory in the preceding pages, or both. A few titles of separate papers have been added, most of which have some close connection with the preceding text. A complete bibliography would be a voluminous affair. For further references the reader is referred especially to the articles numbered 17, 22, 23, 26, 29, 37, 40, and 46 below.

1. *Oeuvres completes de Niels Henrik Abel*, published by Sylow and Lie, 1881. See especially Vol. 1, Memoire XII (1826), p. 145; Vol. 2, Memoire XVII, p. 206.
2. NEUMANN, *Vorlesungen über Riemann's Theorie der Abelschen Integrale*, Leipzig, 1st ed. 1865, 2nd ed. 1884.
3. CLEBSCH AND GORDAN, *Theorie der Abelschen Funktionen*, Leipzig, 1866.
4. WEBER, *Theorie der Abelschen Funktionen vom Geschlecht 3*, Berlin, 1876.
5. KOENIGSBERGER, *Vorlesungen über die Theorie der hyperelliptischen Integrale*, Leipzig, 1878.
6. BRIOT, *Fonctions abeliennes*, Paris, 1879.
7. KRONECKER, *Ueber die Discriminante algebraischer Funktionen einer Variablen*, Journal für Mathematik, XCI (1881), pp. 301–334.
8. KRONECKER, *Grundzüge einer arithmetischen Theorie der algebraischen Grössen* (Festschrift für Kummer), Journal für Mathematik, XCII (1882), pp. 1–122.
9. DEDEKIND AND WEBER, *Theorie der algebraischen Funktionen einer Veränderlichen*, Journal für Mathematik, XCII (1882), pp. 181–290.
10. KLEIN, *Ueber Riemann's Theorie der algebraischen Funktionen und ihre Integrale*, Leipzig, 1882. (Eng. trans, Dover reprint)
11. RIEMANN, *Theorie der Abelschen Funktionen*, Werke, 2nd ed., Leipzig, 1892, pp. 88–142. (Dover reprint)
12. KLEIN, *Autographierte Vorlesungen über Riemannschen Flächen*, Gottingen, 1892.
13. HARKNESS AND MORLEY, *A treatise on the theory of functions*, Macmillan and Co., New York, 1893, reprinted by G. E. Stechert and Co., 1925.
14. BAUR, *Zur Theorie der Funktionen eines cubischen Körpers*, Mathematische Annalen, XLIII (1893), pp. 505–20.
15. PICARD, *Traité d'analyse*, Vol. II, Gauthier-Villars, Paris, 1st ed., 1893, 2nd ed., 1905, 3rd ed., 1925.
16. JORDAN, *Cours d'analyse*, Vol. II, Gauthier-Villars, Paris, 2nd ed., 1894.
17. BRILL AND NOETHER, *Die Entwicklung der Theorie der algebraischen Funktionen in alterer und neuerer Zeit*, Jahresberichte der Deutschen Mathematiker-Vereinigung III, Berlin, 1894, pp. 107–565.

18. APPELL AND GOURSAT, *Theorie des fonctions algebriques et de leurs integrales*, Gauthier-Villars, Paris, 1895, revised by Fatou, 1929.

19. BAUR, *Aufstellung eines vollständigen Systems von Differentialen erster Gattung in einem cubischen Funktionen-körper*, Mathematische Annalen, XLVI (1895), pp. 31–61.

20. STAHL, *Theorie der Abelschen Funktionen*, Leipzig, 1896.

21. BAKER, *Abel's theorem and the allied theory including the theory of the theta functions*, Cambridge, 1897.

22. HANCOCK, *The historical development of abelian functions up to the time of Riemann*, Report of the British Association for the Advancement of Science, Toronto, 1897.

23. PASCAL, *Die algebraischen Funktionen und die Abel'schen Integrale*, Repertorium der höheren Mathematik, revised by Schepp, Teubner, Leipzig, 1900.

24. FORSYTH, *Theory of functions of a complex variable*, Cambridge, 1900. (Dover reprint)

25. HEFFTER, *Zur Theorie der Resultanten*, Mathematische Annalen, LIV (1901), pp. 541–544.

26. WIRTINGER, *Algebraische Funktionen und ihre Integrale*, Encyklopädie der Mathematischen Wissenschaften, II B 2 (1901), pp. 115–175.

27. WEIERSTRASS, *Vorlesungen über die Theorie der Abelschen Transcendenten*, Werke IV, Berlin, 1902.

28. HENSEL UND LANDSBERG, *Theorie der algebraischen Funktionen einer variabeln*, Teubner, Berlin and Leipzig, 1902.

29. BERZOLARI, *Allgemeine Theorie der höheren ebenen algebraischen Kurven*, Encyklopädie der Mathematischen Wissenschaften III C 4 (1906), pp. 313–455.

30. FIELDS, *Theory of the algebraic functions of a complex variable*, Mayer and Müller, Berlin, 1906.

31. BÔCHER, *Introduction to Higher Algebra*, Macmillan and Co., New York, 1907. (Dover reprint)

32. WEBER, *Lehrbuch der Algebra III*, Braunschweig, 1908.

33. STAHL, *Abriss einer Theorie der algebraischen Funktionen einer Veränderlichen in neuer Fassung*, Teubner, Berlin and Leipzig, 1911.

34. NIELSEN, *Elemente der Funktionentheorie*, Teubner, Berlin and Leipzig, 1911.

35. OSGOOD, *Lehrbuch der Funktionentheorie*, Teubner, Berlin and Leipzig, vol. I, 1st ed., 1907, 5th ed., 1928.

36. FIELDS, *On the foundations of the theory of algebraic functions of one variable*, Philosophical Transactions of the Royal Society of London, Series A, Vol. 212, pp. 339–373.

37. EMMY NOETHER, *Die arithmetischen Theorie der algebraischen Funktionen einer Veränderlichen in ihrer Beziehung zu den übrigen Theorien und zu der Zahlkörpertheorie*, Jahresbericht der Deutschen Mathematiker-Vereinigung, XXVIII (1919), pp. 182–203.

38. HENSEL, *Neue Begründung der arithmetischen Theorie der algebraischen Funktionen einer Variablen*, Mathematische Zeitschrift, V (1919), pp. 118–131.

39. SEVERI, *Vorlesungen über algebraische Geometrie, Geometrie auf einer Kurve, Riemannschen Flächen, Abelsche Integrale*, German translation by Läffler, Teubner, Berlin and Leipzig, 1921.

40. HENSEL, *Arithmetische Theorie der algebraischen Funktionen*, Encyklo-pädie der Mathematischen Wissenschaften, II C 5 (1921), pp. 533–650.
41. BLISS, *Birational transformations simplifying singularities of algebraic curves*, Transactions of the American Mathematical Society, XXIV (1922), pp. 274–285.
42. JUNG, *Einführung in die Theorie der algebraischen Funktionen einer Veränderlichen*, Berlin and Leipzig, 1923.
43. BLISS, *The reduction of singularities of plane curves by birational trans-formation*, Bulletin of the American Mathematical Society, XXIX (1923), pp. 161–183.
44. BLISS, *Algebraic functions and their divisors*, Annals of Mathematics, Series 2, XXVI (1924), pp. 95–124.
45. SEVERI, *Trattato di Geometria Algebrica*, Bologna, 1926.
46. JUNG, *Algebraische Funktionen und ihre Integrale*, Pascal's Repertorium I², Teubner, Leipzig, 1927, pp. 849–888.
47. OSGOOD, *Lehrbuch der Funktionentheorie II₂*, Teubner, Leipzig and Berlin, 1932.

INDEX

(The numbers refer to pages)

217

CATALOGUE OF DOVER BOOKS

BOOKS EXPLAINING SCIENCE AND MATHEMATICS

Engineering, technology, applied science etc.

TEACH YOURSELF ELECTRICITY, C. W. Wilman. Electrical resistance, inductance, capacitance, magnets, chemical effects of current, alternating currents, generators and motors, transformers, rectifiers, much more. 230 questions, answers, worked examples. List of units. 115 illus. 194pp. 6⅞ x 4¼.   Clothbound **$2.00**

ELEMENTARY METALLURGY AND METALLOGRAPHY, A. M. Shrager. Basic theory and descriptions of most of the fundamental manufacturing processes involved in metallurgy. Partial contents: the structure of metals; slip, plastic deformation, and recrystalization; iron ore and production of pig iron; chemistry involved in the metallurgy of iron and steel; basic processes such as the Bessemer treatment, open-hearth process, the electric arc furnace —with advantages and disadvantages of each; annealing, hardening, and tempering steel; copper, aluminum, magnesium, and their alloys. For freshman engineers, advanced students in technical high schools, etc. Index. Bibliography. 177 diagrams. 17 tables. 284 questions and problems. 27-page glossary. ix + 389pp. 5⅜ x 8.   S138 Paperbound **$2.25**

BASIC ELECTRICITY, Prepared by the Bureau of Naval Personnel. Originally a training course text for U.S. Navy personnel, this book provides thorough coverage of the basic theory of electricity and its applications. Best book of its kind for either broad or more limited studies of electrical fundamentals . . . for classroom use or home study. Part 1 provides a more limited coverage of theory: fundamental concepts, batteries, the simple circuit, D.C. series and parallel circuits, conductors and wiring techniques, A.C. electricity, inductance and capacitance, etc. Part 2 applies theory to the structure of electrical machines—generators, motors, transformers, magnetic amplifiers. Also deals with more complicated instruments, synchros, servo-mechanisms. The concluding chapters cover electrical drawings and blueprints, wiring diagrams, technical manuals, and safety education. The book contains numerous questions for the student, with answers. Index and six appendices. 345 illustrations. x + 448pp. 6½ x 9¼.   S973 Paperbound **$3.00**

BASIC ELECTRONICS, prepared by the U.S. Navy Training Publications Center. A thorough and comprehensive manual on the fundamentals of electronics. Written clearly, it is equally useful for self-study or course work for those with a knowledge of the principles of basic electricity. Partial contents: Operating Principles of the Electron Tube; Introduction to Transistors; Power Supplies for Electronic Equipment; Tuned Circuits; Electron-Tube Amplifiers; Audio Power Amplifiers; Oscillators; Transmitters; Transmission Lines; Antennas and Propagation; Introduction to Computers; and related topics. Appendix. Index. Hundreds of illustrations and diagrams. vi + 471pp. 6½ x 9¼.   S1076 Paperbound **$2.75**

BASIC THEORY AND APPLICATION OF TRANSISTORS, Prepared by the U.S. Department of the Army. An introductory manual prepared for an army training program. One of the finest available surveys of theory and application of transistor design and operation. Minimal knowledge of physics and theory of electron tubes required. Suitable for textbook use, course supplement, or home study. Chapters: Introduction; fundamental theory of transistors; transistor amplifier fundamentals; parameters, equivalent circuits, and characteristic curves; bias stabilization; transistor analysis and comparison using characteristic curves and charts; audio amplifiers; tuned amplifiers; wide-band amplifiers; oscillators; pulse and switching circuits; modulation, mixing, and demodulation; and additional semiconductor devices. Unabridged, corrected edition. 240 schematic drawings, photographs, wiring diagrams, etc. 2 Appendices. Glossary. Index. 263pp. 6½ x 9¼.   S380 Paperbound **$1.25**

TEACH YOURSELF HEAT ENGINES, E. De Ville. Measurement of heat, development of steam and internal combustion engines, efficiency of an engine, compression-ignition engines, production of steam, the ideal engine, much more. 318 exercises, answers, worked examples. Tables. 76 illus. 220pp. 6⅞ x 4¼.   Clothbound **$2.00**

BOOKS EXPLAINING SCIENCE AND MATHEMATICS

Miscellaneous

ON THE SENSATIONS OF TONE, Hermann Helmholtz. This is an unmatched coordination of such fields as acoustical physics, physiology, experiment, history of music. It covers the entire gamut of musical tone. Partial contents: relation of musical science to acoustics, physical vs. physiological acoustics, composition of vibration, resonance, analysis of tones by sympathetic resonance, beats, chords, tonality, consonant chords, discords, progression of parts, etc. 33 appendixes discuss various aspects of sound, physics, acoustics, music, etc. Translated by A. J. Ellis. New introduction by Prof. Henry Margenau of Yale. 68 figures. 43 musical passages analyzed. Over 100 tables. Index. xix + 576pp. 6⅛ x 9¼.
                                                              S114 Paperbound **$3.00**

MATHEMATICS—INTERMEDIATE TO ADVANCED

General

INTRODUCTION TO APPLIED MATHEMATICS, Francis D. Murnaghan. A practical and thoroughly sound introduction to a number of advanced branches of higher mathematics. Among the selected topics covered in detail are: vector and matrix analysis, partial and differential equations, integral equations, calculus of variations, Laplace transform theory, the vector triple product, linear vector functions, quadratic and bilinear forms, Fourier series, spherical harmonics, Bessel functions, the Heaviside expansion formula, and many others. Extremely useful book for graduate students in physics, engineering, chemistry, and mathematics. Index. 111 study exercises with answers. 41 illustrations. ix + 389pp. 5⅜ x 8½.
                                                                S1042 Paperbound **$2.00**

OPERATIONAL METHODS IN APPLIED MATHEMATICS, H. S. Carslaw and J. C. Jaeger. Explanation of the application of the Laplace Transformation to differential equations, a simple and effective substitute for more difficult and obscure operational methods. Of great practical value to engineers and to all workers in applied mathematics. Chapters on: Ordinary Linear Differential Equations with Constant Coefficients;; Electric Circuit Theory; Dynamical Applications; The Inversion Theorem for the Laplace Transformation; Conduction of Heat; Vibrations of Continuous Mechanical Systems; Hydrodynamics; Impulsive Functions; Chains of Differential Equations; and other related matters. 3 appendices. 153 problems, many with answers. 22 figures. xvi + 359pp. 5⅜ x 8½.   S1011 Paperbound **$2.25**

APPLIED MATHEMATICS FOR RADIO AND COMMUNICATIONS ENGINEERS, C. E. Smith. No extraneous material here!—only the theories, equations, and operations essential and immediately useful for radio work. Can be used as refresher, as handbook of applications and tables, or as full home-study course. Ranges from simplest arithmetic through calculus, series, and wave forms, hyperbolic trigonometry, simultaneous equations in mesh circuits, etc. Supplies applications right along with each math topic discussed. 22 useful tables of functions, formulas, logs, etc. Index. 166 exercises, 140 examples, all with answers. 95 diagrams. Bibliography. x + 336pp. 5⅜ x 8.   S141 Paperbound **$1.75**

Algebra, group theory, determinants, sets, matrix theory

ALGEBRAS AND THEIR ARITHMETICS, L. E. Dickson. Provides the foundation and background necessary to any advanced undergraduate or graduate student studying abstract algebra. Begins with elementary introduction to linear transformations, matrices, field of complex numbers; proceeds to order, basal units, modulus, quaternions, etc.; develops calculus of linears sets, describes various examples of algebras including invariant, difference, nilpotent, semi-simple. "Makes the reader marvel at his genius for clear and profound analysis," Amer. Mathematical Monthly. Index. xii + 241pp. 5⅜ x 8.   S616 Paperbound **$1.50**

THE THEORY OF EQUATIONS WITH AN INTRODUCTION TO THE THEORY OF BINARY ALGEBRAIC FORMS, W. S. Burnside and A. W. Panton. Extremely thorough and concrete discussion of the theory of equations, with extensive detailed treatment of many topics curtailed in later texts. Covers theory of algebraic equations, properties of polynomials, symmetric functions, derived functions, Horner's process, complex numbers and the complex variable, determinants and methods of elimination, invariant theory (nearly 100 pages), transformations, introduction to Galois theory, Abelian equations, and much more. Invaluable supplementary work for modern students and teachers. 759 examples and exercises. Index in each volume. Two volume set. Total of xxiv + 604pp. 5⅜ x 8.   S714 Vol I Paperbound **$1.85**
                                                           S715 Vol II Paperbound **$1.85**
                                                           The set **$3.70**

COMPUTATIONAL METHODS OF LINEAR ALGEBRA, V. N. Faddeeva, translated by C. D. Benster. First English translation of a unique and valuable work, the only work in English presenting a systematic exposition of the most important methods of linear algebra—classical and contemporary. Shows in detail how to derive numerical solutions of problems in mathematical physics which are frequently connected with those of linear algebra. Theory as well as individual practice. Part I surveys the mathematical background that is indispensable to what follows. Parts II and III, the conclusion, set forth the most important methods of solution, for both exact and iterative groups. One of the most outstanding and valuable features of this work is the 23 tables, double and triple checked for accuracy. These tables will not be found elsewhere. Author's preface. Translator's note. New bibliography and index. x + 252pp. 5⅜ x 8.   S424 Paperbound **$1.95**

ALGEBRAIC EQUATIONS, E. Dehn. Careful and complete presentation of Galois' theory of algebraic equations; theories of Lagrange and Galois developed in logical rather than historical form, with a more thorough exposition than in most modern books. Many concrete applications and fully-worked-out examples. Discusses basic theory (very clear exposition of the symmetric group); isomorphic, transitive, and Abelian groups; applications of Lagrange's and Galois' theories; and much more. Newly revised by the author. Index. List of Theorems. xi + 208pp. 5⅜ x 8.   S697 Paperbound **$1.45**

ALGEBRAIC THEORIES, L. E. Dickson. Best thorough introduction to classical topics in higher algebra develops theories centering around matrices, invariants, groups. Higher algebra, Galois theory, finite linear groups, Klein's icosahedron, algebraic invariants, linear transformations, elementary divisors, invariant factors; quadratic, bi-linear, Hermitian forms, singly and in pairs. Proofs rigorous, detailed; topics developed lucidly, in close connection with their most frequent mathematical applications. Formerly "Modern Algebraic Theories." 155 problems. Bibliography. 2 indexes. 285pp. 5⅜ x 8. S547 Paperbound **$1.50**

LECTURES ON THE ICOSAHEDRON AND THE SOLUTION OF EQUATIONS OF THE FIFTH DEGREE, Felix Klein. The solution of quintics in terms of rotation of a regular icosahedron around its axes of symmetry. A classic & indispensable source for those interested in higher algebra, geometry, crystallography. Considerable explanatory material included. 230 footnotes, mostly bibliographic. 2nd edition, xvi + 289pp. 5⅜ x 8. S314 Paperbound **$2.25**

LINEAR GROUPS, WITH AN EXPOSITION OF THE GALOIS FIELD THEORY, L. E. Dickson. The classic exposition of the theory of groups, well within the range of the graduate student. Part I contains the most extensive and thorough presentation of the theory of Galois Fields available, with a wealth of examples and theorems. Part II is a full discussion of linear groups of finite order. Much material in this work is based on Dickson's own contributions. Also includes expositions of Jordan, Lie, Abel, Betti-Mathieu, Hermite, etc. "A milestone in the development of modern algebra," W. Magnus, in his historical introduction to this edition. Index. xv + 312pp. 5⅜ x 8. S482 Paperbound **$1.95**

INTRODUCTION TO THE THEORY OF GROUPS OF FINITE ORDER, R. Carmichael. Examines fundamental theorems and their application. Beginning with sets, systems, permutations, etc., it progresses in easy stages through important types of groups: Abelian, prime power, permutation, etc. Except 1 chapter where matrices are desirable, no higher math needed. 783 exercises, problems. Index. xvi + 447pp. 5⅜ x 8. S300 Paperbound **$2.25**

THEORY OF GROUPS OF FINITE ORDER, W. Burnside. First published some 40 years ago, this is still one of the clearest introductory texts. Partial contents: permutations, groups independent of representation, composition series of a group, isomorphism of a group with itself, Abelian groups, prime power groups, permutation groups, invariants of groups of linear substitution, graphical representation, etc. 45pp. of notes. Indexes. xxiv + 512pp. 5⅜ x 8. S38 Paperbound **$2.75**

CONTINUOUS GROUPS OF TRANSFORMATIONS, L. P. Eisenhart. Intensive study of the theory and geometrical applications of continuous groups of transformations; a standard work on the subject, called forth by the revolution in physics in the 1920's. Covers tensor analysis, Riemannian geometry, canonical parameters, transitivity, imprimitivity, differential invariants, the algebra of constants of structure, differential geometry, contact transformations, etc. "Likely to remain one of the standard works on the subject for many years . . . principal theorems are proved clearly and concisely, and the arrangement of the whole is coherent," MATHEMATICAL GAZETTE. Index. 72-item bibliography. 185 exercises. ix + 301pp. 5⅜ x 8. S781 Paperbound **$2.00**

THE THEORY OF GROUPS AND QUANTUM MECHANICS, H. Weyl. Discussions of Schroedinger's wave equation, de Broglie's waves of a particle, Jordan-Hoelder theorem, Lie's continuous groups of transformations, Pauli exclusion principle, quantization of Maxwell-Dirac field equations, etc. Unitary geometry, quantum theory, groups, application of groups to quantum mechanics, symmetry permutation group, algebra of symmetric transformation, etc. 2nd revised edition. Bibliography. Index. xxii + 422pp. 5⅜ x 8. S269 Paperbound **$2.35**

APPLIED GROUP-THEORETIC AND MATRIX METHODS, Bryan Higman. The first systematic treatment of group and matrix theory for the physical scientist. Contains a comprehensive, easily-followed exposition of the basic ideas of group theory (realized through matrices) and its applications in the various areas of physics and chemstry: tensor analysis, relativity, quantum theory, molecular structure and spectra, and Eddington's quantum relativity. Includes rigorous proofs available only in works of a far more advanced character. 34 figures, numerous tables. Bibliography. Index. xiii + 454pp. 5⅜ x 8⅜. S1147 Paperbound **$2.50**

THE THEORY OF GROUP REPRESENTATIONS, Francis D. Murnaghan. A comprehensive introduction to the theory of group representations. Particular attention is devoted to those groups—mainly the symmetric and rotation groups—which have proved to be of fundamental significance for quantum mechanics (esp. nuclear physics). Also a valuable contribution to the literature on matrices, since the usual representations of groups are groups of matrices. Covers the theory of group integration (as developed by Schur and Weyl), the theory of 2-valued or spin representations, the representations of the symmetric group, the crystallographic groups, the Lorentz group, reducibility (Schur's lemma, Burnside's Theorem, etc.), the alternating group, linear groups, the orthogonal group, etc. Index. List of references. xi + 369pp. 5⅜ x 8½. S1112 Paperbound **$2.35**

THEORY OF SETS, E. Kamke. Clearest, amplest introduction in English, well suited for independent study. Subdivision of main theory, such as theory of sets of points, are discussed, but emphasis is on general theory. Partial contents: rudiments of set theory, arbitrary sets and their cardinal numbers, ordered sets and their order types, well-ordered sets and their cardinal numbers. Bibliography. Key to symbols. Index. vii + 144pp. 5⅜ x 8. S141 Paperbound **$1.35**

THEORY AND APPLICATIONS OF FINITE GROUPS, G. A. Miller, H. F. Blichfeldt, L. E. Dickson. Unusually accurate and authoritative work, each section prepared by a leading specialist: Miller on substitution and abstract groups, Blichfeldt on finite groups of linear homogeneous transformations, Dickson on applications of finite groups. Unlike more modern works, this gives the concrete basis from which abstract group theory arose. Includes Abelian groups, prime-power groups, isomorphisms, matrix forms of linear transformations, Sylow groups, Galois' theory of algebraic equations, duplication of a cube, trisection of an angle, etc. 2 Indexes. 267 problems. xvii + 390pp. 5⅜ x 8. S216 Paperbound **$2.00**

THE THEORY OF DETERMINANTS, MATRICES, AND INVARIANTS, H. W. Turnbull. Important study includes all salient features and major theories. 7 chapters on determinants and matrices cover fundamental properties, Laplace identities, multiplication, linear equations, rank and differentiation, etc. Sections on invariants gives general properties, symbolic and direct methods of reduction, binary and polar forms, general linear transformation, first fundamental theorem, multilinear forms. Following chapters study development and proof of Hilbert's Basis Theorem, Gordan-Hilbert Finiteness Theorem, Clebsch's Theorem, and include discussions of apolarity, canonical forms, geometrical interpretations of algebraic forms, complete system of the general quadric, etc. New preface and appendix. Bibliography. xviii + 374pp. 5⅜ x 8. S699 Paperbound **$2.25**

AN INTRODUCTION TO THE THEORY OF CANONICAL MATRICES, H. W. Turnbull and A. C. Aitken. All principal aspects of the theory of canonical matrices, from definitions and fundamental properties of matrices to the practical applications of their reduction to canonical form. Beginning with matrix multiplications, reciprocals, and partitioned matrices, the authors go on to elementary transformations and bilinear and quadratic forms. Also covers such topics as a rational canonical form for the collineatory group, congruent and conjunctive transformation for quadratic and hermitian forms, unitary and orthogonal transformations, canonical reduction of pencils of matrices, etc. Index. Appendix. Historical notes at chapter ends. Bibliographies. 275 problems. xiv + 200pp. 5⅜ x 8. S177 Paperbound **$1.55**

A TREATISE ON THE THEORY OF DETERMINANTS, T. Muir. Unequalled as an exhaustive compilation of nearly all the known facts about determinants up to the early 1930's. Covers notation and general properties, row and column transformation, symmetry, compound determinants, adjugates, rectangular arrays and matrices, linear dependence, gradients, Jacobians, Hessians, Wronskians, and much more. Invaluable for libraries of industrial and research organizations as well as for student, teacher, and mathematician; very useful in the field of computing machines. Revised and enlarged by W. H. Metzler. Index. 485 problems and scores of numerical examples. iv + 766pp. 5⅜ x 8. S670 Paperbound **$3.00**

THEORY OF DETERMINANTS IN THE HISTORICAL ORDER OF DEVELOPMENT, Sir Thomas Muir. Unabridged reprinting of this complete study of 1,859 papers on determinant theory written between 1693 and 1900. Most important and original sections reproduced, valuable commentary on each. No other work is necessary for determinant research: all types are covered—each subdivision of the theory treated separately; all papers dealing with each type are covered; you are told exactly what each paper is about and how important its contribution is. Each result, theory, extension, or modification is assigned its own identifying numeral so that the full history may be more easily followed. Includes papers on determinants in general, determinants and linear equations, symmetric determinants, alternants, recurrents, determinants having invariant factors, and all other major types. "A model of what such histories ought to be," NATURE. "Mathematicians must ever be grateful to Sir Thomas for his monumental work," AMERICAN MATH MONTHLY. Four volumes bound as two. Indices. Bibliographies. Total of lxxxiv + 1977pp. 5⅜ x 8. S672-3 The set, Clothbound **$12.50**

Calculus and function theory, Fourier theory, infinite series, calculus of variations, real and complex functions

FIVE VOLUME "THEORY OF FUNCTIONS' SET BY KONRAD KNOPP

This five-volume set, prepared by Konrad Knopp, provides a complete and readily followed account of theory of functions. Proofs are given concisely, yet without sacrifice of completeness or rigor. These volumes are used as texts by such universities as M.I.T., University of Chicago, N. Y. City College, and many others. "Excellent introduction . . . remarkably readable, concise, clear, rigorous," JOURNAL OF THE AMERICAN STATISTICAL ASSOCIATION.

ELEMENTS OF THE THEORY OF FUNCTIONS, Konrad Knopp. This book provides the student with background for further volumes in this set, or texts on a similar level. Partial contents: foundations, system of complex numbers and the Gaussian plane of numbers, Riemann sphere of numbers, mapping by linear functions, normal forms, the logarithm, the cyclometric functions and binomial series. "Not only for the young student, but also for the student who knows all about what is in it," MATHEMATICAL JOURNAL. Bibliography. Index. 140pp. 5⅜ x 8. S154 Paperbound **$1.35**

THEORY OF FUNCTIONS, PART I, Konrad Knopp. With volume II, this book provides coverage of basic concepts and theorems. Partial contents: numbers and points, functions of a complex variable, integral of a continuous function, Cauchy's integral theorem, Cauchy's integral formulae, series with variable terms, expansion of analytic functions in power series, analytic continuation and complete definition of analytic functions, entire transcendental functions, Laurent expansion, types of singularities. Bibliography. Index. vii + 146pp. 5⅜ x 8. S156 Paperbound **$1.35**

THEORY OF FUNCTIONS, PART II, Konrad Knopp. Application and further development of general theory, special topics. Single valued functions, entire, Weierstrass, Meromorphic functions. Riemann surfaces. Algebraic functions. Analytical configuration, Riemann surface. Bibliography. Index. x + 150pp. 5⅜ x 8. S157 Paperbound **$1.35**

PROBLEM BOOK IN THE THEORY OF FUNCTIONS, VOLUME 1, Konrad Knopp. Problems in elementary theory, for use with Knopp's THEORY OF FUNCTIONS, or any other text, arranged according to increasing difficulty. Fundamental concepts, sequences of numbers and infinite series, complex variable, integral theorems, development in series, conformal mapping. 182 problems. Answers. viii + 126pp. 5⅜ x 8. S158 Paperbound **$1.35**

PROBLEM BOOK IN THE THEORY OF FUNCTIONS, VOLUME 2, Konrad Knopp. Advanced theory of functions, to be used either with Knopp's THEORY OF FUNCTIONS, or any other comparable text. Singularities, entire & meromorphic functions, periodic, analytic, continuation, multiple-valued functions, Riemann surfaces, conformal mapping. Includes a section of additional elementary problems. "The difficult task of selecting from the immense material of the modern theory of functions the problems just within the reach of the beginner is here masterfully accomplished," AM. MATH. SOC. Answers. 138pp. 5⅜ x 8. S159 Paperbound **$1.35**

A COURSE IN MATHEMATICAL ANALYSIS, Edouard Goursat. Trans. by E. R. Hedrick, O. Dunkel. Classic study of fundamental material thoroughly treated. Exceptionally lucid exposition of wide range of subject matter for student with 1 year of calculus. Vol. 1: Derivatives and Differentials, Definite Integrals, Expansion in Series, Applications to Geometry. Problems. Index. 52 illus. 556pp. Vol. 2, Part I: Functions of a Complex Variable, Conformal Representations, Doubly Periodic Functions, Natural Boundaries, etc. Problems. Index. 38 illus. 269pp. Vol. 2, Part 2: Differential Equations, Cauchy-Lipschitz Method, Non-linear Differential Equations, Simultaneous Equations, etc. Problems. Index. 308pp. 5⅜ x 8.
Vol. 1 S554 Paperbound **$2.50**
Vol. 2 part 1 S555 Paperbound **$1.85**
Vol. 2 part 2 S556 Paperbound **$1.85**
3 vol. set **$6.20**

MODERN THEORIES OF INTEGRATION, H. Kestelman. Connected and concrete coverage, with fully-worked-out proofs for every step. Ranges from elementary definitions through theory of aggregates, sets of points, Riemann and Lebesgue integration, and much more. This new revised and enlarged edition contains a new chapter on Riemann-Stieltjes integration, as well as a supplementary section of 186 exercises. Ideal for the mathematician, student, teacher, or self-studier. Index of Definitions and Symbols. General Index. Bibliography. x + 310pp. 5⅝ x 8⅜. S572 Paperbound **$2.25**

THEORY OF MAXIMA AND MINIMA, H. Hancock. Fullest treatment ever written; only work in English with extended discussion of maxima and minima for functions of 1, 2, or n variables, problems with subsidiary constraints, and relevant quadratic forms. Detailed proof of each important theorem. Covers the Scheeffer and von Dantscher theories, homogeneous quadratic forms, reversion of series, fallacious establishment of maxima and minima, etc. Unsurpassed treatise for advanced students of calculus, mathematicians, economists, statisticians. Index. 24 diagrams. 39 problems, many examples. 193pp. 5⅜ x 8. S665 Paperbound **$1.50**

AN ELEMENTARY TREATISE ON ELLIPTIC FUNCTIONS, A. Cayley. Still the fullest and clearest text on the theories of Jacobi and Legendre for the advanced student (and an excellent supplement for the beginner). A masterpiece of exposition by the great 19th century British mathematician (creator of the theory of matrices and abstract geometry), it covers the addition-theory, Landen's theorem, the 3 kinds of elliptic integrals, transformations, the q-functions, reduction of a differential expression, and much more. Index. xii + 386pp. 5⅜ x 8.
S728 Paperbound **$2.00**

THE APPLICATIONS OF ELLIPTIC FUNCTIONS, A. G. Greenhill. Modern books forego detail for sake of brevity—this book offers complete exposition necessary for proper understanding, use of elliptic integrals. Formulas developed from definite physical, geometric problems; examples representative enough to offer basic information in widely useable form. Elliptic integrals, addition theorem, algebraical form of addition theorem, elliptic integrals of 2nd, 3rd kind, double periodicity, resolution into factors, series, transformation, etc. Introduction. Index. 25 illus. xi + 357pp. 5⅜ x 8. S603 Paperbound **$1.75**

THE THEORY OF FUNCTIONS OF REAL VARIABLES, James Pierpont. A 2-volume authoritative exposition, by one of the foremost mathematicians of his time. Each theorem stated with all conditions, then followed by proof. No need to go through complicated reasoning to discover conditions added without specific mention. Includes a particularly complete, rigorous presentation of theory of measure; and Pierpont's own work on a theory of Lebesgue integrals, and treatment of area of a curved surface. Partial contents, Vol. 1: rational numbers, exponentials, logarithms, point aggregates, maxima, minima, proper integrals, improper integrals, multiple proper integrals, continuity, discontinuity, indeterminate forms. Vol. 2: point sets, proper integrals, series, power series, aggregates, ordinal numbers, discontinuous functions, sub-, infra-uniform convergence, much more. Index. 95 illustrations. 1229pp. 5⅜ x 8. S558-9, 2 volume set, paperbound **$5.20**

FUNCTIONS OF A COMPLEX VARIABLE, James Pierpont. Long one of best in the field. A thorough treatment of fundamental elements, concepts, theorems. A complete study, rigorous, detailed, with carefully selected problems worked out to illustrate each topic. Partial contents: arithmetical operations, real term series, positive term series, exponential functions, integration, analytic functions, asymptotic expansions, functions of Weierstrass, Legendre, etc. Index. List of symbols. 122 illus. 597pp. 5⅜ x 8.   S560 Paperbound **$2.45**

MODERN OPERATIONAL CALCULUS: WITH APPLICATIONS IN TECHNICAL MATHEMATICS, N. W. McLachlan. An introduction to modern operational calculus based upon the Laplace transform, applying it to the solution of ordinary and partial differential equations. For physicists, engineers, and applied mathematicians. Partial contents: Laplace transform, theorems or rules of the operational calculus, solution of ordinary and partial linear differential equations with constant coefficients, evaluation of integrals and establishment of mathematical relationships, derivation of Laplace transforms of various functions, etc. Six appendices deal with Heaviside's unit function, etc. Revised edition. Index. Bibliography. xiv + 218pp. 5⅜ x 8½.   S192 Paperbound **$1.75**

ADVANCED CALCULUS, E. B. Wilson. An unabridged reprinting of the work which continues to be recognized as one of the most comprehensive and useful texts in the field. It contains an immense amount of well-presented, fundamental material, including chapters on vector functions, ordinary differential equations, special functions, calculus of variations, etc., which are excellent introductions to these areas. For students with only one year of calculus, more than 1300 exercises cover both pure math and applications to engineering and physical problems. For engineers, physicists, etc., this work, with its 54 page introductory review, is the ideal reference and refresher. Index. ix + 566pp. 5⅜ x 8.
S504 Paperbound **$2.45**

ASYMPTOTIC EXPANSIONS, A. Erdélyi. The only modern work available in English, this is an unabridged reproduction of a monograph prepared for the Office of Naval Research. It discusses various procedures for asymptotic evaluation of integrals containing a large parameter and solutions of ordinary linear differential equations. Bibliography of 71 items. vi + 108pp. 5⅜ x 8.   S318 Paperbound **$1.35**

INTRODUCTION TO ELLIPTIC FUNCTIONS: with applications, F. Bowman. Concise, practical introduction to elliptic integrals and functions. Beginning with the familiar trigonometric functions, it requires nothing more from the reader than a knowledge of basic principles of differentiation and integration. Discussion confined to the Jacobian functions. Enlarged bibliography. Index. 173 problems and examples. 56 figures, 4 tables. 115pp. 5⅜ x 8.
S922 Paperbound **$1.25**

ON RIEMANN'S THEORY OF ALGEBRAIC FUNCTIONS AND THEIR INTEGRALS: A SUPPLEMENT TO THE USUAL TREATISES, Felix Klein. Klein demonstrates how the mathematical ideas in Riemann's work on Abelian integrals can be arrived at by thinking in terms of the flow of electric current on surfaces. Intuitive explanations, not detailed proofs given in an extremely clear exposition, concentrating on the kinds of functions which can be defined on Riemann surfaces. Also useful as an introduction to the origins of topological problems. Complete and unabridged. Approved translation by Frances Hardcastle. New introduction. 43 figures. Glossary. xii + 76pp. 5⅜ x 8½.   S1072 Paperbound **$1.25**

COLLECTED WORKS OF BERNHARD RIEMANN. This important source book is the first to contain the complete text of both 1892 Werke and the 1902 supplement, unabridged. It contains 31 monographs, 3 complete lecture courses, 15 miscellaneous papers, which have been of enormous importance in relativity, topology, theory of complex variables, and other areas of mathematics. Edited by R. Dedekind, H. Weber, M. Noether, W. Wirtinger. German text. English introduction by Hans Lewy. 690pp. 5⅜ x 8.   S226 Paperbound **$3.75**

THE TAYLOR SERIES, AN INTRODUCTION TO THE THEORY OF FUNCTIONS OF A COMPLEX VARIABLE, P. Dienes. This book investigates the entire realm of analytic functions. Only ordinary calculus is needed, except in the last two chapters. Starting with an introduction to real variables and complex algebra, the properties of infinite series, elementary functions, complex differentiation and integration are carefully derived. Also biuniform mapping, a thorough two part discussion of representation and singularities of analytic functions, overconvergence and gap theorems, divergent series, Taylor series on its circle of convergence, divergence and singularities, etc. Unabridged, corrected reissue of first edition. Preface and index. 186 examples, many fully worked out. 67 figures. xii + 555pp. 5⅜ x 8.
S391 Paperbound **$2.75**

INTRODUCTION TO BESSEL FUNCTIONS, Frank Bowman. A rigorous self-contained exposition providing all necessary material during the development, which requires only some knowledge of calculus and acquaintance with differential equations. A balanced presentation including applications and practical use. Discusses Bessel Functions of Zero Order, of Any Real Order; Modified Bessel Functions of Zero Order; Definite Integrals; Asymptotic Expansions; Bessel's Solution to Kepler's Problem; Circular Membranes; much more. "Clear and straightforward . . . useful not only to students of physics and engineering, but to mathematical students in general," Nature. 226 problems. Short tables of Bessel functions. 27 figures. Index. x + 135pp. 5⅜ x 8.   S462 Paperbound **$1.35**

ELEMENTS OF THE THEORY OF REAL FUNCTIONS, J. E. Littlewood. Based on lectures given at Trinity College, Cambridge, this book has proved to be extremely successful in introducing graduate students to the modern theory of functions. It offers a full and concise coverage of classes and cardinal numbers, well-ordered series, other types of series, and elements of the theory of sets of points. 3rd revised edition. vii + 71pp. 5⅜ x 8.
S171 Clothbound **$2.85**
S172 Paperbound **$1.25**

TRANSCENDENTAL AND ALGEBRAIC NUMBERS, A. O. Gelfond. First English translation of work by leading Soviet mathematician. Thue-Siegel theorem, its p-adic analogue, on approximation of algebraic numbers by numbers in fixed algebraic field; Hermite-Lindemann theorem on transcendency of Bessel functions, solutions of other differential equations; Gelfond-Schneider theorem on transcendency of alpha to power beta; Schneider's work on elliptic functions, with method developed by Gelfond. Translated by L. F. Boron. Index. Bibliography. 200pp. 5⅜ x 8.
S615 Paperbound **$1.75**

ELLIPTIC INTEGRALS, H. Hancock. Invaluable in work involving differential equations containing cubics or quartics under the root sign, where elementary calculus methods are inadequate. Practical solutions to problems that occur in mathematics, engineering, physics: differential equations requiring integration of Lamé's, Briot's, or Bouquet's equations; determination of arc of ellipse, hyperbola, lemniscate; solutions of problems in elastica; motion of a projectile under resistance varying as the cube of the velocity; pendulums; many others. Exposition is in accordance with Legendre-Jacobi theory and includes rigorous discussion of Legendre transformations. 20 figures. 5 place table. Index. 104pp. 5⅛ x 8.
S484 Paperbound **$1.25**

LECTURES ON THE THEORY OF ELLIPTIC FUNCTIONS, H. Hancock. Reissue of the only book in English with so extensive a coverage, especially of Abel, Jacobi, Legendre, Weierstrasse, Hermite, Liouville, and Riemann. Unusual fullness of treatment, plus applications as well as theory, in discussing elliptic function (the universe of elliptic integrals originating in works of Abel and Jacobi), their existence, and ultimate meaning. Use is made of Riemann to provide the most general theory. 40 page table of formulas. 76 figures. xxiii + 498pp.
S483 Paperbound **$2.55**

THE THEORY AND FUNCTIONS OF A REAL VARIABLE AND THE THEORY OF FOURIER'S SERIES, E. W. Hobson. One of the best introductions to set theory and various aspects of functions and Fourier's series. Requires only a good background in calculus. Provides an exhaustive coverage of: metric and descriptive properties of sets of points; transfinite numbers and order types; functions of a real variable; the Riemann and Lebesgue integrals; sequences and series of numbers; power-series; functions representable by series sequences of continuous functions; trigonometrical series; representation of functions by Fourier's series; complete exposition (200pp.) on set theory; and much more. "The best possible guide," Nature. Vol. I: 88 detailed examples, 10 figures. Index. xv + 736pp. Vol. II: 117 detailed examples, 13 figures. Index. x + 780pp. 6⅛ x 9¼.
Vol. I: S387 Paperbound **$3.00**
Vol. II: S388 Paperbound **$3.00**

ALMOST PERIODIC FUNCTIONS, A. S. Besicovitch. This unique and important summary by a well-known mathematician covers in detail the two stages of development in Bohr's theory of almost periodic functions: (1) as a generalization of pure periodicity, with results and proofs; (2) the work done by Stepanoff, Wiener, Weyl, and Bohr in generalizing the theory. Bibliography. xi + 180pp. 5⅜ x 8.
S18 Paperbound **$1.75**

THE ANALYTICAL THEORY OF HEAT, Joseph Fourier. This book, which revolutionized mathematical physics, is listed in the Great Books program, and many other listings of great books. It has been used with profit by generations of mathematicians and physicists who are interested in either heat or in the application of the Fourier integral. Covers cause and reflection of rays of heat, radiant heating, heating of closed spaces, use of trigonometric series in the theory of heat, Fourier integral, etc. Translated by Alexander Freeman. 20 figures. xxii + 466pp. 5⅜ x 8.
S93 Paperbound **$2.50**

AN INTRODUCTION TO FOURIER METHODS AND THE LAPLACE TRANSFORMATION, Philip Franklin. Concentrates upon essentials, enabling the reader with only a working knowledge of calculus to gain an understanding of Fourier methods in a broad sense, suitable for most applications. This work covers complex qualities with methods of computing elementary functions for complex values of the argument and finding approximations by the use of charts; Fourier series and integrals with half-range and complex Fourier series; harmonic analysis; Fourier and Laplace transformations, etc.; partial differential equations with applications to transmission of electricity; etc. The methods developed are related to physical problems of heat flow, vibrations, electrical transmission, electromagnetic radiation, etc. 828 problems with answers. Formerly entitled "Fourier Methods." Bibliography. Index. x + 289pp. 5⅜ x 8.
S452 Paperbound **$2.00**

THE FOURIER INTEGRAL AND CERTAIN OF ITS APPLICATIONS, Norbert Wiener. The only book-length study of the Fourier integral as link between pure and applied math. An expansion of lectures given at Cambridge. Partial contents: Plancherel's theorem, general Tauberian theorem, special Tauberian theorems, generalized harmonic analysis. Bibliography. viii + 201pp. 5⅜ x 8.
S272 Paperbound **$1.50**

Differential equations, ordinary and partial; integral equations

INTRODUCTION TO THE DIFFERENTIAL EQUATIONS OF PHYSICS, L. Hopf. Especially valuable to the engineer with no math beyond elementary calculus. Emphasizing intuitive rather than formal aspects of concepts, the author covers an extensive territory. Partial contents: Law of causality, energy theorem, damped oscillations, coupling by friction, cylindrical and spherical coordinates, heat source, etc. Index. 48 figures. 160pp. 5⅜ x 8.
S120 Paperbound **$1.25**

INTRODUCTION TO THE THEORY OF LINEAR DIFFERENTIAL EQUATIONS, E. G. Poole. Authoritative discussions of important topics, with methods of solution more detailed than usual, for students with background of elementary course in differential equations. Studies existence theorems, linearly independent solutions; equations with constant coefficients; with uniform analytic coefficients; regular singularities; the hypergeometric equation; conformal representation; etc. Exercises. Index. 210pp. 5⅜ x 8.
S629 Paperbound **$1.65**

DIFFERENTIAL EQUATIONS FOR ENGINEERS, P. Franklin. Outgrowth of a course given 10 years at M. I. T. Makes most useful branch of pure math accessible for practical work. Theoretical basis of D.E.'s; solution of ordinary D.E.'s and partial derivatives arising from heat flow, steady-state temperature of a plate, wave equations; analytic functions; convergence of Fourier Series. 400 problems on electricity, vibratory systems, other topics. Formerly "Differential Equations for Electrical Engineers." Index 41 illus. 307pp. 5⅜ x 8.
S601 Paperbound **$1.65**

DIFFERENTIAL EQUATIONS, F. R. Moulton. A detailed, rigorous exposition of all the non-elementary processes of solving ordinary differential equations. Several chapters devoted to the treatment of practical problems, especially those of a physical nature, which are far more advanced than problems usually given as illustrations. Includes analytic differential equations; variations of a parameter; integrals of differential equations; analytic implicit functions; problems of elliptic motion; sine-amplitude functions; deviation of formal bodies; Cauchy-Lipschitz process; linear differential equations with periodic coefficients; differential equations in infinitely many variations; much more. Historical notes. 10 figures. 222 problems. Index. xv + 395pp. 5⅜ x 8.
S451 Paperbound **$2.00**

DIFFERENTIAL AND INTEGRAL EQUATIONS OF MECHANICS AND PHYSICS (DIE DIFFERENTIAL-UND INTEGRALGLEICHUNGEN DER MECHANIK UND PHYSIK), edited by P. Frank and R. von Mises. Most comprehensive and authoritative work on the mathematics of mathematical physics available today in the United States: the standard, definitive reference for teachers, physicists, engineers, and mathematicians—now published (in the original German) at a relatively inexpensive price for the first time! Every chapter in this 2,000-page set is by an expert in his field: Carathéodory, Courant, Frank, Mises, and a dozen others. Vol I, on mathematics, gives concise but complete coverages of advanced calculus, differential equations, integral equations, and potential, and partial differential equations. Index. xxiii + 916pp. Vol. II (physics): classical mechanics, optics, continuous mechanics, heat conduction and diffusion, the stationary and quasi-stationary electromagnetic field, electromagnetic oscillations, and wave mechanics. Index. xxiv + 1106pp. Two volume set. Each volume available separately. 5⅝ x 8⅜.
S787 Vol I Clothbound **$7.50**
S788 Vol II Clothbound **$7.50**
The set **$15.00**

LECTURES ON CAUCHY'S PROBLEM, J. Hadamard. Based on lectures given at Columbia, Rome, this discusses work of Riemann, Kirchhoff, Volterra, and the author's own research on the hyperbolic case in linear partial differential equations. It extends spherical and cylindrical waves to apply to all (normal) hyperbolic equations. Partial contents: Cauchy's problem, fundamental formula, equations with odd number, with even number of independent variables; method of descent. 32 figures. Index. iii + 316pp. 5⅜ x 8.
S105 Paperbound **$1.75**

THEORY OF DIFFERENTIAL EQUATIONS, A. R. Forsyth. Out of print for over a decade, the complete 6 volumes (now bound as 3) of this monumental work represent the most comprehensive treatment of differential equations ever written. Historical presentation includes in 2500 pages every substantial development. Vol. 1, 2: EXACT EQUATIONS, PFAFF'S PROBLEM; ORDINARY EQUATIONS, NOT LINEAR: methods of Grassmann, Clebsch, Lie, Darboux; Cauchy's theorem; branch points; etc. Vol. 3, 4: ORDINARY EQUATIONS, NOT LINEAR; ORDINARY LINEAR EQUATIONS: Zeta Fuchsian functions, general theorems on algebraic integrals, Brun's theorem, equations with uniform periodic coefficients, etc. Vol. 4, 5: PARTIAL DIFFERENTIAL EQUATIONS: 2 existence-theorems, equations of theoretical dynamics, Laplace transformations, general transformation of equations of the 2nd order, much more. Indexes. Total of 2766pp. 5⅜ x 8.
S576-7-8 Clothbound: the set **$15.00**

PARTIAL DIFFERENTIAL EQUATIONS OF MATHEMATICAL PHYSICS, A. G. Webster. A keystone work in the library of every mature physicist, engineer, researcher. Valuable sections on elasticity, compression theory, potential theory, theory of sound, heat conduction, wave propagation, vibration theory. Contents include: deduction of differential equations, vibrations, normal functions, Fourier's series, Cauchy's method, boundary problems, method of Riemann-Volterra. Spherical, cylindrical, ellipsoidal harmonics, applications, etc. 97 figures. vii + 440pp. 5⅜ x 8.
S263 Paperbound **$2.00**

ESSAYS ON THE THEORY OF NUMBERS: 1. CONTINUITY AND IRRATIONAL NUMBERS; 2. THE NATURE AND MEANING OF NUMBERS, Richard Dedekind. The two most important essays on the logical foundations of the number system by the famous German mathematician. The first provides a purely arithmetic and perfectly rigorous foundation for irrational numbers and thereby a rigorous meaning to continuity in analysis. The second essay is an attempt to give a logical basis for transfinite numbers and properties of the natural numbers. Discusses the logical validity of mathematical induction. Authorized English translations by W. W. Deman of "Stetigkeit und irrationale Zahlen" and "Was sind und was sollen die Zahlen?" vii + 115pp. 5⅜ x 8.   T1010 Paperbound **$1.00**

Geometry

THE FOUNDATIONS OF EUCLIDEAN GEOMETRY, H. G. Forder. The first rigorous account of Euclidean geometry, establishing propositions without recourse to empiricism, and without multiplying hypotheses. Corrects many traditional weaknesses of Euclidean proofs, and investigates the problems imposed on the axiom system by the discoveries of Bolyai and Lobachevsky. Some topics discussed are Classes and Relations; Axioms for Magnitudes; Congruence and Similarity; Algebra of Points; Hessenberg's Theorem; Continuity; Existence of Parallels; Reflections; Rotations; Isometries; etc. Invaluable for the light it throws on foundations of math. Lists: Axioms employed, Symbols, Constructions. 295pp. 5⅜ x 8.
S481 Paperbound **$2.00**

ADVANCED EUCLIDEAN GEOMETRY, R. A. Johnson. For years the standard textbook on advanced Euclidean geometry, requires only high school geometry and trigonometry. Explores in unusual detail and gives proofs of hundreds of relatively recent theorems and corollaries, many formerly available only in widely scattered journals. Covers tangent circles, the theorem of Miquel, symmedian point, pedal triangles and circles, the Brocard configuration, and much more. Formerly "Modern Geometry." Index. 107 diagrams. xiii + 319pp. 5⅜ x 8.
S669 Paperbound **$1.65**

HIGHER GEOMETRY: AN INTRODUCTION TO ADVANCED METHODS IN ANALYTIC GEOMETRY, F. S. Woods. Exceptionally thorough study of concepts and methods of advanced algebraic geometry (as distinguished from differential geometry). Exhaustive treatment of 1-, 2-, 3-, and 4-dimensional coordinate systems, leading to n-dimensional geometry in an abstract sense. Covers projectivity, tetracyclical coordinates, contact transformation, pentaspherical coordinates, much more. Based on M.I.T. lectures, requires sound preparation in analytic geometry and some knowledge of determinants. Index. Over 350 exercises. References. 60 figures. x + 423pp. 5⅜ x 8.   S737 Paperbound **$2.00**

CONTEMPORARY GEOMETRY, André Delachet. Translated by Howard G. Bergmann. The recent developments in geometry covered in uncomplicated fashion. Clear discussions of modern thinking about the theory of groups, the concept of abstract geometry, projective geometry, algebraic geometry, vector spaces, new kinds of metric spaces, developments in differential geometry, etc. A large part of the book is devoted to problems, developments, and applications of topology. For advanced undergraduates and graduate students as well as mathematicians in other fields who want a brief introduction to current work in geometry. 39 figures. Index. xix + 94pp. 5⅜ x 8½.   S988 Paperbound **$1.00**

ELEMENTS OF PROJECTIVE GEOMETRY, L. Cremona. Outstanding complete treatment of projective geometry by one of the foremost 19th century geometers. Detailed proofs of all fundamental principles, stress placed on the constructive aspects. Covers homology, law of duality, anharmonic ratios, theorems of Pascal and Brianchon, foci, polar reciprocal figures, etc. Only ordinary geometry necessary to understand this honored classic. Index. Over 150 fully worked out examples and problems. 252 diagrams. xx + 302pp. 5⅜ x 8.   S668 Paperbound **$1.75**

AN INTRODUCTION TO PROJECTIVE GEOMETRY, R. M. Winger. One of the best introductory texts to an important area in modern mathematics. Contains full development of elementary concepts often omitted in other books. Employing the analytic method to capitalize on the student's collegiate training in algebra, analytic geometry and calculus, the author deals with such topics as Essential Constants, Duality, The Line at Infinity, Projective Properties and Double Ratio, Projective Coordinates, The Conic, Collineations and Involutions in One Dimension, Binary Forms, Algebraic Invariants, Analytic Treatment of the Conic, Collineations in the Plane, Cubic Involutions and the Rational Cubic Curve, and a clear discussion of Non-Euclidean Geometry. For senior-college students and graduates. "An excellent textbook . . . very clearly written . . . propositions stated concisely," A. Emch, Am. Math. Monthly. Corrected reprinting. 928 problems. Index. 116 figures. xii + 443pp. 5⅜ x 8.
S949 Paperbound **$2.00**

ALGEBRAIC CURVES, Robert J. Walker, Professor of Mathematics, Cornell University. Fine introduction to algebraic geometry. Presents some of the recently developed algebraic methods of handling problems in algebraic geometry, shows how these methods are related to the older analytic and geometric problems, and applies them to those same geometric problems. Limited to the theory of curves, concentrating on birational transformations. Contents: Algebraic Preliminaries, Projective Spaces, Plane Algebraic Curves, Formal Power Series, Transformations of a Curve, Linear Series. 25 illustrations. Numerous exercises at ends of sections. Index. x + 201pp. 5⅜ x 8½.   S336 Paperbound **$1.60**

THE ADVANCED GEOMETRY OF PLANE CURVES AND THEIR APPLICATIONS, C. Zwikker. An unusual study of many important curves, their geometrical properties and their applications, including discussions of many less well-known curves not often treated in textbooks on synthetic and analytic Euclidean geometry. Includes both algebraic and transcendental curves such as the conic sections, kinked curves, spirals, lemniscates, cycloids, etc. and curves generated as involutes, evolutes, anticaustics, pedals, envelopes and orthogonal trajectories. Dr. Zwikker represents the points of the curves by complex numbers instead of two real Cartesian coordinates, allowing direct and even elegant proofs. Formerly: "Advanced Plane Geometry." 273 figures. xii + 299pp. 5⅜ x 8½. S1078 Paperbound **$2.00**

A TREATISE ON THE DIFFERENTIAL GEOMETRY OF CURVES AND SURFACES, L. P. Eisenhart. Introductory treatise especially for the graduate student, for years a highly successful textbook. More detailed and concrete in approach than most more recent books. Covers space curves, osculating planes, moving axes, Gauss' method, the moving trihedral, geodesics, conformal representation, etc. Last section deals with deformation of surfaces, rectilinear congruences, cyclic systems, etc. Index. 683 problems. 30 diagrams. xii + 474pp. 5⅜ x 8. S667 Paperbound **$2.75**

A TREATISE ON ALGEBRAIC PLANE CURVES, J. L. Coolidge. Unabridged reprinting of one of few full coverages in English, offering detailed introduction to theory of algebraic plane curves and their relations to geometry and analysis. Treats topological properties, Riemann-Roch theorem, all aspects of wide variety of curves including real, covariant, polar, containing series of a given sort, elliptic, polygonal, rational, the pencil, two parameter nets, etc. This volume will enable the reader to appreciate the symbolic notation of Aronhold and Clebsch. Bibliography. Index. 17 illustrations. xxiv + 513pp. 5⅜ x 8. S543 Paperbound **$2.75**

AN INTRODUCTION TO THE GEOMETRY OF N DIMENSIONS, D. M. Y. Sommerville. An introduction presupposing no prior knowledge of the field, the only book in English devoted exclusively to higher dimensional geometry. Discusses fundamental ideas of incidence, parallelism, perpendicularity, angles between linear space; enumerative geometry; analytical geometry from projective and metric points of view; polytopes; elementary ideas in analysis situs; content of hyper-spacial figures. Bibliography. Index. 60 diagrams. 196pp. 5⅜ x 8. S494 Paperbound **$1.50**

GEOMETRY OF FOUR DIMENSIONS, H. P. Manning. Unique in English as a clear, concise introduction. Treatment is synthetic, and mostly Euclidean, although in hyperplanes and hyperspheres at infinity, non-Euclidean geometry is used. Historical introduction. Foundations of 4-dimensional geometry. Perpendicularity, simple angles. Angles of planes, higher order. Symmetry, order, motion; hyperpyramids, hypercones, hyperspheres; figures with parallel elements; volume, hypervolume in space; regular polyhedroids. Glossary. 78 figures. ix + 348pp. 5⅜ x 8. S182 Paperbound **$2.00**

CONVEX FIGURES AND POLYHEDRA, L. A. Lyusternik. An excellent elementary discussion by a leading Russian mathematician. Beginning with the basic concepts of convex figures and bodies and their supporting lines and planes, the author covers such matters as centrally symmetric convex figures, theorems of Euler, Cauchy, Steinitz and Alexandrov on convex polyhedra, linear systems of convex bodies, planar sections of convex bodies, the Brunn-Minkowski inequality and its consequences, and many other related topics. No more than a high school background in mathematics needed for complete understanding. First English translation by T. J. Smith. 182 illustrations. Index. x + 176pp. 5⅜ x 8½. S1021 Paperbound **$1.50**

NON-EUCLIDEAN GEOMETRY, Roberto Bonola. The standard coverage of non-Euclidean geometry. It examines from both a historical and mathematical point of view the geometries which have arisen from a study of Euclid's 5th postulate upon parallel lines. Also included are complete texts, translated, of Bolyai's SCIENCE OF ABSOLUTE SPACE. Lobachevsky's THEORY OF PARALLELS. 180 diagrams. 431pp. 5⅜ x 8. S27 Paperbound **$2.00**

ELEMENTS OF NON-EUCLIDEAN GEOMETRY, D. M. Y. Sommerville. Unique in proceeding step-by-step, in the manner of traditional geometry. Enables the student with only a good knowledge of high school algebra and geometry to grasp elementary hyperbolic, elliptic, analytic non-Euclidean geometries; space curvature and its philosophical implications; theory of radical axes; homothetic centres and systems of circles; parataxy and parallelism; absolute measure; Gauss' proof of the defect area theorem; geodesic representation; much more, all with exceptional clarity. 126 problems at chapter endings provide progressive practice and familiarity. 133 figures. Index. xvi + 274pp. 5⅜ x 8. S460 Paperbound **$1.50**

INTRODUCTORY NON-EUCLIDEAN GEOMETRY, H. P. Manning. Sound elementary introduction to non-Euclidean geometry. The first two thirds (Pangeometry and the Hyperbolic Geometry) require a grasp of plane and solid geometry and trigonometry. The last sections (the Elliptic Geometry and Analytic Non-Euclidean Geometry) necessitate also basic college calculus for understanding the text. The book does not propose to investigate the foundations of geometry, but rather begins with the theorems common to Euclidean and non-Euclidean geometry and then takes up the specific differences between them. A simple and direct account of the bases of this important branch of mathematics for teachers and students. 94 figures. vii + 95pp. 5⅜ x 8. S310 Paperbound **$1.00**

ELEMENTARY CONCEPTS OF TOPOLOGY, P. Alexandroff. First English translation of the famous brief introduction to topology for the beginner or for the mathematician not undertaking extensive study. This unusually useful intuitive approach deals primarily with the concepts of complex, cycle, and homology, and is wholly consistent with current investigations. Ranges from basic concepts of set-theoretic topology to the concept of Betti groups. "Glowing example of harmony between intuition and thought," David Hilbert. Translated by A. E. Farley. Introduction by D. Hilbert. Index. 25 figures. 73pp. 5⅜ x 8.   S747 Paperbound **$1.00**

Number theory

INTRODUCTION TO THE THEORY OF NUMBERS, L. E. Dickson. Thorough, comprehensive approach with adequate coverage of classical literature, an introductory volume beginners can follow. Chapters on divisibility, congruences, quadratic residues & reciprocity, Diophantine equations, etc. Full treatment of binary quadratic forms without usual restriction to integral coefficients. Covers infinitude of primes, least residues, Fermat's theorem, Euler's phi function, Legendre's symbol, Gauss's lemma, automorphs, reduced forms, recent theorems of Thue & Siegel, many more. Much material not readily available elsewhere. 239 problems. Index. I figure. viii + 183pp. 5⅜ x 8.   S342 Paperbound **$1.65**

ELEMENTS OF NUMBER THEORY, I. M. Vinogradov. Detailed 1st course for persons without advanced mathematics; 95% of this book can be understood by readers who have gone no farther than high school algebra. Partial contents: divisibility theory, important number theoretical functions, congruences, primitive roots and indices, etc. Solutions to both problems and exercises. Tables of primes, indices, etc. Covers almost every essential formula in elementary number theory! Translated from Russian. 233 problems, 104 exercises. viii + 227pp. 5⅜ x 8.   S259 Paperbound **$1.60**

THEORY OF NUMBERS and DIOPHANTINE ANALYSIS, R. D. Carmichael. These two complete works in one volume form one of the most lucid introductions to number theory, requiring only a firm foundation in high school mathematics. "Theory of Numbers," partial contents: Eratosthenes' sieve, Euclid's fundamental theorem, G.C.F. and L.C.M. of two or more integers, linear congruences, etc "Diophantine Analysis": rational triangles, Pythagorean triangles, equations of third, fourth, higher degrees, method of functional equations, much more. "Theory of Numbers": 76 problems. Index. 94pp. "Diophantine Analysis": 222 problems. Index. 118pp. 5⅜ x 8.   S529 Paperbound **$1.35**

Numerical analysis, tables

MATHEMATICAL TABLES AND FORMULAS, Compiled by Robert D. Carmichael and Edwin R. Smith. Valuable collection for students, etc. Contains all tables necessary in college algebra and trigonometry, such as five-place common logarithms, logarithmic sines and tangents of small angles, logarithmic trigonometric functions, natural trigonometric functions, four-place antilogarithms, tables for changing from sexagesimal to circular and from circular to sexagesimal measure of angles, etc. Also many tables and formulas not ordinarily accessible, including powers, roots, and reciprocals, exponential and hyperbolic functions, ten-place logarithms of prime numbers, and formulas and theorems from analytical and elementary geometry and from calculus. Explanatory introduction. viii + 269pp. 5⅜ x 8½.
S111 Paperbound **$1.00**

MATHEMATICAL TABLES, H. B. Dwight. Unique for its coverage in one volume of almost every function of importance in applied mathematics, engineering, and the physical sciences. Three extremely fine tables of the three trig functions and their inverse functions to thousandths of radians; natural and common logarithms; squares, cubes; hyperbolic functions and the inverse hyperbolic functions; $(a^2 + b^2)$ exp. ½a; complete elliptic integrals of the 1st and 2nd kind; sine and cosine integrals; exponential integrals Ei(x) and Ei(−x); binomial coefficients; factorials to 250; surface zonal harmonics and first derivatives; Bernoulli and Euler numbers and their logs to base of 10; Gamma function; normal probability integral; over 60 pages of Bessel functions; the Riemann Zeta function. Each table with formulae generally used, sources of more extensive tables, interpolation data, etc. Over half have columns of differences, to facilitate interpolation. Introduction. Index. viii + 231pp. 5⅜ x 8.
S445 Paperbound **$1.75**

TABLES OF FUNCTIONS WITH FORMULAE AND CURVES, E. Jahnke & F. Emde. The world's most comprehensive 1-volume English-text collection of tables, formulae, curves of transcendent functions. 4th corrected edition, new 76-page section giving tables, formulae for elementary functions—not in other English editions. Partial contents: sine, cosine, logarithmic integral; factorial function; error integral; theta functions; elliptic integrals, functions; Legendre, Bessel, Riemann, Mathieu, hypergeometric functions, etc. Supplementary books. Bibliography. Indexed. "Out of the way functions for which we know no other source," SCIENTIFIC COMPUTING SERVICE, Ltd. 212 figures. 400pp. 5⅜ x 8.   S133 Paperbound **$2.00**

Catalogue of Dover Books

JACOBIAN ELLIPTIC FUNCTION TABLES, L. M. Milne-Thomson. An easy to follow, practical book which gives not only useful numerical tables, but also a complete elementary sketch of the application of elliptic functions. It covers Jacobian elliptic functions and a description of their principal properties; complete elliptic integrals; Fourier series and power series expansions; periods, zeros, poles, residues, formulas for special values of the argument; transformations, approximations, elliptic integrals, conformal mapping, factorization of cubic and quartic polynomials; application to the pendulum problem; etc. Tables and graphs form the body of the book: Graph, 5 figure table of the elliptic function sn (u m); cn (u m); dn (u m). 8 figure table of complete elliptic integrals K, K', E, E', and the nome q. 7 figure table of the Jacobian zeta-function Z(u). 3 figures. xi + 123pp. 5⅜ x 8.
S194 Paperbound **$1.35**

TABLES OF INDEFINITE INTEGRALS, G. Petit Bois. Comprehensive and accurate, this orderly grouping of over 2500 of the most useful indefinite integrals will save you hours of laborious mathematical groundwork. After a list of 49 common transformations of integral expressions, with a wide variety of examples, the book takes up algebraic functions, irrational monomials, products and quotients of binomials, transcendental functions, natural logs, etc. You will rarely or never encounter an integral of an algebraic or transcendental function not included here; any more comprehensive set of tables costs at least $12 or $15. Index. 2544 integrals. xii + 154pp. 6⅛ x 9¼.
S225 Paperbound **$2.00**

SUMMATION OF SERIES, Collected by L. B. W. Jolley. Over 1100 common series collected, summed, and grouped for easy reference—for mathematicians, physicists, computer technicians, engineers, and students. Arranged for convenience into categories, such as arithmetical and geometrical progressions, powers and products of natural numbers, figurate and polygonal numbers, inverse natural numbers, exponential and logarithmic series, binomial expansions, simple inverse products, factorials, and trigonometric and hyperbolic expansions. Also included are series representing various Bessel functions, elliptic integrals; discussions of special series involving Legendre polynomials, the zeta function, Bernoulli's function, and similar expressions. Revised, enlarged second edition. New preface. xii + 251pp. 5⅜ x 8½.
S23 Paperbound **$2.25**

A TABLE OF THE INCOMPLETE ELLIPTIC INTEGRAL OF THE THIRD KIND, R. G. Selfridge, J. E. Maxfield. The first complete 6-place tables of values of the incomplete integral of the third kind, prepared under the auspices of the Research Department of the U.S. Naval Ordnance Test Station. Calculated on an IBM type 704 calculator and thoroughly verified by echo-checking and a check integral at the completion of each value of a. Of inestimable value in problems where the surface area of geometrical bodies can only be expressed in terms of the incomplete integral of the third and lower kinds; problems in aero-, fluid-, and thermodynamics involving processes where nonsymmetrical repetitive volumes must be determined; various types of seismological problems; problems of magnetic potentials due to circular current; etc. Foreword. Acknowledgment. Introduction. Use of table. xiv + 805pp. 5⅝ x 8⅜.
S501 Clothbound **$7.50**

PRACTICAL ANALYSIS, GRAPHICAL AND NUMERICAL METHODS, F. A. Willers. Translated by R. T. Beyer. Immensely practical handbook for engineers, showing how to interpolate, use various methods of numerical differentiation and integration, determine the roots of a single algebraic equation, system of linear equations, use empirical formulas, integrate differential equations, etc. Hundreds of shortcuts for arriving at numerical solutions. Special section on American calculating machines, by T. W. Simpson. 132 illustrations. 422pp. 5⅜ x 8.
S273 Paperbound **$2.00**

NUMERICAL INTEGRATION OF DIFFERENTIAL EQUATIONS, A. A. Bennett, W. E. Milne, H. Bateman. Republication of original monograph prepared for National Research Council. New methods of integration of differential equations developed by 3 leading mathematicians: THE INTERPOLATIONAL POLYNOMIAL and SUCCESSIVE APPROXIMATIONS by A. A. Bennett; STEP-BY-STEP METHODS OF INTEGRATION by W. W. Milne; METHODS FOR PARTIAL DIFFERENTIAL EQUATIONS by H. Bateman. Methods for partial differential equations, transition from difference equations to differential equations, solution of differential equations to non-integral values of a parameter will interest mathematicians and physicists. 288 footnotes, mostly bibliographic; 235-item classified bibliography. 108pp. 5⅜ x 8.
S305 Paperbound **$1.35**

INTRODUCTION TO RELAXATION METHODS, F. S. Shaw. Fluid mechanics, design of electrical networks, forces in structural frameworks, stress distribution, buckling, etc. Solve linear simultaneous equations, linear ordinary differential equations, partial differential equations, Eigen-value problems by relaxation methods. Detailed examples throughout. Special tables for dealing with awkwardly-shaped boundaries. Indexes. 253 diagrams. 72 tables. 400pp. 5⅜ x 8.
S244 Paperbound **$2.45**

NUMERICAL SOLUTIONS OF DIFFERENTIAL EQUATIONS, H. Levy & E. A. Baggott. Comprehensive collection of methods for solving ordinary differential equations of first and higher order. All must pass 2 requirements: easy to grasp and practical, more rapid than school methods. Partial contents: graphical integration of differential equations, graphical methods for detailed solution. Numerical solution. Simultaneous equations and equations of 2nd and higher orders. "Should be in the hands of all in research in applied mathematics, teaching," NATURE. 21 figures. viii + 238pp. 5⅜ x 8.
S168 Paperbound **$1.75**

Probability theory and information theory

AN ELEMENTARY INTRODUCTION TO THE THEORY OF PROBABILITY, B. V. Gnedenko and A. Ya. Khinchin. Translated by Leo F. Boron. A clear, compact introduction designed to equip the reader with a fundamental grasp of the theory of probability. It is thorough and authoritative within its purposely restricted range, yet the layman with a background in elementary mathematics will be able to follow it without difficulty. Covers such topics as the processes involved in the calculation of probabilities, conditional probabilities and the multiplication rule, Bayes's formula, Bernoulli's scheme and theorem, random variables and distribution laws, and dispersion and mean deviations. New translation of fifth (revised) Russian edition (1960)—the only translation checked and corrected by Gnedenko. New preface for Dover edition by B. V. Gnedenko. Index. Bibliography. Appendix: Table of values of function $\phi(a)$. xii + 130pp. 5⅜ x 8½.   T155 Paperbound **$1.50**

AN INTRODUCTION TO MATHEMATICAL PROBABILITY, Julian Lowell Coolidge. A thorough introduction which presents the mathematical foundation of the theory of probability. A substantial body of material, yet can be understood with a knowledge of only elementary calculus. Contains: The Scope and Meaning of Mathematical Probability; Elementary Principles of Probability; Bernoulli's Theorem; Mean Value and Dispersion; Geometrical Probability; Probability of Causes; Errors of Observation; Errors in Many Variables; Indirect Observations; The Statistical Theory of Gases; and The Principles of Life Insurance. Six pages of logarithm tables. 4 diagrams. Subject and author indices. xii + 214pp. 5⅜ x 8½.
S258 Paperbound **$1.35**

A GUIDE TO OPERATIONS RESEARCH, W. E. Duckworth. A brief nontechnical exposition of techniques and theories of operational research. A good introduction for the layman; also can provide the initiate with new understandings. No mathematical training needed, yet not an oversimplification. Covers game theory, mathematical analysis, information theory, linear programming, cybernetics, decision theory, etc. Also includes a discussion of the actual organization of an operational research program and an account of the uses of such programs in the oil, chemical, paper, and metallurgical industries, etc. Bibliographies at chapter ends. Appendices. 36 figures. 145pp. 5¼ x 8½.   T1129 Clothbound **$3.50**

MATHEMATICAL FOUNDATIONS OF INFORMATION THEORY, A. I. Khinchin. For the first time mathematicians, statisticians, physicists, cyberneticists, and communications engineers are offered a complete and exact introduction to this relatively new field. Entropy as a measure of a finite scheme, applications to coding theory, study of sources, channels and codes, detailed proofs of both Shannon theorems for any ergodic source and any stationary channel with finite memory, and much more are covered. Bibliography. vii + 120pp. 5⅜ x 8.
S434 Paperbound **$1.35**

SELECTED PAPERS ON NOISE AND STOCHASTIC PROCESS, edited by Prof. Nelson Wax, U. of Illinois. 6 basic papers for newcomers in the field, for those whose work involves noise characteristics. Chandrasekhar, Uhlenbeck & Ornstein, Uhlenbeck & Ming, Rice, Doob. Included is Kac's Chauvenet-Prize winning Random Walk. Extensive bibliography lists 200 articles, up through 1953. 21 figures. 337pp. 6⅛ x 9¼.   S262 Paperbound **$2.50**

THEORY OF PROBABILITY, William Burnside. Synthesis, expansion of individual papers presents numerous problems in classical probability, offering many original views succinctly, effectively. Game theory, cards, selections from groups; geometrical probability in such areas as suppositions as to probability of position of point on a line, points on surface of sphere, etc. Includes methods of approximation, theory of errors, direct calculation of probabilities, etc. Index. 136pp. 5⅜ x 8.   S567 Paperbound **$1.00**

Statistics

ELEMENTARY STATISTICS, WITH APPLICATIONS IN MEDICINE AND THE BIOLOGICAL SCIENCES, F. E. Croxton. A sound introduction to statistics for anyone in the physical sciences, assuming no prior acquaintance and requiring only a modest knowledge of math. All basic formulas carefully explained and illustrated; all necessary reference tables included. From basic terms and concepts, the study proceeds to frequency distribution, linear, non-linear, and multiple correlation, skewness, kurtosis, etc. A large section deals with reliability and significance of statistical methods. Containing concrete examples from medicine and biology, this book will prove unusually helpful to workers in those fields who increasingly must evaluate, check, and interpret statistics. Formerly titled "Elementary Statistics with Applications in Medicine." 101 charts. 57 tables. 14 appendices. Index. iv + 376pp. 5⅜ x 8.
S506 Paperbound **$2.00**

ANALYSIS & DESIGN OF EXPERIMENTS, H. B. Mann. Offers a method for grasping the analysis of variance and variance design within a short time. Partial contents: Chi-square distribution and analysis of variance distribution, matrices, quadratic forms, likelihood ration tests and tests of linear hypotheses, power of analysis, Galois fields, non-orthogonal data, interblock estimates, etc. 15pp. of useful tables. x + 195pp. 5 x 7⅜.   S180 Paperbound **$1.45**

METHODS OF STATISTICS, L. H. C. Tippett. A classic in its field, this unusually complete systematic introduction to statistical methods begins at beginner's level and progresses to advanced levels for experimenters and poll-takers in all fields of statistical research. Supplies fundamental knowledge of virtually all elementary methods in use today by sociologists, psychologists, biologists, engineers, mathematicians, etc. Explains logical and mathematical basis of each method described, with examples for each section. Covers frequency distributions and measures, inference from random samples, errors in large samples, simple analysis of variance, multiple and partial regression and correlation, etc. 4th revised (1952) edition. 16 charts. 5 significance tables. 152-item bibliography. 96 tables. 22 figures. 395pp. 6 x 9.
S228 Clothbound **$7.50**

STATISTICS MANUAL, E. L. Crow, F. A. Davis, M. W. Maxfield. Comprehensive collection of classical, modern statistics methods, prepared under auspices of U. S. Naval Ordnance Test Station, China Lake, Calif. Many examples from ordnance will be valuable to workers in all fields. Emphasis is on use, with information on fiducial limits, sign tests, Chi-square runs, sensitivity, quality control, much more. "Well written . . . excellent reference work," Operations Research. Corrected edition of NAVORD Report 3360 NOTS 948. Introduction. Appendix of 32 tables, charts. Index. Bibliography. 95 illustrations. 306pp. 5⅜ x 8.
S599 Paperbound **$1.75**

Symbolic logic

AN INTRODUCTION TO SYMBOLIC LOGIC, Susanne K. Langer. Probably the clearest book ever written on symbolic logic for the philosopher, general scientist and layman. It will be particularly appreciated by those who have been rebuffed by other introductory works because of insufficient mathematical training. No special knowledge of mathematics is required. Starting with the simplest symbols and conventions, you are led to a remarkable grasp of the Boole-Schroeder and Russell-Whitehead systems clearly and quickly. PARTIAL CONTENTS: Study of forms, Essentials of logical structure, Generalization, Classes, The deductive system of classes, The algebra of logic, Abstraction of interpretation, Calculus of propositions, Assumptions of PRINCIPIA MATHEMATICA, Logistics, Logic of the syllogism, Proofs of theorems. "One of the clearest and simplest introductions to a subject which is very much alive. The style is easy, symbolism is introduced gradually, and the intelligent non-mathematician should have no difficulty in following the argument," MATHEMATICS GAZETTE. Revised, expanded second edition. Truth-value tables. 368pp. 5⅜ x 8.
S164 Paperbound **$1.75**

A SURVEY OF SYMBOLIC LOGIC: THE CLASSIC ALGEBRA OF LOGIC, C. I. Lewis. Classic survey of the field, comprehensive and thorough. Indicates content of major systems, alternative methods of procedure, and relation of these to the Boole-Schroeder algebra and to one another. Contains historical summary, as well as full proofs and applications of the classic, or Boole-Schroeder, algebra of logic. Discusses diagrams for the logical relations of classes, the two-valued algebra, propositional functions of two or more variables, etc. Chapters 5 and 6 of the original edition, which contained material not directly pertinent, have been omitted in this edition at the author's request. Appendix. Bibliography. Index. viii + 352pp. 5⅜ x 8⅜.
S643 Paperbound **$2.00**

INTRODUCTION TO SYMBOLIC LOGIC AND ITS APPLICATIONS, R. Carnap. One of the clearest, most comprehensive, and rigorous introductions to modern symbolic logic by perhaps its greatest living master. Symbolic languages are analyzed and one constructed. Applications to math (symbolic representation of axiom systems for set theory, natural numbers, real numbers, topology, Dedekind and Cantor explanations of continuity), physics (the general analysis of concepts of determination, causality, space-time-topology, based on Einstein), biology (symbolic representation of an axiom system for basic concepts). "A masterpiece," Zentralblatt für Mathematik und ihre Grenzgebiete. Over 300 exercises. 5 figures. Bibliography. Index. xvi + 241pp. 5⅜ x 8.
S453 Paperbound **$1.85**
Clothbound **$4.00**

SYMBOLIC LOGIC, C. I. Lewis, C. H. Langford. Probably the most cited book in symbolic logic, this is one of the fullest treatments of paradoxes. A wide coverage of the entire field of symbolic logic, plus considerable material that has not appeared elsewhere. Basic to the entire volume is the distinction between the logic of extensions and of intensions. Considerable emphasis is placed on converse substitution, while the matrix system presents the supposition of a variety of non-Aristotelian logics. It has especially valuable sections on strict limitations, existence of terms, 2-valued algebra and its extension to propositional functions, truth value systems, the matrix method, implication and deductibility, general theory of propositions, propositions of ordinary discourse, and similar topics. "Authoritative, most valuable," TIMES, London. Bibliography. 506pp. 5⅜ x 8.
S170 Paperbound **$2.35**

THE ELEMENTS OF MATHEMATICAL LOGIC, Paul Rosenbloom. First publication in any language. This book is intended for readers who are mature mathematically, but have no previous training in symbolic logic. It does not limit itself to a single system, but covers the field as a whole. It is a development of lectures given at Lund University, Sweden, in 1948. Partial contents: Logic of classes, fundamental theorems, Boolean algebra, logic of propositions, logic of propositional functions, expressive languages, combinatory logics, development of mathematics within an object language, paradoxes, theorems of Post and Goedel, Church's theorem, and similar topics. iv + 214pp. 5⅜ x 8. S227 Paperbound **$1.45**

GEOLOGY, GEOGRAPHY, METEOROLOGY

PRINCIPLES OF STRATIGRAPHY, A. W. Grabau. Classic of 20th century geology, unmatched in scope and comprehensiveness. Nearly 600 pages cover the structure and origins of every kind of sedimentary, hydrogenic, oceanic, pyroclastic, atmoclastic, hydroclastic, marine hydroclastic, and bioclastic rock; metamorphism; erosion; etc. Includes also the constitution of the atmosphere; morphology of oceans, rivers, glaciers; volcanic activities; faults and earthquakes; and fundamental principles of paleontology (nearly 200 pages). New introduction by Prof. M. Kay, Columbia U. 1277 bibliographical entries. 264 diagrams. Tables, maps, etc. Two volume set. Total of xxxii + 1185pp. 5⅜ x 8.
$\qquad$ S686 Vol I Paperbound **$2.50**
$\qquad$ S687 Vol II Paperbound **$2.50**
$\qquad$ The set **$5.00**

TREATISE ON SEDIMENTATION, William H. Twenhofel. A milestone in the history of geology, this two-volume work, prepared under the auspices of the United States Research Council, contains practically everything known about sedimentation up to 1932. Brings together all the findings of leading American and foreign geologists and geographers and has never been surpassed for completeness, thoroughness of description, or accuracy of detail. Vol. 1 discusses the sources and production of sediments, their transportation, deposition, diagenesis, and lithification. Also modification of sediments by organisms and topographical, climatic, etc. conditions which contribute to the alteration of sedimentary processes. 220 pages deal with products of sedimentation: minerals, limestones, dolomites, coals, etc. Vol. 2 continues the examination of products such as gypsum and saline residues, silica, strontium, manganese, etc. An extensive exposition of structures, textures and colors of sediments: stratification, cross-lamination, ripple mark, oolitic and pisolitic textures, etc. Chapters on environments or realms of sedimentation and field and laboratory techniques are also included. Indispensable to modern-day geologists and students. Index. List of authors cited. 1733-item bibliography. 121 diagrams. Total of xxxiii + 926pp. 5⅜ x 8½.
$\qquad$ Vol. I: S950 Paperbound **$2.50**
$\qquad$ Vol. II: S951 Paperbound **$2.50**
$\qquad$ Two volume set Paperbound **$5.00**

THE EVOLUTION OF THE IGNEOUS ROCKS, N. L. Bowen. Invaluable serious introduction applies techniques of physics and chemistry to explain igneous rock diversity in terms of chemical composition and fractional crystallization. Discusses liquid immiscibility in silicate magmas, crystal sorting, liquid lines of descent, fractional resorption of complex minerals, petrogenesis, etc. Of prime importance to geologists & mining engineers, also to physicists, chemists working with high temperatures and pressures. "Most important," TIMES, London. 3 indexes. 263 bibliographic notes. 82 figures. xviii + 334pp. 5⅜ x 8. $\qquad$ S311 Paperbound **$2.00**

INTERNAL CONSTITUTION OF THE EARTH, edited by Beno Gutenberg. Completely revised. Brought up-to-date, reset. Prepared for the National Research Council this is a complete & thorough coverage of such topics as earth origins, continent formation, nature & behavior of the earth's core, petrology of the crust, cooling forces in the core, seismic & earthquake material, gravity, elastic constants, strain characteristics and similar topics. "One is filled with admiration . . . a high standard . . . there is no reader who will not learn something from this book," London, Edinburgh, Dublin, Philosophic Magazine. Largest bibliography in print: 1127 classified items. Indexes. Tables of constants. 43 diagrams. 439pp. 6⅛ x 9¼.
$\qquad$ S414 Paperbound **$3.00**

HYDROLOGY, edited by Oscar E. Meinzer. Prepared for the National Research Council. Detailed complete reference library on precipitation, evaporation, snow, snow surveying, glaciers, lakes, infiltration, soil moisture, ground water, runoff, drought, physical changes produced by water, hydrology of limestone terranes, etc. Practical in application, especially valuable for engineers. 24 experts have created "the most up-to-date, most complete treatment of the subject," AM. ASSOC. of PETROLEUM GEOLOGISTS. Bibliography. Index. 165 illustrations. xi + 712pp. 6⅛ x 9¼. $\qquad$ S191 Paperbound **$3.25**

SNOW CRYSTALS, W. A. Bentley and W. J. Humphreys. Over 200 pages of Bentley's famous microphotographs of snow flakes—the product of painstaking, methodical work at his Jericho, Vermont studio. The pictures, which also include plates of frost, glaze and dew on vegetation, spider webs, windowpanes; sleet; graupel or soft hail, were chosen both for their scientific interest and their aesthetic qualities. The wonder of nature's diversity is exhibited in the intricate, beautiful patterns of the snow flakes. Introductory text by W. J. Humphreys. Selected bibliography. 2,453 illustrations. 224pp. 8 x 10¼. $\qquad$ T287 Paperbound **$2.95**

PHYSICS OF THE AIR, W. J. Humphreys. A very thorough coverage of classical materials and theories in meteorology . . . written by one of this century's most highly respected physical meteorologists. Contains the standard account in English of atmospheric optics. 5 main sections: Mechanics and Thermodynamics of the Atmosphere, Atmospheric Electricity and Auroras, Meteorological Acoustics, Atmospheric Optics, and Factors of Climatic Control. Under these headings, topics covered are: theoretical relations between temperature, pressure, and volume in the atmosphere; composition, pressure, and density; circulation; evaporation and condensation; fog, clouds, thunderstorms, lightning; aurora polaris; principal ice-age theories; etc. New preface by Prof. Julius London. 226 illustrations. Index. xviii + 676pp. 5⅜ x 8½. $\qquad$ S1044 Paperbound **$3.00**

CHEMISTRY AND PHYSICAL CHEMISTRY

ORGANIC CHEMISTRY, F. C. Whitmore. The entire subject of organic chemistry for the practicing chemist and the advanced student. Storehouse of facts, theories, processes found elsewhere only in specialized journals. Covers aliphatic compounds (500 pages on the properties and synthetic preparation of hydrocarbons, halides, proteins, ketones, etc.), alicyclic compounds, aromatic compounds, heterocyclic compounds, organophosphorus and organometallic compounds. Methods of synthetic preparation analyzed critically throughout. Includes much of biochemical interest. "The scope of this volume is astonishing," INDUSTRIAL AND ENGINEERING CHEMISTRY. 12,000-reference index. 2387-item bibliography. Total of x + 1005pp. 5⅜ x 8.
Two volume set.
S700 Vol I Paperbound **$2.25**
S701 Vol II Paperbound **$2.25**
The set **$4.50**

THE MODERN THEORY OF MOLECULAR STRUCTURE, Bernard Pullman. A reasonably popular account of recent developments in atomic and molecular theory. Contents: The Wave Function and Wave Equations (history and bases of present theories of molecular structure); The Electronic Structure of Atoms (Description and classification of atomic wave functions, etc.); Diatomic Molecules; Non-Conjugated Polyatomic Molecules; Conjugated Polyatomic Molecules; The Structure of Complexes. Minimum of mathematical background needed. New translation by David Antin of "La Structure Moléculaire." Index. Bibliography. vii + 87pp. 5⅜ x 8½.
S987 Paperbound **$1.00**

CATALYSIS AND CATALYSTS, Marcel Prettre, Director, Research Institute on Catalysis. This brief book, translated into English for the first time, is the finest summary of the principal modern concepts, methods, and results of catalysis. Ideal introduction for beginning chemistry and physics students. Chapters: Basic Definitions of Catalysis (true catalysis and generalization of the concept of catalysis); The Scientific Bases of Catalysis (Catalysis and chemical thermodynamics, catalysis and chemical kinetics); Homogeneous Catalysis (acid-base catalysis, etc.); Chain Reactions; Contact Masses; Heterogeneous Catalysis (Mechanisms of contact catalyses, etc.); and Industrial Applications (acids and fertilizers, petroleum and petroleum chemistry, rubber, plastics, synthetic resins, and fibers). Translated by David Antin. Index. vi + 88pp. 5⅜ x 8½.
S998 Paperbound **$1.00**

POLAR MOLECULES, Pieter Debye. This work by Nobel laureate Debye offers a complete guide to fundamental electrostatic field relations, polarizability, molecular structure. Partial contents: electric intensity, displacement and force, polarization by orientation, molar polarization and molar refraction, halogen-hydrides, polar liquids, ionic saturation, dielectric constant, etc. Special chapter considers quantum theory. Indexed. 172pp. 5⅜ x 8.
S64 Paperbound **$1.65**

THE ELECTRONIC THEORY OF ACIDS AND BASES, W. F. Luder and Saverio Zuffanti. The first full systematic presentation of the electronic theory of acids and bases—treating the theory and its ramifications in an uncomplicated manner. Chapters: Historical Background; Atomic Orbitals and Valence; The Electronic Theory of Acids and Bases; Electrophilic and Electrodotic Reagents; Acidic and Basic Radicals; Neutralization; Titrations with Indicators; Displacement; Catalysis; Acid Catalysis; Base Catalysis; Alkoxides and Catalysts; Conclusion. Required reading for all chemists. Second revised (1961) eidtion, with additional examples and references. 3 figures. 9 tables. Index. Bibliography xii + 165pp. 5⅜ x 8.
S201 Paperbound **$1.50**

KINETIC THEORY OF LIQUIDS, J. Frenkel. Regarding the kinetic theory of liquids as a generalization and extension of the theory of solid bodies, this volume covers all types of arrangements of solids, thermal displacements of atoms, interstitial atoms and ions, orientational and rotational motion of molecules, and transition between states of matter. Mathematical theory is developed close to the physical subject matter. 216 bibliographical footnotes. 55 figures. xi + 485pp. 5⅜ x 8.
S95 Paperbound **$2.55**

THE PRINCIPLES OF ELECTROCHEMISTRY, D. A. MacInnes. Basic equations for almost every subfield of electrochemistry from first principles, referring at all times to the soundest and most recent theories and results; unusually useful as text or as reference. Covers coulometers and Faraday's Law, electrolytic conductance, the Debye-Hueckel method for the theoretical calculation of activity coefficients, concentration cells, standard electrode potentials, thermodynamic ionization constants, pH, potentiometric titrations, irreversible phenomena, Planck's equation, and much more. "Excellent treatise," AMERICAN CHEMICAL SOCIETY JOURNAL. "Highly recommended," CHEMICAL AND METALLURGICAL ENGINEERING. 2 Indices. Appendix. 585-item bibliography. 137 figures. 94 tables. ii + 478pp. 5⅝ x 8⅜.
S52 Paperbound **$2.45**

THE PHASE RULE AND ITS APPLICATION, Alexander Findlay. Covering chemical phenomena of 1, 2, 3, 4, and multiple component systems, this "standard work on the subject" (NATURE, London), has been completely revised and brought up to date by A. N. Campbell and N. O. Smith. Brand new material has been added on such matters as binary, tertiary liquid equilibria, solid solutions in ternary systems, quinary systems of salts and water. Completely revised to triangular coordinates in ternary systems, clarified graphical representation, solid models, etc. 9th revised edition. Author, subject indexes. 236 figures. 505 footnotes, mostly bibliographic. xii + 494pp. 5⅜ x 8.
S91 Paperbound **$2.50**

THE SOLUBILITY OF NONELECTROLYTES, Joel H. Hildebrand and Robert L. Scott. The standard work on the subject; still indispensable as a reference source and for classroom work. Partial contents: The Ideal Solution (including Raoult's Law and Henry's Law, etc.); Nonideal Solutions; Intermolecular Forces; The Liquid State; Entropy of Athermal Mixing; Heat of Mixing; Polarity; Hydrogen Bonding; Specific Interactions; "Solvation" and "Association"; Systems of Three or More Components; Vapor Pressure of Binary Liquid Solutions; Mixtures of Gases; Solubility of Gases in Liquids; of Liquids in Liquids; of Solids in Liquids; Evaluation of Solubility Parameters; and other topics. Corrected republication of third (revised) edition. Appendices. Indexes. 138 figures. 111 tables. 1 photograph. iv + 488pp. 5⅜ x 8½.
S1125 Paperbound **$2.50**

TERNARY SYSTEMS: INTRODUCTION TO THE THEORY OF THREE COMPONENT SYSTEMS, G. Masing. Furnishes detailed discussion of representative types of 3-components systems, both in solid models (particularly metallic alloys) and isothermal models. Discusses mechanical mixture without compounds and without solid solutions; unbroken solid solution series; solid solutions with solubility breaks in two binary systems; iron-silicon-aluminum alloys; allotropic forms of iron in ternary system; other topics. Bibliography. Index. 166 illustrations. 178pp. 5⅝ x 8⅜.
S631 Paperbound **$1.50**

THE KINETIC THEORY OF GASES, Leonard B. Loeb, University of California. Comprehensive text and reference book which presents full coverage of basic theory and the important experiments and developments in the field for the student and investigator. Partial contents: The Mechanical Picture of a Perfect Gas, The Mean Free Path—Clausius' Deductions, Distribution of Molecular Velocities, discussions of theory of the problem of specific heats, the contributions of kinetic theory to our knowledge of electrical and magnetic properties of molecules and its application to the conduction of electricity in gases. New 14-page preface to Dover edition by the author. Name, subject indexes. Six appendices. 570-item bibliography. xxxvi + 687pp. 5⅜ x 8½.
S942 Paperbound **$2.95**

IONS IN SOLUTION, Ronald W. Gurney. A thorough and readable introduction covering all the fundamental principles and experiments in the field, by an internationally-known authority. Contains discussions of solvation energy, atomic and molecular ions, lattice energy, transferral of ions, interionic forces, cells and half-cells, transference of electrons, exchange forces, hydrogen ions, the electro-chemical series, and many other related topics. Indispensable to advanced undergraduates and graduate students in electrochemistry. Index. 45 illustrations. 15 tables. vii + 206pp. 5⅜ x 8½.
S124 Paperbound **$1.50**

IONIC PROCESSES IN SOLUTION, Ronald W. Gurney. Lucid, comprehensive examination which brings together the approaches of electrochemistry, thermodynamics, statistical mechanics, electroacoustics, molecular physics, and quantum theory in the interpretation of the behavior of ionic solutions—the most important single work on the subject. More extensive and technical than the author's earlier work (IONS IN SOLUTION), it is a middle-level text for graduate students and researchers in electrochemistry. Covers such matters as Brownian motion in liquids, molecular ions in solution, heat of precipitation, entropy of solution, proton transfers, dissociation constant of nitric acid, viscosity of ionic solutions, etc. 78 illustrations. 47 tables. Name and subject index. ix + 275pp. 5⅜ x 8½.
S134 Paperbound **$1.75**

CRYSTALLOGRAPHIC DATA ON METAL AND ALLOY STRUCTURES, Compiled by A. Taylor and B. J. Kagle, Westinghouse Research Laboratories. Unique collection of the latest crystallographic data on alloys, compounds, and the elements, with lattice spacings expressed uniformly in absolute Angstrom units. Gathers together previously widely-scattered data from the Power Data File of the ATSM, structure reports, and the Landolt-Bornstein Tables, as well as from other original literature. 2300 different compounds listed in the first table. Alloys and Intermetallic Compounds, with much vital information on each. Also listings for nearly 700 Borides, Carbides, Hydrides, Oxides, Nitrides. Also all the necessary data on the crystal structure of 77 elements. vii + 263pp. 5⅜ x 8.
S1013 Paperbound **$2.25**

MATHEMATICAL CRYSTALLOGRAPHY AND THE THEORY OF GROUPS OF MOVEMENTS, Harold Hilton. Classic account of the mathematical theory of crystallography, particularly the geometrical theory of crystal-structure based on the work of Bravais, Jordan, Sohncke, Federow, Schoenflies, and Barlow. Partial contents: The Stereographic Projection, Properties Common to Symmetrical and Asymmetrical Crystals, The Theory of Groups, Coordinates of Equivalent Points, Crystallographic Axes and Axial Ratios, The Forms and Growth of Crystals, Lattices and Translations, The Structure-Theory, Infinite Groups of Movements, Triclinic and Monoclinic Groups, Orthorhombic Groups, etc. Index. 188 figures. xii + 262pp. 5⅜ x 8½.
S1058 Paperbound **$2.00**

CLASSICS IN THE THEORY OF CHEMICAL COMBINATIONS. Edited by O. T. Benfey. Vol. I of the Classics of Science Series, G. Holton, Harvard University, General Editor. This book is a collection of papers representing the major chapters in the development of the valence concept in chemistry. Includes essays by Wöhler and Liebig, Laurent, Williamson, Frankland, Kekulé and Couper, and two by van't Hoff and le Bel, which mark the first extension of the valence concept beyond its purely numerical character. Introduction and epilogue by Prof. Benfey. Index. 9 illustrations. New translation of Kekulé paper by Benfey. xiv + 191pp. 5⅜ x 8½.
S1066 Paperbound **$1.85**

THE CHEMISTRY OF URANIUM: THE ELEMENT, ITS BINARY AND RELATED COMPOUNDS, J. J. Katz and E. Rabinowitch. Vast post-World War II collection and correlation of thousands of AEC reports and published papers in a useful and easily accessible form, still the most complete and up-to-date compilation. Treats "dry uranium chemistry," occurrences, preparation, properties, simple compounds, isotopic composition, extraction from ores, spectra, alloys, etc. Much material available only here. Index. Thousands of evaluated bibliographical references. 324 tables, charts, figures. xxi + 609pp. 5⅜ x 8. S757 Paperbound **$2.95**

THE STORY OF ALCHEMY AND EARLY CHEMISTRY, J. M. Stillman. An authoritative, scholarly work, highly readable, of development of chemical knowledge from 4000 B.C. to downfall of phlogiston theory in late 18th century. Every important figure, many quotations. Brings alive curious, almost incredible history of alchemical beliefs, practices, writings of Arabian Prince Oneeyade, Vincent of Beauvais, Geber, Zosimos, Paracelsus, Vitruvius, scores more. Studies work, thought of Black, Cavendish, Priestley, Van Helmont, Bergman, Lavoisier, Newton, etc. Index. Bibliography. 579pp. 5⅜ x 8. S628 Paperbound **$2.45**

Prices subject to change without notice.

Dover publishes books on art, music, philosophy, literature, languages, history, social sciences, psychology, handcrafts, orientalia, puzzles and entertainments, chess, pets and gardens, books explaining science, intermediate and higher mathematics, mathematical physics, engineering, biological sciences, earth sciences, classics of science, etc. Write to:

Dept. catrr.
Dover Publications, Inc.
180 Varick Street, N.Y. 14, N.Y.